PENGUI

PROJEC

George Dyson was born in 1953. Through his father, a mathematical physicist, his mother, a logician, and his sister, a computer industry analyst, he indirectly witnessed the conjunction of theory, technology and high finance which precipitated the information age. A kayak builder and ethnohistorian, his experience in the Canadian and Alaskan wilderness has sharpened his skills as an observer of the convergence between technology and living things. He is the author of *Darwin among the Machines*, published by Penguin.

PROJECT ORION

The Atomic Spaceship

1957–1965

GEORGE DYSON

PENGUIN BOOKS

PENGUIN BOOKS

Published by the Penguin Group
Penguin Books Ltd, 80 Strand, London WC2R 0RL, England
Penguin Putnam Inc., 375 Hudson Street, New York, New York 10014, USA
Penguin Books Australia Ltd, 250 Camberwell Road, Camberwell, Victoria 3124, Australia
Penguin Books Canada Ltd, 10 Alcorn Avenue, Toronto, Ontario, Canada M4V 3B2
Penguin Books India (P) Ltd, 11, Community Centre, Panchsheel Park, New Delhi – 110 017, India
Penguin Books (NZ) Ltd, Cnr Rosedale and Airborne Roads, Albany, Auckland, New Zealand
Penguin Books (South Africa) (Pty) Ltd, 24 Sturdee Avenue, Rosebank 2196, South Africa

Penguin Books Ltd, Registered Offices: 80 Strand, London WC2R 0RL, England

www.penguin.com

First published in the USA by Henry Holt and Company, LLC 2002
Published in Great Britain by Allen Lane The Penguin Press 2002
Published in Penguin Books 2003
1

Copyright © George Dyson, 2002

The moral right of the author has been asserted

Printed and bound in Great Britain by Clays Ltd, St Ives plc

Except in the United States of America, this book is sold subject
to the condition that it shall not, by way of trade or otherwise, be lent,
re-sold, hired out, or otherwise circulated without the publisher's
prior consent in any form of binding or cover other than that in
which it is published and without a similar condition including this
condition being imposed on the subsequent purchaser

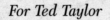
For Ted Taylor

It doomed the mammoths, and it began the setting of that snare that shall catch the sun.

—H.G. WELLS, 1914

CONTENTS

CONTENTS

PREFACE

Bel-Air

In 1957, tail fins, not seat belts, were standard equipment on American cars. Tail fins reached a peak in popularity with the 1957 Chevrolet Bel-Air. Powered by a 235-cubic-inch straight six or a 283-cubic-inch V-8, with either manual overdrive or powerglide automatic transmission, the Bel-Air had a two-tone exterior, accented by anodized aluminum suggesting space-age Los Angeles rather than iron-age Detroit. Optional equipment, besides seat belts, included power windows, six-way power seats, and a built-in electric razor. The Russians were ahead in space, but General Motors was ahead on the road.

This book is the story of Project Orion. In 1957, a small group of scientists, led by physicist Theodore B. Taylor and including my father, Freeman J. Dyson, launched a serious attempt to build an interplanetary spaceship propelled by nuclear bombs. This account, as best as I can reconstruct it, is the story my father could tell me only in fragments at the time.

Orion was a sibling of both *Sputnik* and the Chevrolet Bel-Air. When my father joined Project Orion, he was driving a 1949 Ford. After a year in La Jolla, California, it was time to give up the Ford. "Our poor old car finally gave up the ghost," he reported in his weekly letter home. "So on Friday night we took the old car out for its last run. We went to a big car-dealer in San Diego. We looked at a lot of cars, drove three, and finally bought a 2-year-old Chevrolet at 9 P.M." A turquoise and white 1957 Bel-Air.

To a five-year-old from New Jersey, La Jolla (the jewel) was paradise found. General Atomic, the project's contractor, provided a house with a swimming pool and citrus orchard, draped in bougainvillea and over-looking the Pacific Ocean, which we scanned at sunset for the green flash. Winter swells broke over the reef at Windansea, where a surfing culture as tenacious as the inshore kelp beds had taken hold. Theodore Geisel, better known as Dr. Seuss, visited our three-room schoolhouse at La Jolla Cove. Abalone big enough to resist a tire iron could be gath-ered at low tide. My father and later my thirteen-year-old sister Kata-rina joined the local glider club and spent Saturdays trying to stay aloft in a fabric-covered sailplane winched into the updrafts above the cliffs at Torrey Pines. Jack Kerouac published *On the Road.*

The tail fins on the Chevrolet matched those on the Atlas intercontinental ballistic missiles that Convair Astronautics, a branch of the same corporate family as General Atomic, was building at a new $40 million facility four miles inland. In July 1958 Convair held an open house, pro-viding free hot dogs and the hourly flight of a model ICBM, which, the local paper announced, "will emit a trail of smoke and will complete its trip with a big red flash, simulating the detonation of a warhead." Real Atlas missiles, with a range of 5,000 miles, carried thermonuclear war-heads yielding one hundred Hiroshimas each. The delivery of hydrogen bombs to civilian targets was celebrated with an open house, while Orion, a spaceship that would use bombs to deliver civilians to Mars, Jupiter, and Saturn, was so encumbered by secrecy that until July 1958 even the existence of the project remained publicly unknown.

Much of the record of Project Orion is still classified "Secret— Restricted Data" even though most of what kept the project secret in 1958 is now in the open, except for a few specific technical details. Any danger of Project Orion literature being used for destructive purposes is outweighed by the possibility that knowledge of Orion may be useful in ways that we cannot now predict or understand. Eventually, we will outgrow the use of nuclear energy as a weapon. Project Orion is a monument to those who once believed, or still believe, in turning the power of these weapons into something else.

All the people I visited or revisited in gathering this account believe they contributed to a dream that was nonetheless important for having failed. The years they spent working on Orion were the most exciting of their lives. Would they do it again? Definitely yes. Should we do it now? Probably not.

"We had a wonderfully free time, before any of that fallout stuff came down," says Orion's lead experimentalist, Brian Dunne. "It was a crazy era. All of our values were tweaked because of the cold war. It was a closed society, and all kinds of strange ideas were able to grow."

PROJECT
ORION

1

Sputnik

On October 4, 1957, Earth's first artificial satellite, weighing 184 pounds, was launched. *Sputnik I* circled the earth every ninety minutes for the next three months. *Sputnik II* followed on November 3 and weighed 1,120 pounds, including Laika, the pioneer of space-faring dogs. Earth's third artificial satellite was sent into orbit on January 31, 1958. Launched by a 32-ton Jupiter-C rocket built by the Chrysler Corporation, *Explorer I* weighed 31 pounds.

The race for space had begun. In Washington, D.C., the Advanced Research Projects Agency (then ARPA, now DARPA) was given a small office in the Pentagon and assigned the task of coordinating United States efforts—both civilian and military—to catch up. NASA did not exist until July 1958. All three branches of the United States military had competing designs on space. "If it *flies*, that's our department," claimed the Air Force. "But they're called space*ships*," replied the Navy. "OK, but the Moon is high *ground*," answered the Army, which had already enlisted rocket pioneer Wernher von Braun.

Sputnik caught the American public, but not the United States aerospace establishment, by surprise. American scientists were well aware of the Soviet effort and several United States space programs—including the Atlas and Titan intercontinental ballistic missiles, the Explorer and Vanguard satellite programs, the Rover nuclear rocket project at Livermore and Los Alamos, and even plans for a moon landing—were under way before the Russian Sputniks went up. ARPA's mission was to consolidate existing aerospace projects, differentiate military from civilian objectives, and consider all alternatives, however far-fetched. Things nuclear were viewed with enthusiasm. This was the era of unrestricted atmospheric bomb tests, with the equivalent of several thousand Hiroshimas being exploded from one year to the next.

One of ARPA's alternatives, code-named Project Orion, was an interplanetary spaceship powered by nuclear bombs. Orion was the offspring of an idea first proposed, as an unmanned vehicle, by Los Alamos mathematician Stanislaw Ulam shortly after the Trinity atomic bomb test at Alamogordo, New Mexico, on July 16, 1945. It was typical of Ulam to be thinking about using bombs to deliver missiles, while everyone else was thinking about using missiles to deliver bombs.

To visualize Orion, imagine an enormous one-cylinder external combustion engine: a single piston reciprocating within the combustion chamber of empty space. The ship itself, egg-shaped and the height of a twenty-story building, is the piston, armored by a 1,000-ton pusher plate attached by shock-absorbing legs. The first two hundred explosions, fired at half-second intervals, with a total yield equivalent to some 100,000 tons of TNT, would lift the ship from sea level to 125,000 feet. Each kick adds about 20 miles per hour to the ship's velocity, an impulse equivalent to dropping the ship from a height of 15 feet. Six hundred more explosions, gradually increasing in yield to 5 kilotons each, would loft the ship into a 300-mile orbit around the earth. "I used to have a lot of dreams about watching the flight, the vertical flight," says Ted Taylor, Ulam's younger colleague who founded Project Orion and, as the designer of both the smallest and the largest fission bombs in the United States repertoire, was uniquely qualified to dream where nightmares alone have otherwise led. "The first flight of that thing doing its full mission would be the most spectacular thing that humans had ever seen."

The performance of a conventional rocket is governed by the velocity of its exhaust gases. This is limited by the energy content of the fuel, the efficiency in converting this into kinetic energy via the propellant, and the temperature at which the combustion chamber and rocket nozzles begin to melt. For a chemical rocket, maximum exhaust velocity—about 3 km/sec (6,000 mph)—is limited by the speed to which the energy released by rearranging electrons in a chemical reaction can make the combustion products fly apart. The only way to propel the rocket faster is to leave part of the rocket behind as the next stage continues on. To reach low earth orbit (7 km/sec) requires at least two stages and to reach escape velocity (11 km/sec) at least three—which will get you away from Earth but will not get you back. For a given final payload, each stage adds a factor of about four to the initial mass. Some 16 tons of chemical rocket are required to place a one-ton payload in low earth orbit. A round-trip visit to the moon, requiring five stages, takes almost a thousand tons for every ton that makes it there and back. Voyages to Jupiter, Saturn, or even Mars become prohibitive, which is why we have yet to go beyond the Moon except with one-way, unmanned probes. To really explore the solar system, on a time scale compatible with the careers of individual adventurers, requires high acceleration to get to the places that are interesting, fuel for the return trip, and good brakes so you can stop.

Orion escapes these restrictions because nuclear fission releases a million times the energy of burning chemicals, and because burning the fuel in discrete pulses and at a distance avoids high temperatures within the ship. In a chemical rocket, the fuel, heated by its own combustion, becomes the propellant. Orion's propellant, distinct from the uranium or plutonium used as fuel, can be almost any cheap, inert material that is placed between the pusher and the bomb. It might be as light as polyethylene or as heavy as tungsten, and, on a long voyage, might also include shipboard waste in addition to ice, frozen methane, or other material obtained from the surface of Mars, among the rings of Saturn, or elsewhere the ship decides to stop.

The propellant is vaporized into a jet of plasma by the bomb. In contrast to a rocket, which pushes the propellant away from the ship, Orion pushes the ship away from the propellant—by ejecting slow-moving propellant, igniting the bomb, and then bouncing some of the resulting fast-moving propellant off the bottom of the ship. The bomb debris hits the pusher at roughly a hundred times the speed of a rocket's exhaust, producing temperatures that no rocket nozzle could withstand. For about one three-thousandth of a second the plasma stagnates against the pusher plate at a temperature of about 120,000 degrees. The time is too short for heat to penetrate the pusher, so the ship is able to survive an extended series of pulses, the way someone can run barefoot across a bed of coals without getting burned. Even on an ambitious interplanetary mission, involving several thousand explosions, the total plasmapusher interaction time amounts to less than one second. The high temperatures are safely isolated, in both time and distance, from the ship.

The feature that sold Orion to ARPA in 1958, to the Air Force for seven years, and briefly to NASA in 1963 is its specific impulse—a standard measure for comparing the performance of different forms of propulsion in space. Formally defined as the propellant exhaust velocity divided by the acceleration of gravity, g, specific impulse (Isp) is measured in seconds and can be visualized, informally, as the length of time for which one pound of fuel can generate one pound (on Earth) of thrust. The best chemical rockets achieve a specific impulse of about 430, and reactor-driven nuclear rockets, using existing technology, might reach 1,000. Specific impulse varies as the square root of exhaust temperature, so an internal combustion rocket cannot achieve a much higher specific impulse without melting the ship.

Orion's external combustion engine escapes the temperature limitation, developing far higher Isp: 2,000 to 3,000 for first-generation designs, 4,000 to 6,000 for larger vehicles using existing bombs, possibly an order of magnitude higher if the state of the art was advanced. Other technologies, such as nuclear-electric or solar-electric ion propulsion, offer high specific impulse, but only at very low thrust. Chemical rockets produce high thrust but low specific impulse. Only Orion offers both. And the larger the ship, the higher the Isp. Even the first-generation versions of Orion could, as aerospace historian Scott Lowther describes it, "go from downtown Jackass Flats to Saturn orbit back to low Earth orbit in a single stage."

Project Orion took place from 1957 to 1965 at General Atomic, a division of the General Dynamics Corporation established to develop peaceful uses for atomic energy, usually assumed to include everything nuclear *except* bombs. General Atomic was founded, in 1955, by Frederic de Hoffmann, a young physicist turned entrepreneur who sought to recapture the freewheeling spirit he had known at Los Alamos during the war. General Atomic attracted not only first-class theoretical and experimental talent but the backing of politicians, financiers, and industrialists who, after the success of the Manhattan Project and its hydrogen-bomb successors, were eager to see what de Hoffmann's colleagues might come up with next. There was a narrow window of opportunity between the launch of *Sputnik* and the commitment of the United States to an exclusively chemical approach to space. It was only a time like this and a place like General Atomic that gave a proposal as unorthodox as Orion a chance. Where else could a thirty-two-year-old physicist show up for work the day after *Sputnik,* start daydreaming about how many bombs it would take to put something the size of a nuclear submarine into orbit, and spend the next seven years—with the support of General Dynamics, the AEC, the Air Force, and, to a small extent, even NASA—making a serious effort to get the idea off the ground?

De Hoffmann and Taylor secured a $5,000 study contract from the Albuquerque office of the Atomic Energy Commission, a formality that provided access to the classified information necessary to work on anything having to do with nuclear bombs. On November 3, 1957, the day that *Sputnik II* (with Laika aboard) was launched, General Atomic issued T. B. Taylor's *Note on the Possibility of Nuclear Propulsion of a Very Large Vehicle at Greater than Earth Escape Velocities.* The new project was named Orion—for no particular reason, says Taylor, who just "picked the name out of the sky." Marshall Rosenbluth suggested the code name be spelled O'Ryan—to throw others off the trail.

By the beginning of 1958, plans to build Orion were taking form. Ted Taylor's proposal, submitted to ARPA in early 1958, envisioned a 4,000-ton vehicle, carrying up to 2,600 bombs and capable of orbiting a payload of 1,600 tons. "Dr. Taylor estimated that a fully completed spaceship could be achieved by 1963–1964 and would cost approximately $500,000,000," Second Lieutenant Ronald Prater, one of ARPA's contract monitors, noted after a visit to General Atomic in November 1958. Suggested missions ranged from the ability to deliver "a hydrogen warhead so large

Title frame of flying-model test film presented to ARPA/Air Force sponsors in 1959.

that it would devastate a country one-third the size of the United States" to a grand tour of the solar system that Orion's chief scientists envisioned as an extension of Darwin's voyage of the *Beagle:* a four-year expedition to the moons of Saturn including a two-year stay on Mars. "Saturn by 1970," announced the physicists. "Whoever controls Orion will control the world," claimed General Thomas Power, commander in chief of the Strategic Air Command.

In the early spring of 1958, General Atomic began moving from temporary quarters in the Barnard Street School in downtown San Diego to a spectacular facility on three hundred acres of mesa above the beaches of La Jolla near Torrey Pines. The centerpiece was a circular technical library, two stories high and 135 feet in diameter—exactly the diameter of the 4,000-ton Orion design. The library, which included a cafeteria, provided a sense of scale. Ted Taylor would point to a car or a delivery truck, the size of existing space vehicles, and say, "This is the one for looking through the keyhole." Then he would point to the library and say, "And this is the one for opening the door."

Most technical references to Project Orion remain classified to this day. Even the titles of documents were often classified, leaving only occasional clues to their existence, for instance a reference to Ted Taylor and Marshall Rosenbluth's original report on the possibility of Orion, identified in declassified Air Force correspondence only as GA-292, and by Air Force historians who note that it "included all the necessary practical working features for a very large space vehicle . . . which was sent to ARPA and AFSWC early in 1958." Some of the reasons for this secrecy, such as Orion's potential as a strategic deep-space weapons platform, are now obsolete. Other secrets, especially the details of how to build miniature, directed-energy nuclear explosives using very small amounts of plutonium, remain as sensitive as ever today.

Taylor could supplement the available staff at General Atomic with outside consultants, as long as they had up-to-date Q clearance, the special level of security administered by the AEC under the Atomic Energy Act of 1954. One of the consultants was my father, Freeman J. Dyson, of the Institute for Advanced Study in Princeton, New Jersey, who disappeared periodically to General Atomic with little hint as to what he was working on, though it was possible to guess.

"I have nothing very original to say about Sputniks. I feel very cheerful about them," he wrote to his parents in England on New Year's Day, 1958, flying from New York to San Diego to spend his first ten days consulting on Project Orion with Ted. "It seems to me clear that the Soviet government does not intend to throw bombs at anybody but does intend to dominate the earth by rapid scientific and industrial growth. This will in turn stimulate the Americans to undertake a whole lot of major projects which they would be too parsimonious to do otherwise. There is no question that colonization of the moon and planets will be one of them. I expect eventually to take a hand in this myself."

By springtime, Freeman was spending more and more of his time on the West Coast. "I find myself now in a group of not more than 12 people, all of us under 40, planning an enterprise which will inevitably grow into colossal dimensions," he wrote on April 27 from the Hotel Del Charro, near the beach at La Jolla Shores. "The feeling and atmosphere we are now in must be similar to the atomic bomb project in the earliest days, before even Los Alamos was thought of, when Oppenheimer and Teller and a handful of other people were feeling their way into the problem and establishing the basic ideas for everything which came later. It is characteristic of this very early time that there is no feeling of pressure or urgency, everything is quite informal and relaxed, and we ourselves have difficulty in taking the whole situation seriously. In years to come, when huge projects and whole empires have grown out of this, the early period will have become legendary, and we ourselves will not be able to distinguish our memories of this time from the legends which will grow around us.

"What I have said in this letter is no violation of secrecy," he added, "since I said nothing of what we are doing. Still I would like you to even keep quiet about this, and not tell your friends I am doing anything unusual." In May 1958, Project Orion received permission to reveal the nature of its business, confidentially, and only for recruiting purposes, since it was becoming difficult to hire talent without explaining the project's basic principle and goals. Finally, on July 2, 1958, the existence— but not the name—of the project was made public in a one-page press release issued in Washington, D.C.: "Roy W. Johnson, Director of the Advanced Research Projects Agency, today announced that the Air Research and Development Command has been authorized to let a feasibility study contract with the General Dynamics Corporation's General Atomic Division, located at San Diego, California, related to the possible development of a new concept of propulsion employing controlled nuclear explosions . . . within the atmosphere and beyond. The initial commitment for this study calls for the expenditure of one million dollars during the fiscal year 1959."

I was five years old, and space was within reach in a way that only children of *Sputnik* can understand. In the summer of 1957 we had driven up to the Lick Observatory on Mount Hamilton in California, whose 26-inch refractor was at one time the most powerful telescope in the world. When my father lifted me up to the cold brass eyepiece, Saturn and its rings filled the black, starry night, big as a soup plate, as if the dome we were standing in *was* a spaceship and we had already traveled halfway there. Later that year we scanned the Milky Way as the first Sputniks passed overhead. Under the clear New Jersey winter sky, I learned to recognize the stars and distinguish the planets, guided by a copy of *Find the Constellations* by H. A. Rey, the author also of *Curious George*. "Tonight when I came home from work it was already dark and George said, 'I have just been outside and I could see Venus and Orion,'" Freeman reported to my grandfather in October 1957. "I did not even need to check that his statement was accurate. He has his eyes very wide open for all natural phenomena, birds and butterflies, worms and clouds."

Space travel, in the 1950s, appeared imminent. As the Air Force noted in reviewing the project, "The uses for ORION appeared as limitless as space itself." The children who would be disinherited in the 1960s over the war in Vietnam spent the 1950s believing we would be colonists in space. When it was revealed that the United States government was planning to build a bomb-propelled interplanetary spaceship and that my father intended to be on board, I was among the least surprised. "When I drove George to school this morning I told him about the space-ship," my stepmother reported, in June 1958, when the AEC and Department of Defense first allowed General Atomic to mention the existence of the contract to the press. "He was very excited, asked immediately which planet you will send it to, and whether there would be a little seat right next to you for him to come along."

When my father returned home, I had innumerable questions. "How big is the spaceship? What will it look like? How does it work? Where will you be going and how long will you be gone?"

"I cannot tell you," he answered. "But someday you will find out."

2

The World Set Free

"These atomic bombs which science burst upon the world that night were strange even to the men who used them," wrote H. G. Wells in *The World Set Free*, a prophetic novel appearing at the dawn of World War I. Wells envisioned a future transformed by atomic energy, but feared that the lack of a requisite transformation of human nature would lead to the "Last War"—the one we still refer to, hoping that we have avoided it, as World War III. "The Central European bombs were the same, except that they were larger," Wells explained. "Nothing could have been more obvious to the people of the early twentieth century than the rapidity with which war was becoming impossible. And as certainly they did not see it. They did not see it until the atomic bombs burst in their fumbling hands. . . . Before the last war began it was a matter of common knowledge that a man could carry about in a handbag an amount of latent energy sufficient to wreck half a city . . . and yet the world still, as the Americans used to phrase it, 'fooled around' with the paraphernalia and pretensions of war."

Nuclear fission was unknown in 1914. Wells's atomic bombs, releasing the energy known to fuel the sun, were closer to fusion (hydrogen) than to fission (uranium or plutonium) bombs. Orion would have been powered by small but otherwise conventional fission bombs. Before leaving General Atomic in September 1959, Freeman Dyson did give an informal talk exploring the limits of Orion, taking as an example a hydrogen-bomb-driven interstellar ship that "could get a colony of several thousand people to Alpha Centauri, about 4 light years away, in about 150 years." Only one problem: it would require 25 million hydrogen bombs to get there—and 25 million more bombs if you wanted to stop.

Project Orion's dreams of large-scale transport of passengers and freight around the solar system were, however, fueled by the expectation that small, clean, fission-free or extremely low-fission bombs would become available by the time fleets of bomb-propelled spaceships began to fly. Although small fusion bombs never materialized, the origins and development of Orion were intimately related to the origins and development of the hydrogen bomb. Fusion was in the air in 1956. Early that spring, my father and I were walking home from his office at the Institute for Advanced Study in Princeton, New Jersey, when I found a broken fan belt lying in the road. I asked him what it was. "It's a piece of the sun," he said.

It is not surprising that my father, who had come to America in 1947 as a student of Hans Bethe, would view a fan belt not as a remnant of an automobile but as a remnant of the nearest star. It was Bethe, in 1938, who elucidated the carbon cycle that produces energy via the fusion of hydrogen and helium within the interior of stars. Other reactions in older stars produce the heavier elements resulting in the entirety of our material existence, from Earth's iron core to fan belts thrown by the side of a New Jersey road. "Stars have a life cycle much like animals," Bethe explained when accepting the Nobel Prize. "They get born, they grow, they go through a definite internal development, and finally they die, to give back the material of which they are made so that new stars may live."

"When Bethe's fundamental paper on the carbon cycle nuclear reactions appeared in 1939," explained Stan Ulam, "few, if any, could have guessed or imagined that within a very few years such reactions would be produced on Earth." At least three years before the first fission bombs were exploded, it was recognized that this would produce, for an instant, temperatures and pressures more extreme than those within the interior of the sun. If suitable nuclear fuel were subjected to these temperatures and pressures, a very small sun might be brought into existence, which in the next instant, without the gravity that holds the sun together, would blow itself cataclysmically apart. Splitting the nuclei of heavy elements like uranium (Hiroshima) or plutonium (Nagasaki) releases tremendous energy, but fusing the nuclei of light elements like hydrogen or helium might release a thousand times as much energy or more. Both Moscow and Washington were afraid they might be the next target on the list.

Such a thermonuclear, or "hydrogen," bomb could burn deuterium, a stable and easily separated isotope of hydrogen that constitutes the cheapest fuel available on Earth. The actual cost of deuterium was classified until 1955. "The basic built-in characteristic of all existing weapons," noted Freeman in 1960, "is that it is relatively much cheaper to make a big bang than a small one." In 1950, the cost of adding a kiloton's worth of deuterium to a hydrogen bomb was about sixty cents.

Public debate over Truman's decision to fast-track the development of the hydrogen bomb, against J. Robert Oppenheimer's recommendations as chairman of the General Advisory Committee of the AEC, has eclipsed the preliminaries to these events. The first series of meetings on the prospects for fusion explosions had been held in Oppenheimer's office in Berkeley, early in the summer of 1942. "We were not bound by the known conditions in a given star but we were free within considerable limits to choose our own conditions. We were embarking on astrophysical engineering," remembers Edward Teller. "By the middle of the summer of 1942, we were all convinced that the job could be done and that it would be relatively easy . . . that the atomic bomb could be easily used for a stepping-stone toward a thermonuclear explosion, which we called a 'Super' bomb."

During the Manhattan Project, a small group of physicists, spearheaded by Teller, kept working on the Super bomb and, according to Carson Mark, Hans Bethe's successor as director of Los Alamos's theoretical division, half the division's effort was devoted to the Super between 1946 and 1949. Members of the General Advisory Committee who voiced opposition to its further development, at that time, included not only

Oppenheimer but Enrico Fermi, Isodore Rabi, and James Conant. "Its use would involve a decision to slaughter a vast number of civilians," they concluded on October 30, 1949. "In determining not to proceed to develop the Super bomb, we see a unique opportunity of providing by example some limitations on the totality of war and thus of limiting the fear and arousing the hopes of mankind."

When the decisive technical breakthrough, known as the Teller-Ulam invention, appeared in early 1951, the first meeting to discuss its implications, including both Teller and Bethe, was held in Oppenheimer's office in Princeton. Oppenheimer served as director of the Institute for Advanced Study from 1947 until 1966. The genesis of the hydrogen bomb occurred partly during his tenure at Los Alamos and partly during his tenure at the Institute. The irony of history is that Oppenheimer was vilified for his opposition to deploying the hydrogen bomb, after so actively nurturing the circumstances that led to its design. During his security hearings in 1954, even Oppenheimer acknowledged that the Teller-Ulam invention was irresistible because it was "technically so sweet."

The Institute for Advanced Study, in Princeton, New Jersey, but not *at* Princeton University, occupies eight hundred acres of fields and woodlands that until 1933 was still functioning as Olden Farm. Best known as the place where Albert Einstein spent his later years, it is less known for its contributions to digital computing and the hydrogen bomb. This was no coincidence. The Institute was also home to John von Neumann, who in November 1945 persuaded the Institute trustees to break their rule of supporting only pure science and allow him to build what became the archetype of the modern digital computer, inoculating its 5,000 bytes of high-speed memory with the order codes and subroutines out of which the rudiments of an operating system and the beginnings of the software industry evolved. In 1950 and 1951, even before the machine was fully operational, von Neumann set it to work, once for as many as sixty days nonstop, on a series of calculations that led directly to the first thermonuclear bomb.

In an inconspicuous brick building, paid for by the AEC, at the edge of the Institute's woods and directly across Olden Lane from what later became my father's office in Building E, 40,960 bits of high-speed random

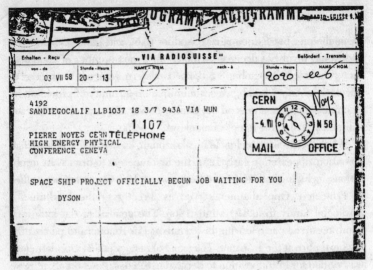

Telegram from Freeman Dyson to Pierre Noyes, July 3, 1958.

access memory flickered to life. This was not the superficial flickering of later computers equipped with banks of diagnostic indicator lights. What von Neumann termed the memory organ of the Institute computer consisted of forty cathode-ray "Williams tubes," each storing 1,024 bits of both data and instructions in a 32 x 32 array of charged spots whose state was read, written, and periodically refreshed by an electron beam scanning across its phosphorescent face. The resulting patterns, shifting 100,000 times per second, *were* the memory, completely unlike the cathode-ray tubes in later computers that merely *display* the contents of memory residing somewhere else. As the first shakedown runs of the new computer were executed, the digital revolution was ignited, but Teller's "Super" fizzled out.

The Super was, as Oppenheimer put it in 1949, "singularly proof against any form of experimental approach." How do you begin to build a hydrogen bomb, when you have no idea whether it is possible or not? You build it numerically, neutron by neutron and nanosecond by nanosecond, in the memory of a computer, first. Ulam, von Neumann, and Nick Metropolis developed the "Monte Carlo Method" of statistical approximation whereby a random sampling of events in an otherwise intractable branching process is followed through a series of representative slices in time, answering the otherwise incalculable question of whether a given configuration would go thermonuclear or not. Computers led to bombs, and bombs led to computers. Although kept largely secret, the push to develop the Super drove the initial development of the digital computers then adapted to other purposes by companies like IBM. Ralph Slutz, who worked with von Neumann on the Institute for Advanced Study computer project, remembers "a couple of people from Los Alamos" showing up as soon as the machine was provisionally operational, "with a program which they were terribly eager to run on the machine . . . starting at midnight, if we would let them have the time."

"As the results of the von Neumann–Evans calculation on the big electronic Princeton machine started to come in, they confirmed broadly what we had shown," recalls Ulam. "In spite of an initial, hopeful-looking 'flare-up,' the whole assembly started to cool down. Every few days Johnny would call in some results. 'Icicles are forming,' he would say." This evidence that the classical Super was a dead end started Ulam thinking. He soon came up with an alternative approach to achieving thermonuclear ignition whose ingenuity, elaborated by Edward Teller, was chilling to those who feared that an enemy might be thinking up a similar design.

The result was the first full-scale fusion device, "Ivy Mike," exploded at Eniwetok Atoll in the South Pacific on November 1, 1952. Mike consisted of an 82-ton tank of liquid deuterium, cooled to minus 250°K and ignited by a TX-5 fission bomb. It yielded 10.4 megatons—almost one thousand Hiroshimas—and a fireball three miles across. The Teller-Ulam invention removed the entire island of Elugelab from the map. Mike's solid-fuel, room-temperature lithium deuteride successors ("Why buy a cow when powdered milk is so cheap?") were soon weaponized, with the help of the Air Force Special Weapons Center (AFSWC), into deliverable packages that could be carried by conventional bombers and eventually by the Atlas and Titan rockets, which were already in the works. In November 1955 the Soviet Union dropped a hydrogen bomb yielding 1.6 megatons from a Tupolev bomber and the race for strategic thermonuclear weapons was on. As rockets grew larger and bombs grew smaller, both sides were pushing toward practical intercontinental ballistic missiles, or ICBMs. Inaccurate guidance, limiting the effectiveness of ballistic missiles against hardened military targets, became less of an impediment as the radius of devastation went up. It was the threat of Soviet thermonuclear ICBMs that led the launch of the Soviet Sputniks to prompt such intense response. "Americans design better automobile tail fins, but we design the best intercontinental ballistic missiles," commented one Russian scientist upon the launch of *Sputnik I.*

Childhood in the 1950s, enthused by dreams of space, was haunted by nightmares about hydrogen bombs. Sometimes my father went to Washington and came home visibly scared. Yet the architects of the H-bomb—people like Stan Ulam, Hans Bethe, Marshall Rosenbluth, and even Edward Teller—were as kind and likable as anyone else. Some, like Teller, were motivated by ideology and others were drawn to the subject simply because, to a physicist, the conditions produced by a thermonuclear explosion were just too interesting to resist. Freeman, a pacifist at the start of World War II, argued during the test-ban debate that "any country which renounces for itself the development of nuclear weapons, without certain knowledge that its adversaries have done the same, is likely to find itself in the position of the Polish Army in 1939, fighting tanks with horses." He had *not* been involved with the development of atomic weapons, having spent the war as a theoretician at RAF Bomber Command, where he learned what conventional bombing could and could not do—and how a new idea, like radar, could tip the scales. "In 1940 we owed our skins to a small number of men who had persevered with the development of weapons through the years when this kind of work was unpopular," he wrote in 1958.

Other physicists, who had helped to develop the A-bomb, thought the H-bomb was going too far. Leo Szilard, who brought the prospect of atomic weapons to Roosevelt's attention in 1939, summed up his thoughts twenty years later in *The Voice of the Dolphins,* a novella about disarmament and interspecies communication in which the dolphins succeed where physicists had failed. Oppenheimer, our neighbor in Princeton, did have a ghostlike quality, but this was the ghost of his broken spirit, not the ghost of "Death, the destroyer of worlds." When Freeman was invited to join Ted Taylor at General Atomic, he went to

Oppenheimer to request a one-year leave. "He was sympathetic," noted Freeman, "and said he felt a certain nostalgia for the days in 1942."

Despite occasional arguments in favor of first use of nuclear weapons, Los Alamos, Hiroshima, and Nagasaki produced a generation of peaceful weaponeers. Many who worked with large thermonuclear weapons systems were more afraid of smaller, tactical nuclear weapons, because their limited power was deceptively tempting and more likely to be used. The details of how to build the small bombs that would have powered Orion remain secret, while the designs of large bombs are better known. RAND studies concluded, behind closed doors, that there could be no such thing as "limited" nuclear war. There was both a cold logic behind the doctrine of Mutual Assured Destruction and a hope that out of this madness a sense of shared humanity might emerge. Once you open Pandora's box, as Ted explains it, you have to keep going, because Hope emerges last. Thermonuclear weapons, while threatening Armageddon, may indeed, as their creators hoped, have prevented "the Last War" as envisioned by H. G. Wells in 1914.

Our only hope was fear. Just as we were building up huge stockpiles of tactical and strategic nuclear weapons and setting in place hair-trigger retaliatory mechanisms that appeared to be leading us from brinkmanship to use, along came the hydrogen bomb. Where kiloton-range weapons had plausible military applications to military targets, megatonrange weapons are useful for threatening wholesale destruction of population centers and little else. The incinerations of Dresden and Hamburg by conventional bombing in World War II were explained as fortuitous if unfortunate accidents; no one fully understood the fuel requirements and meteorological conditions that caused a firestorm to form. Thermonuclear weapons could deliver these results reliably every time. When the Soviet Union exploded a three-stage bomb yielding nearly 60 megatons on October 30, 1961, it was estimated that, for a moment, the energy flux exceeded 1 percent of the entire output of the sun. Enough was enough. It was this ability to produce temperatures of a hundred million degrees, and more, that kept the cold war cold.

The genesis of Project Orion was both technically and politically interwoven with the development of hydrogen bombs. Practical two-stage thermonuclear devices required compact fission primaries to trigger thermonuclear explosions, producing a renaissance in fission-weapon design. Instead of simply exploding a stockpile weapon and measuring its yield, weaponeers began to study how the energy of a fission explosion could be directed and channeled and how that energy might be transformed. This opened two new fields of theoretical and technical expertise: bomb physics, concerned with what happens immediately; and weapons effects, concerned with what happens next. Project Orion attracted some of weaponeering's most creative minds. Ted Taylor had a gift for designing bombs and gathered around him those with gifts for predicting the results. It was people like Marshall Rosenbluth, Burt Freeman, Charles Loomis, and Harris Mayer, among others, who had the theoretical and computational tools, developed for thermonuclear weapons, to investigate the feasibility of Ted Taylor's plan.

"By the time we started work on Orion," explains Ted, "there were a whole lot of checked-out possibilities for tailoring the effects of the primary by fiddling around with the design so it would change the relative fraction of energy, in neutrons, in penetrating gammas, high-speed debris, and so on. We could pick out what we wanted, which was momentum stretched out over a long enough time so the pressures weren't intolerable but short enough so that the heat transfer wasn't intolerable either. We had a whole array of possible ways of designing the explosives to do that. This was toward what many people called the golden age of nuclear weaponeering. Orion would have gotten nowhere without some deep familiarity, mostly by Burt Freeman and Marshall Rosenbluth and then Bud Pyatt. Without their knowledge of how to do all that, the whole project would not have made sense."

Orion was the answer to the question, "What's next?" The physicists who spent the war at Los Alamos found it the most exciting time of their lives. After the end of the war there was a period of declining excitement, and then along came the hydrogen bomb. And then after the hydrogen bomb had been developed, once again the spirit of excitement of Los Alamos went into decline. "That was a time of exodus from Los Alamos," says Burt Freeman, who left Los Alamos to work on Orion with Ted. "The programs had come to a certain point and a lot of the original people that were involved with the development had left, and there was this feeling of a loss of mission there. I was looking for a new challenge, and reigniting that sense of excitement and team spirit was a big plus. Those were the good old days. And, I must say, I haven't experienced that sort of environment since."

Orion was the Teller-Ulam invention turned inside out. How to use the energy of a nuclear explosion to drive a spaceship has much in common with the problem of how to use the energy of a nuclear explosion to drive a thermonuclear reaction in a hydrogen bomb. The difficulty with the classical Super—detonating a large fission bomb next to a container of deuterium—was that the fuel would both be physically disrupted by the explosion and lose energy through radiation before it could reach the temperatures and pressures required to ignite. This was described as comparable to lighting a lump of coal with a match. Ulam's insight, delivered by Teller, was to channel the radiation produced by the primary into a cavity between a heavy, opaque outer radiation case and an inner cylindrical uranium "pusher" propelled violently inward by the pressure on its outer surface—much like Orion's pusher plate receiving a kick from a bomb. This shock compresses and heats the thermonuclear fuel, including a central "spark plug" of fissionable material, strongly enough to ignite. Since the radiation from the explosion of the primary travels much faster than the hydrodynamic shock wave, the secondary has a chance to go thermonuclear before being blown apart.

This brought the interactions between matter and radiation into a regime that was largely unexplored. What happens at the suddenly shocked surface? How energetically is the pusher propelled as a result? How transparent or how opaque to radiation is the intervening material at the time? These are exactly the questions whose answers would determine whether it is possible to propel a spaceship with nuclear bombs.

3

Ulam's Demon

Stanislaw Ulam, whose role in the Teller-Ulam invention remains disputed by Edward Teller, is securely on record as the principal inventor of space propulsion by nuclear bombs. "The day after Trinity he found himself thinking about propelling something into a ballistic trajectory," says Ted. In 1959, the AEC patented the concept of a bomb-propelled space vehicle in his and Cornelius Everett's name. "It does not matter," Ulam once said in response to a summary of Project Orion that omitted his paternity from the account. "After all, it is MY patent!" Nuclear pulse propulsion was only one of Ulam's progeny of ideas, from pure mathematics through weapons physics to what is now called the science of complexity, and is associated, thanks in part to Ulam, with his adopted home of Santa Fe.

"He was a maverick, a very complicated man, a Pole, and, above all, a study in contrasts and contradictions," says his wife, Francoise. "He lived mainly in the confines of his mind." He was also gregarious. "Many of us at the laboratory who were associated with him knew how much he disliked being alone, how he would summon us at odd times to be rescued from the loneliness of some hotel room, or from the four walls of his office, after he had exhausted his daily round of long-distance calls," says his mathematical colleague Gian-Carlo Rota. "One day I mustered the courage to ask him why he constantly wanted company and his answer gave him away. 'When I am alone,' he admitted, 'I am forced to think things out.'"

"Ulam knew something about everything," says Brian Dunne, who remembers driving the Ulams down to Point Loma from La Jolla in his Volkswagen to watch the launch of one of the explosive-driven models of Orion that were being tested in 1959. The flights depended on precisely timed sequential charges, and Ulam helped obtain some of the low-jitter detonators developed at Los Alamos to ensure the perfectly symmetrical implosion that triggers the explosion of a bomb. "He was a real singularity in many ways," confirms Bruno Augenstein, a RAND analyst and architect of the United States ICBM program who intersected periodically with Ulam during the H-bomb years. "He was simultaneously one of the smartest people that I've ever met and one of the laziest—an interesting combination." Francoise disagrees: "With his aristocratic nonchalance he gave the appearance of being lazy, but in reality he pushed himself mentally, all the time." Claire Ulam, age nine in 1953, was overheard telling a friend that "all my father does is think, think, think!"

Ulam emigrated from Poland to the United States in 1935 to join von Neumann at the Institute for Advanced Study. In 1941, upon acquiring United States citizenship, he tried to enlist in the Air Force, hoping to become a navigator if not a pilot, but due to his age and imperfect eyesight his appliction was turned down. In 1943 he asked von Neumann how he might assist in the war effort, and, as Ulam recalls, "Johnny answered with an intimation that there was interesting work going on— he could not tell me where." Ulam then received an invitation, signed by Hans Bethe, "to join an unidentified project that was doing important work, the physics having something to do with the interior of stars." He accepted, on the strength of Bethe's reputation, without knowing what he had agreed to, or where. "Soon after, other people I knew well began to vanish one after the other. Finally I learned that we were going to New Mexico, to a place not far from Santa Fe."

The Ulams, with daughter Claire on the way, arrived in Los Alamos in February 1944. "In the entire history of science there had never been anything even remotely approaching such a concentration," he noted, astonished at the team of scientists that Oppenheimer had assembled on the mesa above Santa Fe. "At thirty-four I was already one of the older people." Ulam found wartime Los Alamos a refreshing contrast to academic life. "People here were willing to assume minor roles for the sake of contributing to a common enterprise," he noted. "Jules Verne had anticipated this when he wrote about the collective effort needed for his 'Voyage to the Moon.'" Ulam's exposure to physics revealed gifts that otherwise might have gone unrecognized this late in a mathematical career. "I found out that the main ability to have was a visual, and also an almost tactile, way to imagine the physical situation, rather than a merely logical picture of the problems. One can imagine the sub-atomic world almost tangibly, and manipulate the picture dimensionally and qualitatively, before calculating more precise relationships."

For fifty years, we have separated the uses of nuclear energy into two distinct regimes: reactors and bombs. The nuclear establishment does its best to preserve the distinction: making sure that bombs *do* blow up and that reactors *don't*. The spectrum between reactors and bombs, however, is a continuum. Some of the earliest ideas for nuclear propulsion fell in the middle, intermediate between an overheated reactor and a fizzling fission bomb. The minutes of an informal meeting on nuclear rockets, held at Los Alamos on January 17, 1949, and recorded by Frederic de Hoffmann, note that "the group took as its premise that an effective method for the delivery of nuclear bombs had to be available" and considered at least one design where the "nuclear motor becomes a bomb on landing," concluding that the resulting hybrid would be inefficient both as a rocket and as a bomb. "It would also be feasible to shoot at the moon and thus obtain interesting physics data," the group added. Attendees included George Gamow, Edward Teller, and Fred Reines, as well as Ulam and de Hoffmann.

"The idea of nuclear propulsion of space vehicles was born as soon as nuclear energy became a reality," Ulam recalls. "It was an obvious thought to try and use its more powerful concentration of energy to propel vehicles with a very large payload for ambitious voyages of space exploration or even for excursions to the moon. I think Feynman was the first in Los Alamos during the war to talk about using an atomic reactor which would heat hydrogen and expel the gas at high velocity." These ideas became the basis of separate Livermore and Los Alamos efforts, later consolidated as Project Rover (named, by Herbert York, after the fictional Rover Boys) and the NERVA (Nuclear Energy for Rocket Vehicle Application) program, which remained active until 1973. All these nuclear rockets—and the parallel project to build a nuclear-powered airplane—would have been dirty at the best of times and disastrous if anything went wrong. "Fission product decay heat would cause melting and/or vaporization of the reactor within about 30 seconds after shutdown if the coolant is shut off or exhausted," noted R. W. Bussard in reviewing the prospects for a nuclear-powered Atlas missile in 1956.

Ulam began thinking about propulsion by external nuclear explosions in 1946. Preliminary calculations were recorded in a still-classified memorandum coauthored with Fred Reines in 1947. Johndale Solem, a Los Alamos physicist who has been studying next-generation Orion-type vehicles for deflection of asteroids on collision course with Earth, confirms having seen the original memo when cleaning out the T-Division safe. "I asked Fred Reines about it and he said, 'Well, Stan talked me into that one.' He wasn't about to admit he was involved in the beginning of Orion. The stuff we were throwing out here went to archives somewhere."

"I heard Stan talk about this in—maybe it was 1948," remembers Harris Mayer, a Los Alamos colleague whose insights into the opacity of matter at high temperatures were relevant both to Orion and to the hydrogen bomb. "We knew a lot about nuclear bombs. At that time we didn't know about hydrogen bombs. But his idea was very simple. If you threw a nuclear bomb out the back of a rocket ship, it exploded and gave it a kick. Now he was thinking of a rocket ship of the conventional size and class, something like the Atlas; the whole ship is maybe 100 tons. We were just brainstorming, that was the level of it, and recognized immediately that this was not a manned ship. The accelerations would just crush a person into a blot. So we didn't worry about all the other things, radioactivity and so on. And nobody did anything about it."

In 1955, with Cornelius Everett, Ulam produced a more detailed report, *On a Method of Propulsion of Projectiles by Means of External*

Nuclear Explosions, issued as a classified Los Alamos document, LAMS-1955. Having the document number match the year of publication was a singularity of which Ulam was especially proud. "Repeated nuclear explosions outside the body of a projectile are considered as providing a means to accelerate such objects to velocities of the order of 10^6 cm/sec . . . in the range of the missiles considered for intercontinental warfare and even more perhaps, for escape from the earth's gravitational field, for unmanned vehicles," Ulam and Everett explained. In reviewing the thinking behind these ideas, "some of which originated as long as ten years ago," Ulam and Everett followed the logical progression that leads from the energy limitations of conventional rockets to the temperature limitations of an internal combustion nuclear rocket to the breakthrough that becomes possible if you take a nuclear reactor to its extreme—the explosion of a bomb—and isolate the resulting high temperatures from the ship. "The scheme proposed in the present report involves the use of a series of expendable reactors (fission bombs) ejected and detonated at a considerable distance from the vehicle, which liberate the required energy in an external 'motor' consisting essentially of empty space. The critical question about such a method concerns its ability to draw on the real reserves of nuclear power liberated at bomb temperatures without smashing or melting the vehicle."

Ulam and Everett proposed ejecting disks of lightweight plastic propellant separately from the bombs. "The vehicle is considered to be saucer-shaped, of diameter about 10 meters, sufficient at any rate to intercept all or most of the exploding propellant. Its final mass is perhaps 12 tons. . . . The bombs are ejected at something like one-second intervals from the base of the rocket and are detonated at a distance of some 50 meters from the base. Synchronized with this, disk-shaped masses of propellant are ejected in such a way that the rocket-propellant distance is about 10 meters at the instant the exploding bomb hits it. The propellant is raised to high temperature, and, in expanding, transmits momentum to the vehicle." The ship would carry about fifty bombs, each weighing about half a ton, of roughly one kiloton yield. "The accelerations of the order of 10,000 g are certainly large," they admitted. Passengers or fragile cargo would be prohibited, and control mechanisms would have to be hardened against shock.

After hearing the news that *Sputnik* had been launched, Ted Taylor began thinking about adding shock absorbers to make the impulse tolerable to a human crew. "That night of thinking about the thing," he recalls, "I derived for myself the notion that if you really added together the features that you wanted of any vehicles for exploring the solar system—the whole thing, not just near in—you're led directly to energy on the scale of a lot of nuclear weapons. And having been led to that, in thinking about what might be done, I began saying, 'Gee, that's what Stan Ulam's been talking about all these years.' I had read LAMS-1955, and Stan and I, every now and then we'd get together at his house or in his office or somewhere, eating lunch in the cafeteria, and talk about his propulsion idea, and how to get people interested in it and get it off the ground."

When the proposal for Project Orion was first circulated in Washington in 1958, both Hans Bethe and Stan Ulam lent support. Ulam testified in favor of Orion before the Joint Committee on Atomic Energy, explaining to the assembled congressmen in January 1958 that "it is almost like Jules Verne's idea of shooting a rocket to the moon." In April he spoke again to the committee, emphasizing that "it appears that a big ship, with payloads of the order of 1,000 or several thousands of tons, can be made to travel by such propulsion. . . . These planned vehicles are very large affairs. It is not a question of 'space capsules' but comfortable quarters for occupants of such a ship." In response to concerns that General Atomic was absconding with a concept originated at the national weapons lab, he wrote to Senator Clinton P. Anderson, chairman of the committee, that "Dr. Taylor is one of the most inventive young scientists in this country, and if not for him, the project would probably still be in the form of a purely theoretical scheme."

"The spaceship could transport hundreds or thousands of people," Ulam later explained. He tried to interest George Kistiakowsky, President Eisenhower's scientific advisor, "but his reception of it was not enthusiastic." Ulam's own ideas for space travel left the limited horizons of Washington far behind. On April 1, 1958, he wrote a brief Los Alamos report, *On the Possibility of Extracting Energy from Gravitational Systems by Navigating Space Vehicles*, describing how a spacecraft might operate as a gravitational "Maxwell's demon," amplifying a limited supply of fuel and propellant by using computational intelligence to

One-meter-diameter tethered model suspended from the Atlas missile test tower at Point Loma in preparation for single-shot high-explosive tests.

select a trajectory that harvested energy from celestial bodies as it passed by.

James Clerk Maxwell was the author of Maxwell's equations formalizing the concept of an electromagnetic field and namesake for the Maxwellian distribution of kinetic energy among the particles of a gas. In 1867 he conceived an imaginary being—termed "Maxwell's demon" by William Thomson (Lord Kelvin) in 1874—"whose faculties are so sharpened that he can follow every molecule in its course." The demon appears to defy the second law of thermodynamics by heating a compartment in an otherwise closed system, without the expenditure of physical work, by opening and closing a vanishingly small trap door to let high-velocity molecules in and low-velocity molecules out. Resolving this apparent paradox led to advances first in thermodynamics and later in quantum mechanics. Leo Szilard showed in 1929 that even if the operation of the trap door is perfectly effortless, the cost of making the observations required to distinguish fast molecules from slow molecules assures that the laws of thermodynamics are upheld.

A Maxwellian distribution of energy among a collection of particles in thermodynamic equilibrium implies the equipartition of energy, meaning that kinetic energy tends to equalize across the particle population over time. Light particles end up moving at relatively high velocities and heavy particles end up moving relatively slowly. A 4,000-ton spaceship ends up moving faster than a planet—given enough time. If applying the kinetics of a gas to interplanetary transport seems far-fetched, remember that Maxwell first developed these ideas, later adapted to thermodynamics, in an attempt to explain the distribution, by size and velocity, of particles that make up Saturn's rings.

"As examples of the situation we have in mind," explained Ulam, "assume a rocket cruising between the sun and Jupiter, i.e., in an orbit approximately that of Mars, with an energy in reserve which would allow the kinetic energy of the vehicle to increase by a factor like 2. The question is whether, by planning suitable approaches to Jupiter and then closer approaches to the sun, it could acquire, say, 10 times more energy. It is clear, on general thermodynamic grounds, that 'in general' the equipartition of energy may take place. . . . Nothing is said, however, about the times necessary for effecting this. They might be of super-astronomical lengths. . . . With an operating intelligence perhaps this approach to near-equilibrium could be made vastly more rapid. The problem is whether, by steering the rocket, one can to some modest extent acquire the properties of a Maxwell demon, i.e., plan the changes in the trajectory in such a way as to shorten by many orders of magnitude the time necessary for acquisition of very high velocities."

"I remember Stan talking about being able to make a Maxwell's demon, that it could be a possible physical thing," Ted Taylor recalls. Ulam hinted that he was thinking about the still-classified possibilities of Orion, whose cruising speed, for the 4,000-ton version, was estimated at 20 km/second. "The above discussion is, of course, intended for a purely theoretical, mathematical question," he wrote. "Even so, during the next few decades large objects may be constructed with a cruising velocity of 20 kilometers a second, and there will still be some additional energy left." Although gravitational energy is available apparently for free, the intelligence required to operate such an equipartition engine would have its costs, especially when even small computers, slower than a pocket calculator of today, consumed kilowatts to operate at kilocycle speeds while weighing tons. "The computations required to plan changes in the trajectory might be of prohibitive length and complication," Ulam warned.

Project Orion had Ulam's enthusiastic support. He lobbied Congress, pushed for support within Los Alamos, and encouraged Ted and the rest of the Orion gang. "Meteors, some of which come in at thirty kilometers per second, do not get excessively chewed up, even though presumably they were not especially engineered for it," he wrote to Ted in 1962, when there were worries about whether the surface of the pusher plate could withstand being hit by the propellant cloud. After the death of Project Orion he continued to believe in its resurrection, perhaps as a joint U.S.-U.S.S.R. mission at some more cooperative time. Outshadowed by the success of the Teller-Ulam invention, Orion was a hope that returned to confinement after the 1963 atmospheric test-ban treaty began to close the lid on Pandora's box.

"It was such a crazy idea, really. One of those wonderful dreams," says Francoise Ulam. "Oh, but they had a good time in California, and we went and visited them once and saw one little puff. The little thing went off and then came back with a parachute, at Point Loma. They had fun, but did they really think it would go?"

4

General Atomic

"I wanted to do something about the hydrogen bomb and nobody else wanted to," complains Edward Teller, remembering the postwar years at Los Alamos, before the explosion of "Joe 1," the first Soviet A-bomb in August 1949. "Bradbury practically forbade me to work on it. And the one man who wanted to do it more than I was Freddy de Hoffmann."

Frederic de Hoffmann, a Viennese student in his last year of physics at Harvard, arrived at Lamy, New Mexico, the railhead for Los Alamos, aboard the Santa Fe *Super Chief* just after Christmas of 1943. He was nineteen years old, unusual even for Los Alamos, which was "in the hands of youngsters," as Francoise Ulam, then twenty-five, recalls. He was immediately interviewed by Edward Teller, the Super Chief himself.

"That nuclear fission could theoretically be turned into a nuclear explosive was known to me from my physical chemistry courses at Harvard," de Hoffmann wrote. "That there was indeed such a project to do so took me by complete surprise." He worked on a wide range of problems in Hans Bethe's theoretical division, including the first criticality experiments, performed with a device known as the Dragon. A cylindrical slug of uranium hydride, dropped by hand through a uranium hydride ring, would go super-critical for a fraction of a second. This was equivalent to suddenly pulling all the control rods out of a nuclear reactor, or tickling the tail of an atomic bomb. The Dragon produced, for an instant, the kind of near-disaster that reactor engineers would soon go into business trying to prevent. Later in the war, de Hoffmann's group made critical mass measurements on mocked-up bomb assemblies, approximating spherical configurations by surrounding a 6.2-kg sphere of plutonium 239 with cubes of neutron-reflecting tamper material set in place by hand. De Hoffmann's friend Harry Daghlian received a lethal dose of radiation, on August 21, 1945, as a result of accidentally assembling a critical mass. "We had a rule not to work alone at night and furthermore always to add the last uranium brick from the side," said de Hoffmann. "Harry Daghlian was alone at night and added the fatal brick from the top when it slipped from his hand."

It was de Hoffmann who performed the initial computations for Edward Teller on the feasibility of the Super bomb. He also calculated the ballistic trajectories for "Fat Man" and "Little Boy," the first two air-dropped atomic bombs. "Making the bomb tables for Hiroshima and Nagasaki is etched so strongly in my mind because it really brought me to the reality of the end use of our scientific and technical experimentation." When de Hoffmann returned to Los Alamos in early 1949, he worked with Teller on the Super full-time. "Even before the Soviet explosion he felt that the hydrogen bomb must be our main task," explained Teller. "Now he acted like a man who has been freed from a terrible restriction."

When the Teller-Ulam invention surfaced, Ulam and Teller coauthored a report. "What we wrote up was really qualitative," says Teller. "I gave the quantitative detail to Freddy de Hoffmann. In a very short time, in a week, he wrote it up, and put it in under my name alone." De Hoffmann became Teller's protégé and general factotum, acting as his official deputy during the years 1949–1951. "I remember one flight back to Los Alamos from an American Physical Society conference in Los Angeles, where Teller and I were on the same plane," Ted Taylor recalls. "Then the plane landed in Phoenix with engine trouble. We spent six or eight hours there talking quite freely about bombs and so on. And then we got on the plane and he had called Freddy, who drove to

Albuquerque and met the plane in the middle of the night." At General Atomic, de Hoffmann established a motor pool, with visitors of any importance being assigned a car and driver during their stay. "I think one of the reasons Freddy used to make such a big point about drivers," Ted speculates, "is that he had been a driver himself."

After leaving Los Alamos, de Hoffmann collaborated with Hans Bethe and Sylvan Schweber at Cornell on a now classic text, *Mesons and Fields,* completed his Ph.D., and eventually became chairman of the Committee of Senior Reviewers of the AEC. He helped to enforce AEC security rules, deciding what nuclear information should be kept secret and what information, such as the design of commercial reactors, could safely be revealed. When the United Nations held the first Atoms for Peace conference in Geneva in the summer of 1955, de Hoffmann was one of an international team of scientific secretaries assigned to determine, in advance of the official conference, not only what information would be exchanged, but how to distribute public credit for efforts that had been conducted in secrecy so far. The role of international diplomat suited de Hoffmann well. As an undergraduate at Harvard he had founded an organization called the United Nations Council that "invited big wheels to come down from New York and give a talk," according to classmate Ralph Stahl, who joined General Atomic in 1956. "Fred would go down to the railroad station and meet the guest and take him out to dinner and then introduce him. It was a wonderful way to get to meet really important people."

The Geneva conference was the first meeting between nuclear scientists from East and West. Although the details of civilian reactor design would not be declassified by the AEC until June of 1956, the foundations of a new industry were established and an international community among nuclear scientists was formed. Fission power plants were already being planned, and it was widely assumed that something like the Teller-Ulam invention would soon precipitate an advance from fission to fusion power as dramatic as the recent leap from fission to fusion bombs. Controlled fusion, classified under the code name "Project Sherwood," appeared closer in 1955 than it does today.

Big business was watching. General Dynamics, with close to $1 billion in sales, was the largest defense contractor in the United States. Its

Electric Boat Division in Groton, Connecticut, was building nuclear submarines and its Convair Astronautics Division in San Diego was building Atlas ICBMs. The chairman of General Dynamics, John Jay Hopkins, believed it was time to enter the nuclear energy business and asked Edward Teller for advice. Teller answered: "Frederic de Hoffmann." Hopkins gave de Hoffmann $10 million to start things up. "We are establishing here a timeless institution, a thing of the mind and spirit, devoted to Man's progress," he proclaimed at the founding of de Hoffmann's laboratory in 1956.

"Freddy de Hoffmann was Napoleonic by nature," explains Brian Dunne. "He studied Napoleon's life as a boy. He had this dream, this vision, but it was driven by grandiosity. Those kinds of fevers are catching things." Not only did he "have the AEC in his pocket," a prerequisite to getting reactor designs licensed for commercial use, he understood and was able to transcend the factions that had divided the nuclear weapons community since the end of World War II. "You've got the Livermore gang and you've got the Los Alamos gang, two different cultures," says Dunne. "Acolytes of Teller, disciples of Bethe. They are different tribes, warring tribes. Teller and Freddy de Hoffmann had this relationship that was separate from the tribal wars."

General Atomic was founded on July 18, 1955. De Hoffmann began assembling the nucleus of his staff, beginning with physicist Ed Creutz, who had worked on the first homogeneous-fuel reactor, the "water boiler," at Los Alamos, and conducted the first full-scale high-explosive test of an implosion assembly, the day before the Alamogordo test. After the war, Creutz was giving a talk on reactor physics and needed to give a rough estimate of how many neutrons are released at each fission of a uranium nucleus, a number still classified at the time. Knowing the value was more than 2 and less than 3, he said 2.5, precisely the value that was supposed to be kept unknown. Creutz was soon visited by de Hoffmann, who notified him, politely, that he had violated security rules. The next time Creutz heard from de Hoffmann it was to offer him a job. "He asked me if I would care to join him in the creation of a new atomic energy company," says Creutz. "I said, 'That would be fun but would cost millions of dollars.' He said, 'We have ten million. Now we need to recruit the best people in the business to do the job right.'"

They also needed a name. "I suggested a couple of things, like 'Useful Atoms' or something like that, something silly," remembers Creutz. "De Hoffmann said, 'No. I've got a better idea. We'll call it General Atomic.'" Money was no obstacle. "Somebody said de Hoffmann was a man who knew every millionaire in the world," continues Creutz. "That's probably a slight exaggeration. He knew an awful lot of rich and influential people, and John Jay Hopkins—the father of General Dynamics—was very fond of Fred, and had a lot of contacts. So Fred was very good at not only going to people and getting money but going to people and getting them to go to people to get money."

De Hoffmann and Hopkins flew around the United States looking at potential laboratory sites, courted by local politicians wherever they went. They distilled the prospects down to Cambridge, Massachusetts, in the East and either Monterey or San Diego in the West. Mayor Charles C. Dail of San Diego, already home to Convair, held the winning hand: vacant "pueblo land" remaining from the original Spanish grant to the Pueblo of San Diego in 1791. The boundaries extended from the Pacific Ocean inland to where Interstate 805 is today and northward up the coast past La Jolla to Del Mar. Large areas remained unencumbered in 1956. "Because the early city fathers were inclined to dispose of it too easily (North Island was sold for a barrel of whiskey), the city charter of 1889 contained a provision that no pueblo land be sold until 1930," it was reported in announcing a plebiscite on whether to grant General Atomic a laboratory site. "The 1931 charter contained a provision that no pueblo land north of the San Diego River could be sold without a council ordinance and majority approval of the voters. Proposition H authorizes sale and conveyance of 320 acres of pueblo land to General Atomic for a nuclear research center on the east side of Highway 101 half a mile north of La Jolla Junction. It requires majority approval." The measure passed by a margin of more than 6 to 1.

General Atomic—now General Atomics—occupies some of the most expensive real estate in the United States. The nearby oceanfront bluffs and canyons, south of another 1,000 acres of pueblo land that became Torrey Pines State Park, are now rimmed with multimillion-dollar homes. De Hoffmann's was one of the first. The University of California at San Diego, immediately south of General Atomic, has expanded to fill

the land it was later granted. A checkerboard of pharmaceutical companies, research institutes, medical clinics, and the odd brokerage firm has
saturated the landscape far into the desert inland.

In 1956 the Torrey Pines mesa was largely untouched. La Jolla was a
quiet retirement enclave, and to the north, between the outpost of the
Scripps Institution of Oceanography and the horse-racing track at Del
Mar, there was little development except an abandoned World War II
military staging base and the occasional gas station as Highway 101
meandered its way, pre-interstate, up the coast. "Mayor Dail, Fred,
Hopkins, and I visited the land, which was then a cow pasture," recalls
Creutz. "Stepping carefully we walked around the mesa, and in the distance was the dome of Palomar observatory. We pointed this out to Hopkins, who said, not as another person might, 'Oh, we can see the dome,'
but, 'Oh, they can see us.'"

Within two years de Hoffmann transformed the site into a Xanadu.
"If science is to flourish," he said in reviewing the successes of Los
Alamos, "conditions for men in their twenties should be made as ideal
as possible." During the Manhattan Project, he noted, "the distinction
between pure science and application was nonexistent." At General
Atomic, theoreticians, experimentalists, and technicians worked in close
proximity, while academic traditions such as weekly colloquia, visiting
fellowships, and peer-reviewed publications coexisted with an aggres-
sive patent department and glossy annual reports. Guest speakers as far
removed from nuclear physics as Margaret Mead were brought in to
give talks.

The architects hired to design the laboratory, says Creutz, "came up
with what they called a 'campus plan': here's the physics building, here's
a street, here's the chemistry building. I don't want that. I had seen
unfortunate divisions separating the contributions by various disci-
plines on some university campuses. I want the chemistry building and
the physics building to be the same building. I don't want people to feel
they are separate entities if we're working together on new ideas, so I
came up with the circular plan, with the library in the center." The
library was encompassed by a large, three-quarter-of-a-circle building,
appearing from above like Saturn with a bite taken out of its rings. Satellite laboratories were distributed elsewhere about the site.

By June 1958 there were four laboratory buildings, a prototype reactor capable of pulses up to 1,500 megawatts, a 32-million-electron-volt linear accelerator, a critical-assembly building, and a 48,000-square-foot administration building, flanked by a garden featuring a 250-foot-long ornamental lagoon. A year later there were 250,000 square feet of buildings, housing some 100 individual laboratories, and another 100,000 square feet of laboratories were being built. By 1960 there were 700 technical people on staff, more than 100 with Ph.D.s.

The site also included a health club, medical facility, tennis courts, swimming pool, and cafeteria. "It was a fabulously plush time at General Atomic in those days," says Kedar (Bud) Pyatt, a young physicist who arrived in 1959. "It was really due to Freddy's attitude. He sold John Jay Hopkins on the idea, give him ten years and enough money and he would—I loved the speech he always gave—'bring the sun down to the earth.' Freddy's attitude was: give me a room full of theoretical physicists and I'll conquer the world. He told Ted and Lothar Nordheim, 'Here's the money to support the hiring of ten young theorists per year. You don't have to have a project for them to work on, just hire ten young theorists.' I took the job and came there and asked what was I supposed to do. And Ted's comment was, 'Why don't you read for a while and think of something you can do that's creative.' It was Nirvana on earth for a physicist."

"Freddy de Hoffmann was my first encounter with the world of Big Business," remembers Freeman. "He was a first-rate physicist who also just had a good head for business. I had never before met anybody with the authority to make decisions so quickly and with so little fuss." Most of General Atomic's staff had worked on big projects during the recent war. Technical and political obstacles were seen as challenges to be overcome. If specialized tools or facilities were needed they were either purchased or they were built. Nothing, except the construction of nuclear explosives—a province that belonged to Los Alamos, Livermore, and Sandia National Laboratories—was out of bounds. According to David Weiss, who joined General Atomic in 1959 when it appeared that test versions of Orion might soon be launched, de Hoffmann "wanted to build the whole thing himself, like in a nineteenth-century shipyard, where you had your own foundry to make castings for all the metal parts."

Marshall Rosenbluth (left) and Ted Taylor (right) with memorial plaque to Frederic de Hoffmann at General Atomic (now General Atomics) headquarters, La Jolla, California, November 1999.

"Freddy behaved as king of the realm," explains Ted. "He could do whatever he wanted, and that meant that things could happen fast. Something new would turn up in Orion, and within minutes of the time Freddy was told about it, he would go get somebody to do something constructive about it, like setting up meetings with people in Washington." His access to the highest levels of government, industry, and academia was unmatched.

"De Hoffmann loved to collect Nobel laureates. It was almost like collecting butterflies," says Brian Dunne. He also collected patents. "Every year Freddy de Hoffmann would go before the board of General Dynamics, and he'd walk in and lay down a string of patents in front of these General Dynamics directors, and they would think this was the coming wealth of the future, and they'd give him the money."

Despite the initial emphasis on peaceful atoms, a large share of General Atomic's cash flow came from weapons-related contracts with the AEC and the Department of Defense. Besides possible military applications of Orion, and the recurring problem of producing tritium for thermonuclear weapons, there was a classified ship reactor program and a series of small self-contained reactors to supply electricity for surveillance platforms in space. The Air Force Special Weapons Center in Albuquerque, New Mexico, administered the Orion contract for ARPA and kept the money flowing to General Atomic for other projects including Project Defender (ballistic missile defense), Casaba-Howitzer (directed-energy weapons), TREES (Transient Radiation Effects on Electronic Systems), and a whole series of weapons-effects studies that sometimes came close to infringing on weapon design. "Where do you draw the line between effects and design?" asks Burt Freeman. "We got our hands slapped a bit, on that. The effects are design-dependent. And the weapon designer, not having any concern about effects, stops at a place where he feels that his job is done. Now, the effects person wants to pick them up, but there's a gray area in between, in time or space, where the one has to start and the other stop."

No one except Freddy de Hoffmann could get away with hiring some of the leading talent away from the two national weapons laboratories, to work on a project involving large numbers of bombs, without drawing fire from the AEC. At General Atomic, AEC security procedures were visible but unobtrusive. "Anything involving bomb data had to be in special safes and under much more physical protection than ordinary military secrets," Freeman remembers. "There was one building called the H building—it's the shape of an H—and that's where everything was. It had the appropriate guards, but once you had the badge and the guards knew who you were it was easy enough to get in and out. But there were rules; for instance if we brought in a visitor we couldn't let him go to the bathroom by himself."

Air Force physicists, Air Force officers, and Air Force generals made regular visits to General Atomic, and always came away impressed. "They were in awe when they came out here," remembers Brian Dunne. "A lot of it was Freddy with his round buildings and swimming pools and tennis courts. They had never seen a facility of that kind—and the quality of people that he attracted." Air Force Colonel Don Prickett, a physicist and one of the AFSWC project officers responsible for Project Orion, attended the briefing on Project Orion at General Atomic with General Thomas Power of the Strategic Air Command, who made the statement that "whoever controls Orion will control the world." Prickett remembers General Power's enthusiasm for Orion, and the dinner that followed the briefing. "It was the last abalone I ever had."

Without Frederic de Hoffmann and General Atomic, Project Orion would never have had a chance. "When you look back on the architecture—the buildings and the way it's put together—somebody put a lot of money in," says physicist Bill Vulliet, who came to General Atomic from Convair in July 1958. "And for a long time after they got the buildings, there was still a lot of money flowing in there. And it's my guess— just a guess—that it was the bomb, and the end of the war, that allowed this to last such a long time. And physicists were closer to God than anybody else."

5

TRIGA

Project Orion was launched officially in 1958, but its crew began to assemble in 1956. When General Atomic received the green light from John Jay Hopkins, Frederic de Hoffmann did not wait around for buildings to get built. Operating out of an office within General Dynamics' Stromberg-Carlson Division on Hancock Street in downtown San Diego, near what is now Lindbergh Field, he went straight to work, without laboratories and tennis courts but with people and ideas. In January 1956 de Hoffmann's new company rented an abandoned schoolhouse near Point Loma, vacant since the closure of the Frontier housing project that had accommodated aircraft workers during the war. In 1943, Robert Oppenheimer and the U.S. Army had requisitioned the Los Alamos Ranch School to house the initial group of physicists assembled to build an atomic bomb. Thirteen years later, de Hoffmann reinvited many of the same nuclear physicists, and their promising younger colleagues, to gather at the Barnard Street School for the summer of 1956.

De Hoffmann's first target for recruitment from Los Alamos was Lois Iles—secretary of the Theoretical Division. According to Harris Mayer, "That's when Carson Mark hit the roof: 'You can take my Ted Taylor, you can take my scientists, but you can't take Lois Iles!'" Lois Iles did not want to work directly for de Hoffmann, but agreed to come to San Diego if she could work for somebody else, so, says Ed Creutz, "Fred then hired me, and Lois came to work for me. For the first year, Lois and I were the personnel department. In the summer of '56, she made all of the arrangements for the visitors and consultants. I think that she and I hired at least a hundred people with no other help." Lois Iles stayed on through all of Project Orion, and, as Ted puts it, "She had a lot to do with how fast everything went."

F. W. (Bill) Simpson, then the technical librarian for the AEC in Washington, D.C., was flown out to San Diego by de Hoffmann on February 28, 1956. "Fred spent most of two days with me, with a driver, showing me around town," Simpson remembers. "And he took me to the little red schoolhouse. It was dusty and cobwebby, and it looked like hell. Well, by the end of April, they had cleaned that place up, and painted things, and it was sparkling new-looking. And in the patio he had picnic benches and huge palm trees and a lot of bougainvillea and other things. They were in these huge nursery containers, looking forward to a place where they could be planted permanently. And he said, to the guy in charge of the grounds, 'I want flowers and blossoms. When people think of California, they think of flowers and blossoms. So get me some.'" De Hoffmann's instructions to Simpson, who became one of General Atomic's first employees, were to order enough books and journals so the physicists would have a working library as well as bougainvillea when they showed up. And they did.

In contrast to the Jeeps and barracks of Los Alamos, de Hoffmann insisted that transportation and accommodations be first class. "That first summer was just fabulous," remembers Ralph Stahl. "The first thing de Hoffmann did in preparation for that summer, he established a motor pool. Nice cars and drivers." Freeman Dyson wanted to see the California desert and mentioned this to his driver, who "was buying up land in El Cajon just at the right time, and didn't need to be a chauffeur anymore" and spent an entire Sunday giving him a tour. "De Hoffmann rented lovely houses for all of the visitors," says Jonny Stahl, who worked in the stenographic pool. "They weren't paid, but boy they had a lovely place to live and nice things to do for the summer." Jonny remembers deciphering Teller's Hungarian accent during the day and lengthy Scrabble tournaments at night. "I beat them all. I was very good at that. That's what I remember about that summer, that I could beat these brilliant people at Scrabble."

"Those of us who started General Atomic didn't much know the meaning of working hours," de Hoffmann explained. "We didn't know the words 9 to 5." Ed Creutz, director of the laboratory that did not yet exist, helped set up the lunch tables in the courtyard of the school. "We covered these with blackboards, complete with chalk and erasers. The idea was to continue thought and discussion during lunch." The schoolhouse came to life. "The drinking fountains were down very low for children and the blackboards were low," remembered Brian Dunne, Ted's college roommate from Caltech who soon joined the schoolhouse gang. "The machine shop used to be the kindergarten and all the drawers were way down there next to the floor."

Participants in the summer-long workshop ranged from well-knowns such as Edward Teller, Hans Bethe, and Marshall Rosenbluth to people like Manhattan Project nuclear chemist Bob Duffield, who had played a supporting role in the development of the atomic bomb. "Plutonium— it's warm, it's decaying all the time," explains Dunne. "They made this tiny piece of it, and it was so valuable they didn't dare send it by airplane to Los Alamos. They didn't even dare send it by train. They looked around for the most reliable way to get it there. And they chose Bob Duffield to haul it there in his old Oldsmobile." When General Atomic decided to send a prototype reactor to the second Geneva conference on peaceful uses of atomic energy in September 1958, it was Bob Duffield who got it there in working order and on time.

By 1956, the first micrograms of plutonium metal that had been produced in Chicago in November 1943 had grown into an industry whose scale was known to people like de Hoffmann but still largely hidden from public view. Enormous, industrial-scale operations such as Hanford in Washington State and Oak Ridge in Tennessee, built during the Manhattan Project, had expanded their production after the war, supplying the growing stockpile of U.S. weapons and a growing number of nuclear tests. The launch of the *Nautilus* in 1955 led the way to a fleet of nuclear submarines, and nuclear-powered aircraft, nuclear-powered surface ships, and nuclear-powered space vehicles were expected to be next. Amounts, costs, and production capacities of nuclear material were still strictly classified, leading to a vast invisible economy governed by the AEC. It was evident to General Dynamics, and others, that nuclear power stations would be the way to connect this hidden economy to the visible economy, with what promised to be lucrative results.

"We all knew even in 1937 that the world would soon run out of coal and oil," says Freeman, who, with many of his colleagues, expected a world dominated by nuclear power long before the century was out. Freddy's invitation to La Jolla was a chance to repeat some of the technical challenges of Los Alamos, without the bomb project's moral qualms. "It was a marvelous summer," says Freeman, who lived in an apartment at the foot of Nautilus Street, a block from the legendary surfing beach at Windansea. "We had all of these people lecturing in the mornings and then having brainstorming sessions in the afternoons. I've never been involved in anything that worked so well. Freddy was the conductor of the orchestra. He never seemed to be harassed and he never seemed to be exerting authority, but somehow he made everything happen. He was always there when you needed him." The first order of business was to decide what kinds of reactors the group should design. It was Edward Teller, according to Ted, who stood up and said: "What the world needs is a safe reactor." Not only idiot-proof, but Ph.D.-proof. Inherent safety "must be guaranteed by the laws of nature and not merely by the details of its engineering," Freeman explained.

"There was a meeting at my house late one afternoon and into the night," recalls de Hoffmann. "We decided to decide what nuclear product was needed. We felt an ultra-safe research reactor was a finite enough project, that we could tackle this head-on and bring it about. Two of the younger members of the group, Freeman Dyson and Ted Taylor, were so inspired that, that night, they invented the uranium-zirconium hydride reactor." The patent was granted to Freeman Dyson, Ted Taylor, and Andrew McReynolds, whose rights were sold, according to custom, to General Atomic for one dollar each. This was the best three dollars that General Atomic ever spent. The reactor became known as TRIGA: Training, Research, Isotopes, General Atomic. Some

General Atomic from the air, looking north, 1964.

sixty-five TRIGAs have been installed on five continents, making it the best-selling reactor in the world. Producing everything from short-lived isotopes for use in hospitals to pulses as high as 2,000 megawatts for scientific research, TRIGA is the only nuclear reactor design that has consistently turned a profit for forty years.

Most nuclear reactors are governed by control rods of neutron-absorbing material inserted into the chain-reacting fissile core. Control rods make the difference between a critical mass that forms a reactor and a critical mass that forms a fizzling atomic bomb. "The result of suddenly pulling out the control rods," Freeman explains, "would in most cases be a catastrophic accident, including as one of its minor consequences the death of the idiot who pulled the rods." Such an accident would be similar to what did happen at Los Alamos when a neutron-reflecting brick slipped from Harry Daghlian's hand, or what might have happened if the two parts of the super-critical Dragon had become jammed. Reactors have elaborate safety mechanisms to ensure that the control rods cannot be suddenly removed. This was not enough for Teller, who, as Freeman relates, decided that they needed to design a reactor that would be "safe even in the hands of an idiot clever enough to bypass the entire control system and blow out the control rods with dynamite." Teller pushed for the safe reactor with the same intensity he had pushed for the hydrogen bomb. "Some of his ideas were brilliant, some were practical, and a few were brilliant and practical," Freeman says. "His intuition and my mathematics fitted together in the design of the safe reactor just as Dick Feynman's intuition and my mathematics had fitted together in the understanding of the electron."

To make TRIGA inherently safe required a prompt negative temperature coefficient, meaning that as soon as the reactor core starts heating up, the rate of fission immediately drops. The key physical principle is the warm neutron effect: neutrons are *less* likely to produce fission as their temperature goes up. Conventional reactors achieve a negative temperature coefficient by surrounding the fuel elements with a moderator such as water that raises the neutron temperature as it heats up. But if the control rods are removed suddenly, this external thermal moderation may not have time to take effect before the reactor core overheats and melts. If an effective moderator, such as hydrogen, could be incorporated *within* the fuel, the rise in neutron temperature would be prompt. TRIGA's inventors theorized that zirconium hydride would do the job. Hydrogen atoms are bound within a tetrahedral lattice of zirconium—which has one of the lowest neutron capture cross sections of any structural material—so that the evenly spaced quantum energy levels of the bound hydrogen maximize the warm neutron effect. Massoud Simnad, an Iranian metallurgist, soon developed an alloy of uranium hydride and zirconium hydride that worked as the theoreticians hoped. Some of TRIGA's prototype fuel elements have remained in operation for more than forty years.

As warm-neutron theory was translated into a working reactor, the foundations of Project Orion began to form. Just as at Los Alamos, the barriers between theoreticians and engineers were lowered and everything moved faster as a result. "I am amusing myself with uranium reactors and I find it absorbingly interesting to think about them," Freeman wrote to his parents in August 1956. "Probably this summer is a turningpoint in my life. I find the atomic energy business not only congenial, but also find I am good at it. My real talent is perhaps not so much in pure science as in the practical development of it. Just as Papa would never make music to himself in an ivory tower but always in the context of a particular group of people who would play it." It was Stanley Koutz, Peter Fortescue, Brian Dunne, Robert Duffield, Ralph Stahl, and other experimentalists, technicians, and engineers who translated the theory of warm neutrons into a working reactor in under two years. "Freeman's warm-neutron paper was like the first draft of what you'd put on a patent application," says Dunne. "He gave guesses as to the total amount of U-238, U-235, zirconium, and hydrogen. It was a description of a workable reactor. I was struggling around trying to find one, and there it was, and it was clear."

The first prototype TRIGA was operational in May 1958. By September, when TRIGA was exhibited in Geneva, orders were pouring in. "TRIGA was one of the grandest exhibits in the show—everyone wanted to see the blue light," says Brian Dunne. "They sold those things like hotcakes. Without TRIGA on the rails and selling briskly none of these other things would have been as easy." TRIGA gave General Atomic credibility in high places and Project Orion was next. The sales pitch to the board of General Dynamics was simple. "Here's the guy who invented TRIGA, and now he's really got this big, fantastic idea," says Ed Creutz.

In June 1959, de Hoffmann brought in Niels Bohr, who had tried to engage Churchill, Roosevelt, and Stalin in a joint dialogue on atomic weapons and had initiated the 1955 Geneva conference on peaceful uses of atomic energy, to dedicate the new lab at Torrey Pines. The ceremony was followed by a demonstration putting the reactor's inherent safety to the test. "Niels Bohr pressed the switch and a muffled hiss was heard from the sudden release of compressed air that was used to pull the control rods at high speed out of the TRIGA core," Freeman reported. "The pointer on the large dial, which was graduated to show the power output of the TRIGA in megawatts, swung over instantaneously to 1,500 megawatts and then quickly subsided to half a megawatt. After the ceremony we went and saw it sitting quietly at the bottom of its pool of cooling water. Here it was. It was hard to believe. How could one believe that nature would pay attention to all the theoretical arguments and calculations that we had fought over in the schoolhouse three years earlier? But here was the proof. Warm neutrons really worked."

Bohr, who "loved technical toys, just the opposite of Oppenheimer," according to Freeman, wanted to know what Ted and Freeman were up to next. "Being a Danish citizen and having no need to know, we couldn't tell him any of the details about the project," says Ted. "But on his own, apparently, in the course of a few hours he decided that it made sense." Late that night, over one of the glass tables beside the pool at the Hotel Del Charro, Bohr told Ted and Marshall Rosenbluth that he "had been looking for some really dramatic effort conceived in the United States that we could then go to the Soviets with and say, 'Let's do this together.'" Bohr continued to advocate an international Orion program until his death in 1962, sending Freddy de Hoffmann, among others, "a strong letter on that subject" and inspiring Ted with a hope "that the flag that would fly at every place Orion took people to would be the U.N. flag."

On July 3, before Bohr left La Jolla, he joined Freeman for an evening picnic at La Jolla Shores. "For about half an hour Bohr talked to me alone as we walked up and down the beach," Freeman reported. "He at once understood and was enthusiastic about our space-ship. He thinks of it as something with which one may once again try to make a reasonable bargain with Russia. It was a tantalizing experience, as his voice is anyway almost too low to hear, and each time a wave broke his wisdom was irreparably lost."

6

Critical Mass

Theodore B. Taylor was born in Mexico City, to American parents, in 1925. His mother, the daughter of Congregational missionaries, obtained a Ph.D. in Mexican literature and his father was general secretary of the YMCA. When Charles Lindbergh landed in Mexico City in 1927, two-year-old Ted, still in his father's arms, was among the delegation who assembled at the airfield, foreshadowing Lindbergh's support for Project Orion as a member of the Air Force's Space Advisory Committee in 1961. Few families owe as much to the Old Testament as Ted's. "My grandfather oversaw the building of a Congregational church in the middle of Guadalajara, which is still there," Ted explains. "In the midst of delivering a sermon in this small church in Guadalajara, a Mexican came running down the aisle with a big long knife and lunged at him at the pulpit. And he just automatically held his big Bible up against his chest, and the knife penetrated the Bible from Genesis to Leviticus, and stopped."

Ted attended the American School in Mexico City until his graduation at age fifteen in 1941. It was outside of school that his future avocation became known. "I was attracted to explosions from the very beginning," he says. "I was given a chemistry set when I was seven or eight and that rapidly turned into a laboratory for making explosives, with one restriction set down by my mother: never, never under any circumstances was I allowed to make nitroglycerine. So I didn't. Just picric acid and nitrogen iodide and so on. I was fascinated by explosions. I still am. I love to watch them and be responsible for them and set them off. Without any attraction to the damage. It's the act of the exploding, putting a little sack full of potassium chlorate and sulfur on a streetcar track in Mexico City. And no one got hurt." Ted's destiny as the leader of Project Orion was already at work. "I hated to just fiddle around," he remembers. "I wanted to go to extremes. Even one cherry bomb under a fifty-gallon drum, it goes up about fifteen feet."

Ted showed no particular interest in physics, but an intuitive grasp of elastic scattering, chain reactions, and reflected shock waves was sharpened by the billiards he played after school. With three or four friends who found themselves "at loose ends," he started hanging out at a nearby chess-and-billiards parlor after classes were dismissed at one in the afternoon. "There were other places, not so close to the school, where the billiard balls were really spherical and the tables were very heavy and the balls would bounce very nicely," says Ted. "We found that there were various degrees of accuracy with which you could call a shot depending on how heavy and flat and rigid the table was."

Finished with high school in Mexico City but too young for college in the United States, Ted was sent to Exeter Academy in New Hampshire for a year. A class taught by Mr. Little sparked his interest in physics. "I spent all my time on Millikan's oil drop experiment, trying to find ways to reduce the number of electrons that were isolated in each droplet, trying to get it down close to one. I got fascinated with that and didn't do anything else," recalls Ted, who received a D.

In 1942, after a year at Exeter, Ted enrolled at Caltech, joining the Navy V-12 program that obligated students to a postgraduate commission after having their way paid through school. "I flipped a coin and one side was Army and one side was Navy, and it turned up Navy," he says. "If it had been Army I would have been at the front in six months." He received his degree in physics in 1945 and was at midshipman's school in Fort Schuyler, New York, in August when reports of Hiroshima came in. "When I heard the news I was totally shocked. I had no intimations of anything remotely like the Manhattan Project, even though I was a physicist." His fellow midshipmen looked to Ted for an explanation of the atomic bomb. "I couldn't even make up anything credible. Oliver Selfridge, hardly a model midshipman but a very bright mathematician from MIT, had picked up some information about nuclear fission before it was covered by the Manhattan Project's cloak of secrecy, and instantly became our battalion's expert on the awesome events."

Ted wrote to his mother that same afternoon. "I said that I didn't know what was going to happen to me, but I did know one thing, and that was that I would never work on nuclear weapons. Four years later I was not only working on nuclear weapons at Los Alamos, but doing so with considerable enthusiasm. It turned out I was really good at it." With the war over and his year of sea duty fulfilled, Ted resigned from the Navy in June 1946, returning home to Mexico City before enrolling in the physics department at UC Berkeley to pursue a Ph.D. With two fellow graduate students, he drafted a proposal for a worldwide strike of nuclear physicists against nuclear weapons. Oppenheimer, sensing danger, persuaded him to destroy the document and advised him never to mention it again.

Ted collaborated with Robert Serber, coauthoring a paper on nuclear structure and securing a part-time job at the Radiation Laboratory in the Berkeley hills. He married Caro Arnim, started a family, and all was going well, until he flunked his preliminary exams—twice. This disqualified him as a candidate for a Ph.D. "I just wasn't interested in mechanics and heat, and the modern physics thing I really fouled up." No one in the physics department could bend the university's rules. "Dreams of settling down with Caro and some children to teach physics in some agreeable place vanished. I thought I had no qualifications to do anything else. Our future looked grim." Robert Serber, who had given the first lectures on how to build an atomic bomb—issued (secretly) in April 1943 as Los Alamos Laboratory Document No. 1, *The Los Alamos Primer*—contacted Carson Mark at Los Alamos and recommended Taylor for a job. In August 1949 Ted was offered a position, pending security clearance, to work on "problems in neutron diffusion theory" in the Theoretical Division at a salary of $375 a month. "I didn't know whether I was going to be working on nuclear weapons, and didn't ask."

Ted, Caro, and four-month-old Clare drove their 1941 Buick to Los Alamos in November 1949. "Within twenty-four hours of our arrival at Los Alamos I was deeply immersed in the nuclear weapons program. I was doing exactly what I had vowed four years earlier I would never do." Although T-Division was in high gear attempting to build the Super, Carson Mark assigned Ted to work under Jack Smith, a former student of Hans Bethe's who was investigating implosion assemblies for conventional fission bombs. "Within a week I was hooked on understanding what went on at these enormously high energy densities, clear off any human scale. I was getting stacks of IBM printouts of implosion systems and looking at them: what columns are pressures, what were densities, and so on. I found myself right off the bat asking questions: 'Why do we do this? Why do we do that? Why do we just take a full stockpile bomb out to Eniwetok'—we didn't have the Nevada Test Site yet—'and always test the whole thing? Why don't we find out a lot more, about what's going on in the middle particularly, where there are uncertainties in how well things converge?' By January of 1950 I had done a lot of calculations that people had not done before, with relatively small amounts of plutonium and highly enriched uranium in the cores."

While others were consumed with developing the Super, Ted devoted his attention to fission bombs. Within four years Ted's designs included the smallest, the largest, and the most efficient fission devices ever exploded. At least one of these records still stands. This was the Super Oralloy Bomb (SOB), which yielded 500 kilotons in the Ivy King test at Eniwetok on November 15, 1952. The SOB went into production as the Mark 18 stockpile warhead of which about ninety were eventually deployed. Ted's goal had been to produce a fission weapon so powerful that there would be no need to deploy the hydrogen bomb. He went to the Pentagon for two weeks in November 1950, spending much of the time "drawing circles on photographs, of Baikul and Moscow and so on, looking to see what a 500-kiloton fission bomb would do, and always being disappointed when it didn't wipe out everything." Thirty-six years later he would find himself in Red Square, thinking back to "placing the sharp point of a compass exactly where I was now standing, and drawing circles corresponding to distances at which moderate and severe damage would result from our dropping a 500-kiloton bomb several thousand feet above that point." By this time Ted was working to dismantle the stockpile he had helped design. "I suddenly came back to the present, looked around, saw perhaps a couple of thousand happy-looking people, including several wedding parties, walking about enjoying the sights. There came over me an overpowering sense of the insanity of what I was doing more than thirty-six years ago."

In 1950 Ted's fascination was unrestrained. "I had complete freedom to work on any new weapon concept I chose," he says. "It's an exhilarating experience to look at what's going on theoretically, on paper, inside something the size of a baseball that has the same amount of energy as a pile of high explosive as big as the White House—all that in a little handful. I went crazy over that. A big high. The highs needed fixes. And we got those twice a year easily. The fix was a combination of seeing one of these things go off—'Aha! It worked!'—and seeing how the next one might be even more spectacular."

Little bureaucracy stood in the way. "In my seven years at the laboratory I never had to participate in the writing of a single proposal," says Ted. "In Los Alamos in the '50s somebody would get an idea and go down the hall and get Preston Hammer to put it on the computer and six weeks later you get printouts and find out whether the guess was right. If the results came out interesting you go up and talk to Carson Mark and he often would find some flaw. Or he'd say something like, 'Well, I'll be damned' and then you'd cut across the overpass to the middle of the laboratory, and find MacDougall, the head of the explosives division, and he'd say, 'That sounds great! We'll put it on the fission committee agenda.' A week, two weeks later we'd have a fission-weapon committee meeting, and sometimes flaws turned up there. When they didn't, OK, we'll put it on the list. List for what? List for testing, either in Nevada or out in Eniwetok, quite often in less than a year from the initial concept to the successful test." There was some official paperwork, but it was not much. "The laboratory's director, Norris Bradbury, had to get authorization from Washington for each test, but I had the impression this was usually pro forma. He would in effect say, 'Here is something new we have come up with. Do you want it?' The answer almost invariably was 'You bet!'"

The race for smaller and more clever bomb designs was not only against the Soviets, but between the two competing weapons labs in the United States. "Ted and I were friendly competitors while he was at Los Alamos," says Morris (Moe) Scharff, a weapons physicist who joined Ted at General Atomic in 1959 to work on Orion when "there just wasn't as much doing, as much excitement, at Livermore" during the temporary bomb-test moratorium of 1958–1961. "I had been Livermore's Ted Taylor," he explains. "They would try to build smaller and better bombs and we would try to build even smaller and even better ones." Most of them worked. In contrast to the string of failures in rocketry, there were no duds until the United States' eighteenth nuclear test. Ted remembers witnessing only one failure, Redwing Yuma at Eniwetok in 1956, that "scarcely blew off the top of the supporting tower, and drew some cheers from those of us at Los Alamos because it had been designed at Livermore."

By the early 1950s, says Freeman, "a large part of Los Alamos was working on one or another of Ted's ideas. At this point it became rather embarrassing that he still was in a junior position and without any degree." In 1953 Ted was given paid leave to obtain a Ph.D. from Hans Bethe at Cornell. Ted's designs continued to be built and tested while he was gone. He remembers it being "unbearably exciting," as a graduate student, to receive an occasional cryptic phone call from Carson Mark: "Well, how did the wasp go? —Just great!" In 1954 Ted submitted his thesis, on an optical model of nuclei, and underwent his final oral exam. After the exam, he was asked to leave the room and return in an hour, when mathematician Mark Kac, one-third of his committee, announced, "We'll tell you right now before you decide to jump out the window that you passed." Bethe commented, diplomatically, that Ted's performance was not of the quality that his thesis had led them to expect.

With Ph.D. in hand, the Taylors, now with three children, returned to Los Alamos in May 1954. Ted resumed designing bombs. "A great part of the small-bomb development of the last five years was directly due to Ted," Freeman acknowledged in 1958. Ted's designs were not only smaller but also more powerful. He helped develop the concept of boosting, now a standard feature in all United States stockpile fission-weapon designs. Adding a few grams of deuterium and tritium to the core of a fission weapon—in effect a small fusion spark plug—could release a burst of high-energy neutrons at just the right instant, giving a spectacular boost in efficiency and yield. The mere existence of boosting was kept secret until 1972, and the fact that gaseous deuterium and tritium is utilized was declassified only in 1983. Ted attributes the idea to the encouragement he received from Carson Mark. "I was playing around with the middle of implosions, the last millimeter or two, and Carson said, 'Keep your eyes open for high temperatures.' Because there's always a possibility that you could put some deuterium inside, and get neutrons out. Which had all kinds of implications."

Greenhouse Item, yielding 45.5 kilotons at Eniwetok on May 24, 1951, was the first proof of the boosting principle, following Greenhouse George on May 8, whose 225-kiloton yield was the first thermonuclear fusion on a measurable scale. Greenhouse Dog, yielding 81 kilotons on April 7, 1951, in a mock-up of a radiation implosion, was the first test in the series and the first test witnessed firsthand by Ted—from fifteen miles away. "The explosion was every bit as awesome as I had expected—roughly five times as big as the one that destroyed Hiroshima. The countdown started close to dawn . . . one minute . . . thirty seconds (put on your dark goggles) . . . fifteen . . . four, three, two, one: instant light, almost blinding through the goggles, and heat that persisted for a time that seemed interminable. I was sure I was getting instant sunburn, and the back of my neck felt hot from heat reflected off the beach house behind us. Goggles came off after a few seconds. The fireball was still glowing like a setting sun over a clear horizon, a purple and brown cloud rising so fast that in less than a minute we had to crane our necks to see the top. I had forgotten about the shock wave, a surprisingly sharp, loud crack that broke several martini glasses on the shelf of the beach house bar. The sight was beautiful at first, in an awesome way, then turned ugly and seemed threatening as the gray-brown cloud spread and began drifting toward us. I tried hard to shake off the feelings of exhilaration, and think about the deeper meanings of all this, without success. It was just plain thrilling." The test produced some severe fallout over the support facilities, but, says Ted, "the only formal protective action I remember about the incident was cancellation of the outdoor movie that night."

In 1958, few within the nuclear or military establishment would have taken Project Orion seriously if not for Ted Taylor's track record at designing very small bombs. Plutonium and highly enriched uranium were far too expensive and strategically important to consider using thousands of bombs' worth for voyages in space. "We didn't have an infinite amount of plutonium," says Freeman. "Now of course we do." According to Ted, the amount of plutonium needed to produce a useful explosion was far less than anyone had thought. The same curiosity that drove Ted to design the SOB also drove him to think about really, really small atomic bombs. "It was curiosity rather than some talent I had for calculating. It was wondering, 'What's the limit?' I wanted a panoramic view." Ted's interest in low-yield explosions was not because he perceived a need for them—he had no inkling of Orion at that time—but because you could learn more by exploring the delicate balances involved. "I said, why don't we build things with much less plutonium in there and see what's going on in the middle with much more sensitivity. We can do things at around a kiloton instead of what was then the predicted yield of a stockpile bomb, eighty kilotons—it was that for years. To make small yields with big implosion assemblies, that got fascinating. I was focusing my attention on the inner fifty grams, one hundred grams, kilogram, et cetera, pushing things as far as one could go, never mind that you wind up in some cases with shells less than a millimeter thick. Who's going to make those? As it turned out it was very worthwhile to find some way to make those."

"Pursuing these limits became an obsession," Ted admitted in 1986. "What is the absolute lower limit to the total weight of a complete fission explosive? What is the smallest amount of plutonium or uranium 235 that can be made to explode? What is the smallest possible diameter of a nuclear weapon that could be fired out of a gun?" The answers were surprising. "I was narrowing my focus, getting the quantities of plutonium that one could use to make nuclear explosions, down into less than a kilogram. Quite a bit less." This is golf ball, not baseball, size. When John McPhee profiled Ted and his warnings about nuclear terrorism for *The New Yorker* in 1973, Ted could reveal much less than can be revealed today. At that time the smallest known warhead was the Davy Crockett, something less than 12 inches in diameter with a weight of about 60 pounds. McPhee credited Ted with its design, although Ted had been working on much smaller bombs. "I tried to find out what was the smallest bomb you could produce, and it was a lot smaller than Davy Crockett, but it was never built in those years," says Ted. "It certainly has been since then. It was a full implosion bomb that you could hold in one hand that was about six inches in diameter."

Whether anyone *wanted* nuclear field artillery, nuclear demolition charges, or a nuclear-equipped infantry was not a concern of Ted's—though he did collaborate, with George Gamow, on an informal study titled "What the World Needs Is a Good Two-Kiloton Bomb." The prospect of small, tactical, battlefield nuclear weapons was greeted with enthusiasm by the AEC and the Pentagon, and, says Ted, "less than

	Recoverable Test Vehicle	Orbital Test Vehicle	Interplanetary Ship	Advanced Interplanetary Ship
Gross Weight	50 - 100 tons	880 tons	4000 tons	10,000 tons
Propulsion system empty weight (Pusher, shock absorbers, storage and delivery)	45 tons	370 tons	1700 tons	3250 tons
Specific Impulse	variable up to 3000 sec	3000 to 6000 sec	4000 sec	12,000 sec
Diameter	40 ft	80 ft	135 ft	185 ft
Height	50 ft	120 ft	200 ft	280 ft
Average total acceleration of ship	2 - 4 g	2 g	variable up to 2 g	variable up to 4 g
Vacuum yield per charge	.1 - .5 KT	.8 - 3 KT	~ 5 KT	~15 KT
Sea level yield per charge	3 tons	.03 KT	.15 KT	.35 KT
Number of explosions to reach 125,000'	100 - 200	200	200	200
Total yield to 125,000'	~2 KT	~ 20 KT	~ 100 KT	~250 KT
Total number of explosions to reach 300 mi orbit	--	800	800	800
Total yield to reach 300 mi orbit	--	.450 - 1.8 MT	3 MT	9 MT
Payloads	(I_{sp} = 3000 sec)			
300 mi orbit (V = 10 km/sec)	--	300 tons	1600 tons	6100 tons
Soft lunar landing (V = 15.5 km/sec)	--	170 tons	1200 tons	5700 tons
Soft lunar landing and return to 300 mi orbit or Mars orbit and return to 300 mi orbit } (V = 21 km/sec)	--	80 tons	800 tons	5300 tons
Earth's surface to Venus orbit to Mars orbit to 300 mile earth orbit (V = 30 km/sec)	--	--	200 tons	4500 tons
Earth's surface to inner satellite of Saturn and return to 300 mi Earth orbit. ~3 year round trip (V = 100 km/sec)	--	--	--	1300 tons

Proposed Orion vehicle parameters, late 1958 or early 1959.

three years later, after astonishingly creative actions by a variety of groups of people at Los Alamos, Gamow's original goals had been considerably surpassed." When Orion raised the possibility of using low-yield bombs for constructive purposes, it was a long-awaited opportunity for Ted. "With that sort of background, the idea of thousands of explosions, up close and personal, was extremely attractive," he says.

"Ted Taylor spent a lot of time thinking about small-yield nuclear weapons," recalls his Los Alamos colleague Harris Mayer. "'What's the smallest bomb we can make?' And he knew a great deal about these and how to make them. He also knew all about the economics of the nuclear bomb business at the time. As to having one thousand bombs, nobody else would think of that, but Ted Taylor would say, 'Why stop at a thousand bombs? Make them with very small amounts of fissile material. Make them very intelligently so you could get reasonable yield out of very small amounts.' So he's talking about something in which one thousand bombs wasn't too much drain on a stockpile."

"One of the big questions, a large part of the whole project which I cannot talk about freely, is just how much plutonium you need," Freeman explains. "One of the things that made Orion very attractive is the trade-off between plutonium and high explosive. In the ordinary bombs we use for the stockpile, all kinds, it doesn't matter whether they are high yield or low yield, the military likes minimum weight and minimum volume, so you tend to use a rather small amount of high explosive because high explosive quickly becomes the dominating mass. For what we wanted to do it was an advantage to have a huge amount of high explosive because that would also absorb neutrons and be the shielding for the ship. Then you need a lot less plutonium. And the question how much less I cannot discuss. The whole economy of the thing depended on that. These were all very nonstandard bombs, which meant nobody believed us; the numbers clearly didn't add up if you took the standard kind of bombs. This is also an interesting question from the point of view of the terrorist bomb problem. If you have a bunch of people wanting to blow up the World Trade Center or something, they might have no difficulty getting large amounts of high explosive. So it is important not to declassify all that stuff."

Ted was the first to raise the alarm. "The use of small numbers of covertly delivered nuclear explosives by groups of people that are not clearly identified with a national government is more probable, in the near future, than the open use of nuclear weapons by a nation for military purposes," he warned in 1966. Retaliation offered no deterrent to foreign subnational groups, or to "an extremist group of U.S. citizens who believe they are trying to save the U.S." Sent by the AEC on a tour of nuclear facilities to evaluate nonproliferation safeguards, he had been profoundly shocked. "At Nuclear Fuel Services' commercial nuclear fuel reprocessing plant in West Valley, New York," he reported, "several containers with separated plutonium nitrate solution, enough in the aggregate for at least two atomic bombs, were in a small shack a few feet from an ordinary chain-link fence and more than 100 yards from the plant entrance, where the 'guard' had no weapon of any kind." The same tenacious imagination that drove Ted's hopes for using bombs in space would later drive his fears about their falling into the wrong hands on the ground.

Ted met Freeman Dyson for the first time when he arrived at Cornell in January 1953, where Freeman had been teaching since 1951. Freeman and Ted, both without Ph.D.s, possessed different yet complementary skills. When they joined forces, first on TRIGA and then on Orion, it had the effect of bringing two subcritical masses together and forming a critical assembly that suddenly ignites. "The year that Freeman spent at La Jolla was the happiest in his life," says Harris Mayer. "This was a confluence of people and time and spirit. And Ted Taylor was the essential part of that. Freeman was almost in love with Ted Taylor. Ted had a fantastic imagination. So did Freeman. But Ted had more of an instinct than Freeman for how mechanical things worked. Freeman appreciated that. He saw in Ted not only imagination but this sort of a feeling for practical things."

"Ted Taylor had a unique approach," explains Moe Scharff. "It wasn't the usual moving ahead by small consecutive steps. He'd look for the ideal way of doing something. Then he would figure out how nature would constrain things, and back off just a little. And then he'd push for that result, even if it meant taking a huge step."

7

QED

In September 1932, about the time that seven-year-old Ted Taylor began experimenting with chemical explosives in Mexico City, Freeman Dyson, then eight, was sent away from home in Winchester, England, to attend the Twyford School. "It was an abominable school but had an excellent library so that was my refuge," he says. "There was lots and lots of stuff about electrons and electricity and radio waves and all sorts of things, but nobody ever mentioned protons. I remember asking people, 'Why is it that they only talk about electrons and not about protons?' Nobody seemed to know."

Among the books that captured Freeman's imagination was *From the Earth to the Moon and a Trip Around It*, by Jules Verne. Shortly before his ninth birthday—December 15, 1932—Freeman began to write a sequel, *Sir Phillip Roberts's Erolunar Collision*, concerning a predicted collision between the asteroid Eros and the Moon. Freeman's unfinished account of South African astronomer Sir Phillip's preparations for a voyage to observe the collision closely followed the precedent of Jules Verne: "'Accounting for delays,' said Sir Phillip, when General Mason had told him of his idea, 'and the journey, and preparations on the

Moon, we will still have well over ten years to make our cannon, projectile, and gun-cotton, we will use gun-cotton, it is much better than ordinary powder, therefore we can make our expedition much larger than Barbicane's; don't worry about money, subscriptions will be almost infinite.'"

While Ted was learning how to make gun-cotton, Freeman was theorizing about propelling a 15-foot diameter spaceship to the Moon. Gun-cotton, or nitrocellulose, detonates at nearly twice the speed of dynamite and was introduced in 1865, the year that Jules Verne published the first installment of his book. Freeman estimated that Sir Phillip's launching gun—or Columbiad, as Verne referred to it—would be two miles in length, uncannily close to the dimensions of more recent proposals for chemical-fueled space-launching guns. Sir Phillip's ten-year development schedule corresponds exactly to the plans for a 1968 Mars mission that accompanied Freeman and Ted's sales pitch for Project Orion in 1958.

Freeman first estimated how large a Moon-based Columbiad it would take to escape from the Moon's gravitational field for the return to Earth. He then estimated how large a terrestrial Columbiad it would take to send the lunar Columbiad to the Moon. The second-stage Columbiad would be left on the Moon for future use, a strategy quite different from the single-use, multiple-stage rockets in which the Apollo astronauts finally did make the trip. Orion goes one step better, dispensing with the Columbiad entirely—though when they built their flying model, the Orioneers used a shallow tub and a one-pound charge of gunpowder for the initial kick.

The progenitor of Orion was not Wernher, but Verne. "When I thought about space travel in those days, I was thinking about the huge guns that I read about in the stories of Jules Verne," Freeman explains. "Rockets had nothing to do with it. The Martians in Wells's *War of the Worlds* did not come in rockets. They came in artillery shells." On December 19, 1934, Freeman witnessed his first rocket launch, reinforcing his conviction that Verne's was the better approach. A German entrepreneur, Gerhard Zucker, had arrived in England to promote postal rocketry, supporting his venture by selling collectible Rocket Mail stamps. "Herr Zucker stated that he hoped to construct a large rocket here in England," the British Interplanetary Society reported, "with a view to establishing a regular rocket postal service between England and the continent. After which, he envisions the formation of a company for the manufacture of postal rockets for world distribution."

The Dysons had a weekend cottage near Lymington, almost exactly where Zucker decided to launch. "They had this very impressive-looking rocket," Freeman remembers. "They set it up with great ceremony on this rather derelict piece of land where we lived, which was sort of a mudflat on the coast opposite the Isle of Wight. They had some dignitaries from London who came down, and ceremoniously put this bag of mail with special stamps into the rocket. Then they launched and the thing zoomed up into the sky very beautifully. But then it turned around and came back almost exactly where it took off and landed with a big splash in the mud. So they went out and retrieved it and the mail went over later on the boat."

Within ten years, Zucker's successors were routinely sending rockets across the English Channel, having switched from delivering letters to delivering bombs. Freeman was working as a civilian statistician for the Royal Air Force Bomber Command when he first encountered the rockets of Wernher von Braun. "In London we were very grateful to Wernher von Braun," he explains. "We knew that each V-2 cost as much to produce as a high-performance fighter aircraft." German airplanes were inflicting heavy Allied losses, whereas V-2s exploded haphazardly and only once. It was when V-2s began falling on southern England at 3,500 miles per hour that Freeman first thought about rockets, not guns, as vehicles for reaching space. "I remember being very delighted to learn that the V-2 really existed. It was a big step forward. It went 50 miles up and 250 miles horizontal. If you could do that much you could get into space. And then I was rather disappointed. If the Germans could do that well, I expected that we would have our own secret projects. Probably we would be doing much better. At the end of the war I found out there was really nothing on our side. We had to start over again from scratch."

In 1947 Freeman left England to study physics with Hans Bethe at Cornell. Theoretical physics and experimental physics were separate trades, but graduate students were expected to become familiar with both. Millikan's oil drop experiment, which had drawn Ted into physics six years earlier, did not go as well in Freeman's hands. Millikan had shown how to measure the charge of the individual electron by balancing microscopic droplets of oil between the force of gravity pulling them downward and the force of an electric field pulling them up. "I had my oil drops floating nicely, and then I grabbed hold of the wrong knob to adjust the electric field," says Freeman. "They found me stretched out on the floor, and that finished my career as an experimenter."

Many of the physicists who had spent the war building the bomb with Bethe at Los Alamos were now reassembled under Bethe's leadership at Cornell. Freeman became familiar with the Manhattan Project's chief protagonists and the political forces in which their work had become enmeshed. He felt a moral and technical kinship with those who had spent the war calculating how to build atomic weapons, just as he had spent the war calculating how to maximize the destructive effects of conventional bombs. "The sin of the physicists at Los Alamos did not lie in their having built a lethal weapon," he later explained. "They did not just build the bomb. They enjoyed building it. They had the best time of their lives building it. That, I believe, is what Oppenheimer had in mind when he said that they had sinned."

Of all the Los Alamos gang, Richard Feynman influenced Freeman the most. Bethe assigned Freeman to work on a problem known as quantum electrodynamics, or QED. In 1947, there was a quagmire of incomplete and contradictory approaches to the relation between matter and electromagnetic fields. "The problem," according to Freeman, "was simply that there existed no accurate theory to describe the everyday behavior of atoms and electrons emitting and absorbing light." In the aftermath of the war physicists had returned to their laboratories, built new equipment, and were making new observations and discoveries with unprecedented precision but without a consistent mathematical framework to explain the results. Feynman had developed a system of QED that produced all the right answers, but his unorthodox techniques were viewed by the physics establishment as mathematically opaque. "Dick was using his own private quantum mechanics that

Freeman Dyson (carrying briefcase) at the Point Loma test site, summer 1959. Clockwise from top, surrounding the meter model: Ed Day, Walt England, Brian Dunne, Perry Ritter, Jim Morris, Michael Feeney, W. B. McKinney, Michael Ames.

nobody else could understand," Freeman later explained. "He was struggling, more intensely than I had seen anyone struggle, to understand the workings of nature by rebuilding physics from the bottom up."

Feynman revealed his methods to Freeman, who then went to Ann Arbor to attend a series of lectures by mathematical physicist Julian Schwinger, whose approach to QED was as precise, orderly, and complicated as Dick's "Feynman diagrams" were simple and unexplained. "Dyson was probably the only person who thoroughly understood both methods," Bethe observed. The third piece in the puzzle came from Sin-Itiro Tomonaga in Japan, who had developed a parallel theory of QED in complete isolation during the war. This arrived unexpectedly in Hans Bethe's mailbox at Cornell, and thus Freeman found himself in the middle of a deep mathematical conflict in the spring and summer of 1948. Tomonaga, Schwinger, and Feynman had each arrived at the same physics by taking a different mathematical approach. In September, while Freeman was returning by Greyhound bus from Berkeley to

Chicago, the puzzle was suddenly resolved. "The roads were too bumpy for me to read, and so I sat and looked out of the window and fell into a comfortable stupor," he remembers. "As we were droning across Nebraska on the third day, something suddenly happened. Feynman's pictures and Schwinger's equations began sorting themselves out in my head with a clarity they had never had before. For the first time I was able to put them all together. I had no pencil and paper, but everything was so clear I did not have to write it down."

On October 6, 1948, Freeman submitted "The Radiation Theories of Tomonaga, Schwinger, and Feynman" to *The Physical Review*. This demonstrated the mathematical equivalence of the Feynman and Schwinger theories and presented a simpler method of applying Schwinger and Tomonaga's theory to specific problems, "the simplification being the greater the more complicated the problem." Soon after the paper appeared on February 1, 1949, Freeman was offered a professorship at Cornell by Bethe and a permanent membership at the Institute for Advanced Study by Robert Oppenheimer. He never obtained a Ph.D.

The mathematical elucidation of QED advanced our understanding of how the strange workings of quantum mechanics constitute the universe in which we live. "The picture of the world that we have finally reached is the following," Freeman explained in 1953. "Some 10 or 20 qualitatively different quantum fields exist. Each fills the whole of space and has its own particular properties. There is nothing else except these fields; the whole of the material universe is built of them. . . . Even to a hardened theoretical physicist it remains perpetually astonishing that our solid world of trees and stones can be built of quantum fields and nothing else. The quantum field seems far too fluid and insubstantial to be the basic stuff of the universe. Yet we have learned gradually to accept the fact that the laws of quantum mechanics impose their own peculiar rigidity upon the fields they govern, a rigidity which is alien to our intuitive conceptions but which nonetheless effectively holds the earth in place."

QED's mathematical precision could be applied to a wide spectrum of physical events—from the behavior of an individual electron to the behavior of a 4,000-ton spaceship propelled by exploding bombs. To describe the extent of the domain of QED, Freeman divided the whole of physics into three compartments: "In the first compartment we put our knowledge of nuclear structure, protons, neutrons, mesons, neutrinos, and the interactions of these particles with one another. In the second compartment we put theories of the large-scale structure and geometry of the universe, including Einstein's general theory of gravitation. In the third compartment we put our knowledge of all other phenomena, everything intermediate in scale between an atomic nucleus and a massive star. The third compartment includes the whole of classical mechanics, optics and electrodynamics, special relativity and extranuclear atomic physics. The first two compartments are full of undigested experimental information, empirical rules, and mutually contradictory assumptions. These fields are only beginning to be explored and organized. On the other hand, the third compartment is unified by a logically consistent theory . . . quantum electrodynamics. . . . It is the only field in which we can choose a hypothetical experiment and predict the result to five places of decimals, confident that the theory takes into account all the factors that are involved."

This view of the world was mathematically abstract—the perfect complement to the hands-on technical imagination that was Ted's. Freeman might grab the wrong knob in an experiment, but he could calculate exactly how the electrons, if not the physicist, should behave. The question of Orion's feasibility—once the rearrangement of nuclei in the first few microseconds of the bomb's explosion was completed—fell within the domain of QED. When Freeman said he believed that Orion would work as Ted Taylor hoped, skeptics listened. They knew that Ted could design the bombs and that Freeman could calculate what would happen next. Driving a 4,000-ton ship with nuclear explosions would be difficult. "What you need is momentum and not energy," Freeman explains. "A nuclear explosion gives you a lot of energy but very little momentum." This was the basic problem, and Freeman's job was to help decide whether making the translation from the energy of a bomb to the momentum of a ship was feasible or not.

The way the numbers turned out, he believed the answer was yes. Problems as diverse as the opacity of a stagnating plasma, stability of the ship, convective ablation of the pusher, optimum launch trajectory through the atmosphere, effects of fallout, design of test containment

facilities, mission planning to the outer planets, and military implications received Freeman's attention over the project's first twelve
months. "We skimmed the cream off a multitude of technical problems
in the most diverse branches of physics and engineering," he said. "In
the early days of the project we were all amateurs. Everybody did a little of everything. There was no division of the staff into physicists and
engineers. The ethos of engineering is very different from that of
physics. A good physicist is a man with original ideas. A good engineer
is a man who makes a design that works with as few original ideas as
possible."

"He had a good sense of what he was good at," says Ted. "In the
course of his deciding whether to stay with the project and resign from
the Institute, he said he had to make a choice between being a very
good theoretical physicist or the best engineer ever. He was not sitting
on the side doing esoteric plasma physics calculations, or simply dream-
ing about what kind of a bed he'd sleep in. He was doing the real engineering, providing a framework so it could all fit together as Orion
evolved." In the end, Freeman chose to return to physics, after fifteen
months that he remembers as the most exciting of his scientific life.
"When I left the project in September 1959, the number of employees
had risen to fifty; we had together solved to our satisfaction most of the
basic problems of vehicle design, the technical feasibility of our concept
had been clearly established, and the government had decided not to
take us seriously. Wernher von Braun and his chemical rockets had won
the battle for government support, and the pattern of the space program
was set in a way that left no place for us."

Project Orion spanned all three compartments into which Freeman
had divided our knowledge of the world. The third compartment,
encompassing most of the design and operation of Orion, lay within the
bounds of QED. From there, Orion offered a window into the other two
compartments where so much remained to be explored and understood:
the mysteries of the atomic nucleus, which Ted and his colleagues were
fiddling with by designing and exploding bombs, and the mysteries of
the large-scale structure of the universe, being revealed by the expansion of science into space. "The general feeling when I arrived was one
of great enthusiasm from Freeman and Ted," says Pierre Noyes, who

consulted part-time for Orion during the summer of 1958. "Freeman said one of the reasons he was pushing Orion was it could take a lot of people, including older people like himself." As Bruno Augenstein describes it, the allure of Orion's high performance is that "even quite adventurous missions may well be realistically accomplishable in times commensurate with the productive lives of individual scientists."

"I saw in half an hour that it was the thing all the space-flight projects had been praying for," Freeman wrote in July 1958, when his optimism was at its height. "I have never had any reason to change this opinion. It will work, and it will open the skies to us. The problem is of course to convince oneself that one can sit on top of a bomb without being fried. If you do not think about it carefully, it looks obvious that you can't do it. Ted's genius was the courage that led him to question the obvious impossibility. Ted and I will fly together to Los Alamos this evening. We travel like Paul and Barnabas. Golly, this life is good."

8

Lew Allen's Balls

In 1952, at the Nevada Test Site, Ted Taylor added to his already considerable reputation by holding up a small parabolic mirror and lighting a cigarette with an atomic bomb. The fireball was twelve miles away. "I carefully extinguished the cigarette and saved it for a while in my desk drawer at Los Alamos," he says. "Sometime, probably in a state of excitement about some new kind of bomb, I must have smoked it by mistake."

Those who were designing, building, stockpiling, and attempting to understand the effects of nuclear weapons in the 1950s were concerned either with destroying things like cities and hardened missile silos, or with nominally constructive applications like melting oil out of the Alberta tar sands and digging a sea-level Panama Canal. Putting something as expensive as a 4,000-ton spaceship within a few hundred feet of a series of nuclear explosions was going to be a hard sell, even for Ted. Without some material evidence of survivability, even the most enthusiastic officials at the AEC or within the Pentagon would be unlikely to lend support. Fortuitously, evidence was at hand: a series of tests known as "Lew Allen's Balls" (also referred to, according to Burt Freeman, "as Ogle's balls, after Bill Ogle, the great atmospheric test director who was responsible for much progress over many years"). This was the third key ingredient—between the concept of Stan Ulam and the incentive provided by *Sputnik*—from which Project Orion was being assembled in the back of Ted Taylor's mind.

Lew Allen was an Air Force physicist, born in 1925, who had been assigned to Los Alamos in the early 1950s and rose rapidly through the ranks. He later became Secretary of the Air Force and, after retiring with the rank of four-star general, director of the Jet Propulsion Laboratory at Caltech. Lew Allen and Ted Taylor became close friends at Los Alamos and on the islands encircling the lagoon at Eniwetok, where they collaborated on a number of tests. After leaving Los Alamos Lew Allen joined the Office of Special Projects at the Air Force Special Weapons Center at Kirtland Air Force Base in Albuquerque, where he became the first project officer responsible for Orion when the monitoring of ARPA's contract with General Atomic was assigned to AFSWC by the Air Force Research and Development Command in 1958. He was skeptical enough, as an administrator, to be given oversight over the project, and optimistic enough, as a physicist, to recognize the value in giving Orion contractual support. "It was a remarkable period in the Air Force, in which they really encouraged brilliant young technicians to remain technicians and not lose their skills as they advanced in the Air Force," says Bud Pyatt. "I don't think that happens today." As JPL's *Voyager* 2 space probe headed out toward Neptune and Uranus, after sending back pictures of the moons of Jupiter in 1979 and the moons of Saturn in 1981, there was an old Orion hand—Lew Allen—at the helm.

It was a shortage of tritium that led to "Lew Allen's Balls." In the mid-1950s, as new weapon designs such as Ted's went into production, the AEC began to worry, behind closed doors, that we might not have enough tritium to keep the stockpile up to date. Tritium, an unstable isotope of hydrogen with two extra neutrons in its nucleus, occurs naturally in seawater as one part in 10^{18} of ordinary hydrogen, produced by collisions with cosmic rays. Since tritium decays 5.5 percent per year, tritium-boosted fission weapons and tritium-initiated thermonuclear warheads have to be periodically replenished and cannot simply be left stockpiled on the shelf. Producing tritium by neutron bombardment in special reactors is expensive and slow. Tritium is also produced during thermonuclear explosions, and that gave Ted an idea. Why not use the neutron flux from a nearby explosion to produce tritium, and then go in and harvest the results?

"Ted was not devoid of wild ideas," Lew Allen explains. "One of the ideas he had when he was at Los Alamos was that one could use a thermonuclear weapon to produce fissionable material, or tritium, by exploding it over a basin which contained raw material that would be transmuted by the neutrons from the bomb. Could you put a covering on the basin in such a way that it wouldn't get torn up by the bomb, because you'd probably want to do more than one bomb? How would material behave in a fireball? So I did a set of experiments aimed at looking at that.

"One of the experiments was to hang some spheres of raw material, surrounded by a fairly thick layer of graphite, from the tower of a bomb, and then see if we could recover the spheres—they were steel spheres with a capsule of material inside—and find out if the material really transmuted, and remained in the matrix. The idea was the carbon would protect the steel spheres, which would go flying away and embed themselves in the sand out in Eniwetok and then we'd recover them. And that worked. I also had some big cylindrical disks of steel with material inside them that we placed at the base of the tower to see how they would survive: three or four feet across and six or eight inches high. That could well be where Ted began thinking about what bombs did to big plates."

The surprise result—and one of the germs of Orion—was that some of the spheres were propelled farther than could be explained by blast effect alone. "We had trouble finding some of those steel spheres," Allen says. "We had thought we could find them using metal detectors. We hadn't realized that the sand at the base of that tower—there had been other shots there before—was littered with pieces of metal, fragments of the tower and what have you, so the metal detector just rang all the time. We ended up taking huge road scrapers and scraping off the top six or eight inches of the sand and just simply following along behind them and uncovering these things." One of the later tests happened to

UNCLASSIFIED

CONFIDENTIAL

SECRET

UNCLASSIFIED

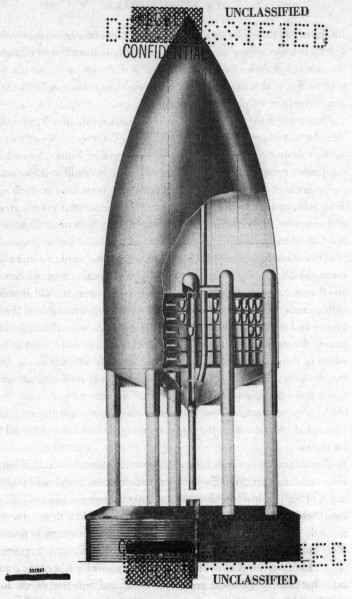

Proposed 200-ton test vehicle, 1962: 30 feet in diameter, 0.78-second pulse period, 75-foot separation distance, 1.9-g acceleration, 220-pound charges, yield unknown.

be one of Ted's early boosted designs—a test named "Viper" that was "a big step on the boosting front, a different design of a booster. I probably shouldn't go into that," says Ted.

Lew Allen performed a similar series of experiments in Nevada, hanging spheres of material from shot towers in the desert during the Teapot test series in April 1955. "A number of these objects were subsequently recovered and examined," according to Bruno Augenstein at RAND. "From their condition and final landing places, it could be reasonably established that the bodies had been 'propelled' by some mechanism of the nuclear blast." The results, both from Nevada and Eniwetok, attracted notice at RAND and among Edward Teller's group at Livermore who had been looking, independently and in advance of *Sputnik*, at the possibility of a bomb-propelled, ablation-driven upper stage for thermonuclear ICBMs. At a February 1957 conference, Livermore physicist Tom Wainwright noted that nonmetallic material such as Bakelite suffered markedly less ablation, a phenomenon that became the key to protecting Orion's pusher plate from repeated blasts. "When placed about 100 feet from the center of explosions of 15 to 25 kilotons, plastic specimens suffered very much smaller mass losses," he wrote. Nothing came of the Livermore proposal, which died quietly in the interim between Ulam's 1955 study and the frenzy over *Sputnik* amid which Project Orion was launched.

After the atmospheric test ban put an end to such experiments, Lew Allen's balls remained among the relics from the era when Orion stood on the verge of advancing to nuclear tests. "They are still there," says Bud Pyatt, who has periodically returned to Eniwetok to study evidence from previous tests. "You can go and see these famous iron balls that, in terms of temperature, were within the 150,000 degrees Kelvin range of the fireball. The phenomena of the self-protection from ablation through the creation of a hot layer that was opaque enough to protect the remainder of the ball from any of the radiation were important observations in terms of could we create a layer or pusher that could exist that close to a nuclear explosion?" Why and how the objects survived so well was not fully understood in 1956, prompting a small group of curious physicists to take advantage of bomb-development and stockpile-reliability tests. "There are still several dozen completely unexplained weapons effects—and all we did was to keep testing the stockpile weapons, without trying to understand them," says Ted. "We knew much more about how to make bombs than about what they did."

According to Ted, it was Lew Allen's experiments that helped convince the skeptics—including himself. "Being able to preserve things that were within twenty feet from the center of the explosion, of tens of kilotons, was a big surprise to a lot of people. That we had those data and had photographs of spheres of metal that had been protected with graphite, showing no sign of any unusual explosion, is what led me to the feasibility of the concept as a whole." As Freeman remembers it, "These experiments helped us to persuade people that the idea of an Orion ship surviving inside a succession of fireballs was not absurd. They showed that solid objects survived much better than most people expected. They were important to us because we could say, 'Look, this piece of plastic lost only X millimeters of its surface sitting inside a fireball for half a second.' That made Orion seem less crazy."

When Lew Allen describes what Ted was thinking about in 1955, it sounds a lot like Orion, upside down: "You carved a big hemispherical basin, somewhere in some remote area, and then you shot relatively clean bombs off at the center of curvature of this thing. Because they were clean and because you designed this basin so that stuff didn't go flying out, you didn't contaminate the air or the surroundings very much at all. You banged off a certain number of these things—I've forgotten how many, about a dozen, say—and then you came back in and mined the products which would be either tritium or lithium 6 and fissionable thorium. The economics were really not unreasonable. It looked like all you needed as a covering was asphalt. The asphalt would ablate and it had enough flexibility that it wouldn't go rippling and tearing off, and the tests in the Pacific showed that the materials would stay in the matrix you prepared. Outside of this little tiny handicap, that one really didn't want to go banging off bombs all over the place, it looked like it would work pretty well. This was just before *Sputnik*. Ted could well have been thinking about the fact that he was not only flooding the stuff with neutrons, but he was also pushing on it pretty hard."

This scheme was known as BATS—for Bomb Assisted Tritium Supply. Orion was BATS turned right-side up. "Ted was a practical scientist who had participated in the design of some of the key weapons up there at Los Alamos, and was fully accepted in the theoretical community as being a real guy, not an off-the-wall guy," explains Lew Allen. "So, when he came up with these various schemes, I think if anybody else had done it, they would have been cast aside fairly quickly, but when he came up with them, they had a certain aura of plausibility about them just because of Ted.

"When Orion began, shooting bombs off in the atmosphere was really common," Allen continues. "That is, one was doing it all the time, and those of us in the business felt that most of the effects that people were concerned about were significantly exaggerated and that there really wasn't that big a problem. Obviously, the thoughts on that changed. But at least for a while there, the idea was not at all unreasonable. So, in the initial year or so at least, the issues were: 'Would a thing like this work?' It had so many technical challenges and it scaled up into such a big thing. Could you really make it work? It wasn't until later, when the test-ban treaty began to get signed, that people began to say, 'Hey, wait a minute! Suppose this does work, would we really want to start shooting off the bombs?' All of us were skeptical that you would ever actually do this, but felt that it was such an imaginative and exciting idea that it was certainly worthy of the research that had to be done."

9

ARPA

General Atomic's proposal for a nuclear bomb–propelled space vehicle spent the first six months of 1958 bouncing from desk to desk. Officials who thought the idea was crazy were reluctant to say no and officials who thought the idea had potential were reluctant to say yes. Orion was orphaned from the start. For the entire seven years of its existence, the project was plagued, politically, by the features that made it so appealing to people like Freeman and Ted. Our military space program was unable to wholeheartedly adopt a project aimed at peacefully exploring the solar system. Our nonmilitary space program was unable to wholeheartedly adopt a project driven by bombs. For a brief moment in history, the Advanced Research Projects Agency (ARPA) was in the business of doing both.

Ted Taylor's diplomacy, Freddy de Hoffmann's influence within General Dynamics and the AEC, and the efforts of individuals such as Lew Allen within the military establishment eventually achieved a compromise giving Project Orion a chance. In early 1958, there were a half-dozen places where Orion could seek support: General Dynamics, the AEC, the Pentagon, Congress, ARPA, and NASA—which had not yet been formed. "Several important people have said, 'Yes, this is very important. In fact it is so important that I cannot possibly do anything about it until Congress decides who is to handle it,'" Freeman reported after a visit to Washington with Ted in the spring of 1958. "Congress is just now in the middle of creating a new Space Agency to administer all nonmilitary schemes of this kind."

Congress was a slow way to launch anything into space. In January 1958, just as Secretary of Defense Neil H. McElroy was creating ARPA, the United States Congress Joint Committee on Atomic Energy (JCAE) held a series of hearings on outer space propulsion by nuclear energy before a number of influential congressmen, including Senator Clinton P. Anderson of New Mexico, chairman of the Subcommittee on Outer Space Propulsion, and Senator Albert Gore of Tennessee. The assembled congressmen had two main questions for the physicists, who included Stan Ulam from Los Alamos and Theodore Merkle from Livermore: Were the Russians using nuclear energy to launch their Sputniks? Could the United States use nuclear energy to regain the lead? Senator John Pastore of Rhode Island asked Dr. Ulam: "Do you believe in the admonition that the nation that controls outer space will control the world?" Ulam, having already hinted at possibilities such as Orion, replied: "If some nation controls travel in space and is in possession of the Moon, it ipso facto, it seems to me, dominates this planet too." The subsequent questioning of Dr. Merkle went adrift:

> **Representative James T. Patterson (Connecticut):** Is there any theory that states after you get a certain distance from our earth in space then the atmosphere becomes comparable to the one we live in now?
>
> **Dr. Theodore Merkle:** I am not sure I quite understand your question.
>
> **Representative Patterson:** I do not know just how to put it myself.
>
> **Dr. Merkle:** Let me put it this way: the earth's atmosphere which you are currently breathing gets thinner and thinner as you increase the distance from the earth.
>
> **Representative Patterson:** When you arrive at a certain point, then does it reverse itself?

Dr. Merkle: No, indeed, sir. After you get up a few hundred miles the atmosphere disappears and it never again reappears. Space is truly empty.

It was this political vacuum, in the aftermath of *Sputnik*, that gave Project Orion its chance. General Dynamics sponsored Orion's nine-month initial incubation at General Atomic, hoping to recoup this investment through research and development contracts once the project got off the ground. Someday, fleets of Orion ships might be cruising space under the General Dynamics label in the same way that General Dynamics' Electric Boat division, starting with the 3,500-ton *Nautilus*, had become the leading brand in nuclear submarines. Orion would have been "built like a submarine, not an airplane," says Freeman, who remembers that "the Electric Boat division of General Dynamics was to some extent involved. We did talk with them about how you build submarines and I think a couple of those people came to talk to Ted. They would have got the contract if the thing had gone ahead."

Physicist Herbert York, an advisor to Eisenhower who was appointed the first director of the Livermore laboratory in 1952 and the first technical director of ARPA in 1958, remembers John Jay Hopkins asking his advice about whether General Dynamics should lend more support. "I said that from a government point of view it was worth putting in some small amount of money, like a million dollars, to get the thinking further along, but that if I was involved in investing General Dynamics money I wouldn't put a nickel in." In 1958 General Dynamics was in the process of losing a fortune on an ill-fated attempt to enter the commercial aviation market with the Convair 880 jetliner, and inclined to side with York. Their backing was contingent on the government picking up the tab for most of the expenses along the way.

The AEC was firmly on board. Without their blessing, it would have been impossible for a private contractor, acting independently from the weapons labs, to undertake a project involving nuclear secrets and nuclear bombs. Orion's first contract, for $5,000 in January 1958, was with the AEC, but this was for the provision of classified information (including the results from Lew Allen's tests), not research or development costs. The AEC had to be careful not to alienate the military establishment by appearing to be making their own preemptive bid for space. Herbert York, who began testifying before the JCAE in 1953, emphasizes that political battles larger than Orion were being fought. "The JCAE had been the most important committee, and they knew that space was going to take that away, so they tried very hard to get the responsibility for space," he says. "Which they couldn't do. It's entirely possible that their hidden agenda was to somehow or other make it evident that space propulsion and nuclear energy were so intrinsically and powerfully connected that they had to be kept connected. That's a suspicious thought—but the JCAE was really losing its position. And so was the AEC."

Establishing NASA required an act of Congress, whereas the Department of Defense was able to establish ARPA by executive order as an immediate response to *Sputnik*'s launch. "It was Secretary of Defense Neil H. McElroy's personal answer to *Sputnik*," says York. The first task was to prevent rivalries between the Army, Navy, and Air Force from getting in the way. The conflicts arose not only over military activities; all three services viewed peaceful exploration of space as a desirable extension of their turf, and their contractors sought prestige in the peaceful "conquest" of space. There was also a military imperative to promote nonmilitary projects, since it was essential for reconnaissance, guidance, and other defense objectives to establish a precedent that national boundaries were not being violated by spacecraft flying overhead. In anticipation of NASA's formation, ARPA was chartered to consolidate everything—military and nonmilitary—for a year or so and then, once NASA was established, divide things up. "I played a key role," says York, "in getting ARPA going into a lot of things, and then taking them out of it when it was time to do so. The most difficult thing I did was getting ARPA out of the big space-transport business because von Braun and the Army were determined to keep it in. But the president wanted them out." When ARPA undertook sponsorship of Project Orion, the assumption was that this was a long-range, deep-space venture that would be transferred to NASA once things got sorted out.

General Atomic's proposal was a radical departure from anything under consideration in 1958. While the United States was struggling to launch low-Earth-orbit satellites weighing fewer than one hundred pounds, Ted was proposing interplanetary payloads of one thousand tons. "I remember the document," says Air Force Colonel Don Prickett. "Ted brought it to the Pentagon. I had what they called a nuclear desk at that time, and I saw it and read it. Of course I take off on anything like that. We fired it back down to Lew Allen at Kirtland for a comment. And then, as I remember, it went to RAND for a comment. I didn't know Ted from Adam's off ox, but it was an intriguing proposal and at a time that we didn't have much in the way of propulsion systems. The Russians were running away from us."

Orion attracted interest within the Air Force, but no one was able to come up with a plausible military requirement for sending a 4,000-ton spaceship to Mars or points beyond. The Moon was already spoken for by the Army and von Braun. The military *was* interested in the capabilities of a large, manned observation and fire-control platform, but even in 1958 it was evident (if secret) that by the time Orion could be developed, unmanned satellites would be sending high-resolution imagery back to Earth. Orion scaled up better than it scaled down. There were no immediate military requirements for anything that large, other than the argument that if we did not build Orion the Russians might build it first. "Luckily the work we are doing here is not regarded as having military importance," Freeman reported in June 1958. "I think this is a mistake, but I am happy to leave the generals out of it as long as possible."

The proposal kept landing back at ARPA on Herbert York's desk. Finally it stuck. "We asked the government for a few million dollars to get the thing started," Freeman explained when the contract was signed. "The committee which reviews such proposals has at least 500 proposals a year to look at, most of them crazy or stupid, but all of them asking for a few million dollars to get started, all of them submitted by people who get very indignant when they are refused. So naturally the committee was inclined to say no to us. The thing looks completely crazy at first sight. So we had to wear down their resistance, getting various other influential people in the government to believe in us and put in good words for us, and so on. On the whole the committee has not treated us badly. They gave us a number of meetings to explain what we wanted to do, and in the end they agreed to give us the money. The whole procedure took about six months.

"One reason why things were slow," Freeman continued, "is that we shall be under the responsibility of a civilian space agency which will undertake all long-range scientific programs concerned with space and not for directly military purposes. This Space Agency does not yet exist and will probably start next year. Meanwhile we are being paid by the Defense Department out of its research funds. So the contract had to be approved both by the Defense people and by the people who are going to run the Space Agency. I think in the long run this Space Agency will turn out very well. It has enthusiastic support in Congress, and it will probably be able to see us through to the end."

The Orion team lobbied hard. Bethe lobbied James Killian, chairman of Eisenhower's Presidential Science Advisory Committee. Ulam lobbied Congress via the Joint Committee on Atomic Energy. Lewis Strauss, chairman of the AEC, lobbied both ARPA and the Department of Defense. Lew Allen remembers it was Edward Teller who first told him of the project, diverting him from Albuquerque to La Jolla to meet with Ted Taylor, urging the Air Force to lend support.

After it was decided, in early 1958, that the Air Force should not undertake Orion directly, Lew Allen recommended that ARPA fund the project, but as a modest theoretical effort that would reduce both the political liability and the cost. "Conceptually at least, the whole thing looks feasible except for the very serious objection that during the initial liftoff from the earth and while in the dense atmosphere the entire vehicle is immersed within the weapon fireball," he wrote in May 1958. "It may be possible to design for survival but it will not be trivial. Although there are many reservations in our minds regarding the feasibility of the scheme, the possible ultimate reward is so high that we feel strongly that further research should be carried out. General Atomic has done the work so far on an unfunded contract with AEC and are now asking for something like $4,000,000 to carry out an ambitious program involving much experimentation. We have heard that ARPA was considering such a sum favorably. We feel that that amount is too imaginative and recommend that a more modest effort be supported at present, at most a few hundred thousand to fund more study over the next year. The idea is exciting, the reward for success immense, the chance for success slim, but the chance that the study will uncover variants or new ideas of more practical importance is very high."

Herb York was in a bind. As Eisenhower's representative, he was skeptical of the Air Force's tendency to build expensive weapon systems not required for fighting wars. On the other hand, ARPA's mission was to leave no alternative unturned. Politicians tended to be overawed by scientists like Bethe, Dyson, or Rosenbluth, but this did not work on a physicist like York. "Smart people are just as capable of being naïve as dumb people. Maybe more so," he argues. He also refused to believe the estimated costs. "It wasn't just Orion. Almost every cost estimate made by a physicist is wildly wrong, and the better the physicist the worse it is."

York was also a space enthusiast. "I came out of the 1930s space cadet tradition, Buck Rogers and science fiction," he explains. "I was interested in astronomy. Among the very first books I read was a very particular book called *Astronomy for Amateurs,* by a French astronomer called Camille Flammarion, which a somewhat eccentric uncle gave to me when I was eight or nine years old." As a member of the von Neumann committee that set the United States, long in advance of *Sputnik,* on the path toward both peaceful launch vehicles and H-bomb-carrying ICBMs, York helped guide the decisions that set the global agenda for space. In 1958, he wrote a classified report for Killian and Eisenhower that laid out plans for a series of large boosters and called for reaching the Moon in ten to twenty years—which turned out to be right. But in the 1950s, ICBMs came first, and those in York's position kept their dreams to themselves. "In the back of everybody's minds, what stimulated all of us, von Neumann and everyone else—maybe not everyone else, but most of the people—was the long-range possibility, the ultimate idea of Man flying out into the universe. But it wasn't what we were working on," he says.

Upon his appointment as technical director of ARPA, on March 17, 1958, York found a proposal for a 4,000-ton interplanetary spaceship on his desk. "It was the time after *Sputnik* when everybody was looking for some kind of an answer and thinking that technology was the likeli-

Free flight of 1-meter, high-explosive-driven model, version 1, October 1959.

est place to look, and so a lot of stuff that would be too far out under ordinary circumstances managed to get included inside the envelope," he explains. He authorized a one-year feasibility study, with, according to AFSWC officials, "the verbal understanding that the contract would be extended at a somewhat higher rate if it proved technically impossible to disprove feasibility at the end of the first year." York believed the idea, however improbable, should be given a chance. "It was a unique time. When we were getting ARPA started we were willing to take some fliers. I never thought it was feasible, but that's OK, I thought it was interesting. And of sufficiently dramatic ultimate potential that even very low feasibility merited some attention. I tried to put that combination together somehow and multiply that out."

The result of ARPA's decision was Air Force Contract AF 18(600)-1812, "Feasibility Study of a Nuclear Bomb Propelled Space Vehicle," dated June 30, 1958, between the USAF Air Research and Development Command and the General Atomic division of General Dynamics Corporation. "Preliminary studies have indicated that it is conceivable to use nuclear bombs as the energy source to propel a very large, manned vehicle to very high velocities" is the opening sentence in the included four-page Statement of Work. In a total of twenty-three pages, the conceptual and contractual framework was established for the ensuing seven years of work.

"If the concept is feasible," the contract explains, "it may be possible to propel a vehicle weighing several thousand tons to velocities several times earth escape velocities. Such a vehicle would represent a major advance in the field of space propulsion. The Concept which will be under study by the Contractor is, briefly, as follows: A circular disk of material, which is called the pusher, is connected through a shock-absorbing mechanism to the ship proper, which is above the pusher–shock-absorber assembly. A number of nuclear bombs, which are stored in the ship, are fired periodically below the pusher. Each bomb is surrounded by a mass of material called the propellant. As a result of each explosion, the propellant contained within the solid angle subtended by the pusher strikes the pusher and drives it upward into the shock absorbers, which then deliver a structurally tolerable impulse to the ship."

The amount of the contract was $949,550 with a fixed fee of $50,200 for a total of $999,750. "There must have been a million-dollar limit," says Ed Giller, a young physicist and Air Force colonel who had flown the first P-38 fighter into combat in Europe and was effectively running things at AFSWC in 1958. "Right up against the peg!" says Don Prickett.

The next problem was what to do with the money. ARPA could not just hand over a million dollars to General Atomic and walk away. Officially, the contract was administered by the Air Research and Development Command, through the Air Force's Los Angeles office via the San Diego Air Procurement District, with technical cognizance and reporting assigned to AFSWC at Kirtland Air Force Base in Albuquerque. Procuring the design for a nuclear bomb–propelled spaceship had little in common with procuring engine parts or runway paint, and bureaucratic wrangling between La Jolla and Los Angeles set in immediately, starting with procedures for transferring classified AEC documents to the Department of Defense and ending with a dispute over whether Project Orion consultants could bill the contractor for actual costs or standard per diem for their hotels. "We do not consider the primary role of General Atomic to be the engineering of existing concepts into slightly improved products," General Atomic's contract administrator answered the San Diego Air Procurement District, which had requested General Atomic to procure less-expensive physicists and keep them closer to home. "The cost of hotel accommodations, for example, in some of the larger cities I have mentioned run well in excess of $10 and approach, in New York at least, $15 to $20 per night."

AFSWC, composed largely of Air Force physicists, intermediated and soon assumed complete control. "The technical people enjoyed it and wanted to work on it," says Giller. "I remember flying a B-25 out to General Atomic, stuffing people in the back of the airplane, noisier than hell. We'd fly out and visit them, and then we'd fly back." General Atomic was five miles west of Miramar Naval Air Station. Flying out from Albuquerque to visit General Atomic was a favorite way to get in some flight time, check up on the Orion contract, and perhaps run into Hans Bethe or other luminary physicists over lunch. Orion and AFSWC were a perfect match.

"We [AFSWC] were standing around not doing anything," explains Giller, "when they [ARPA] had the money so they gave it to us." AFSWC had been established, shortly after the Ivy Mike explosion at Eniwetok, to weaponize a liquid-deuterium hydrogen bomb so that it could be delivered by our largest bomber, the B-36. "We kept it the deepest dark secret," says York—negating the weapon's value as a deterrent, since "something the Russians knew nothing about couldn't possibly deter them." Before this predicament was resolved, next-generation solid-fuel H-bombs made the project obsolete. AFSWC suddenly had a lot of highly trained physicists looking for something to do. "I went to the Air Force and said, 'Send me all your Ph.D.s,'" Giller remembers. "All these people who had their commitment deferred while they got a doctorate and then they owed two years. A lot of the other labs said, 'They only have two years and then they're gone.' I said, 'I don't care. If one stays it's worth it.' So they all came with enthusiasm and energy and wanting to do something. We turned them loose."

Orion was irresistible. "I remember talking to Herb York about it," says Ed Giller. "They had some money and we wanted it. Herb didn't even have an office, he was just parked someplace in Washington. We all showed up and said, 'Herb, we'll do it, we'll do it. What is it? You got money, you got an idea? We can spend it.' Our little group at Kirtland was really gung ho to find anything new. This excited us. So we went out and tried to grab it, as the contract monitor, put it that way. We were in the nuclear game, but weren't building anything. We were the marriage fraternity between the bomb and the carrying fraternity, and we were trying to break that mold. It was just a gung ho, 'We can do anything. You want to go to Mars? We're ready.'"

ARPA remained behind the scenes, but continued to lend support. Roy W. Johnson, the head of ARPA when Orion was initially funded, told a Senate Aeronautical and Space Sciences Subcommittee in 1959 that at first "it looked screwball; it doesn't look quite as screwball today." He described Orion to the senators as follows: "This is quite a little trick. First of all, you use bombs, and you use a lot of them. The trick is the creation of a spring mechanism on the platform. This is a peculiar thing; it won't work with anything little like a hundred tons. You are going to have to have several thousand tons; it has got to be real big or it won't work, and it has a springing device, against which the shock wave thrusts. Driving the vehicle, of course, the shock must be absorbed sufficiently so that the inhabitants of it are not killed, but so that thrust is still obtained. Some of the very finest scientists in the country have conceived this and are working on it."

Thanks to ARPA, a small group of Air Force physicists who had been assembled in Albuquerque to squeeze a single H-bomb into a ten-engine B-36 bomber found themselves instead assigned to help Ted Taylor send 2,600 atomic bombs on their way to Mars. It was a marriage made in heaven. The honeymoon cost $999,750 and lasted for thirteen months.

"Herb York had just left Livermore, and things nuclear were high on the totem pole," Giller explains. "They were really the thing. Congress was all excited about things nuclear and so were all the services. Everybody's got to have his own bomb. The Marines, Army, Navy, and Air Force. There was no NASA, and ARPA had just been launched. The Advanced Research Projects Agency—you couldn't get any more advanced than that. It's in that general atmosphere. Space is out there, nuclear is good—or not bad, I'll put it that way. And a bunch of scientists—not crackpot scientists—got interested in it for the science, not necessarily for the mission. They realize they have to have a mission, but some of the scientists, like Lew Allen and Jack Welch, wanted it for science as much as anyone else. It was in that atmosphere that it was born—before all the naysayers got a chance to stop it before it got started. They showed up a little bit later, and they began to question the rationality and the cost."

10

Columbus

"We shall know what we go to Mars for, only after we get there," wrote Freeman Dyson in May 1958. "You might as well ask Columbus why he wasted his time discovering America when he could have been improving the methods of Spanish sheep-farming. It is lucky that the U.S. government like Queen Isabella is willing to pay for the ships."

Officially, Project Orion was a feasibility study. No development allowed. Even building the 1-meter flying model was outside the scope of ARPA's contract and was initially paid for out of General Atomic's $50,200 "overhead," not directly from ARPA funds. Among Orion's true believers, however, the question was not if the ship would fly, but when. Ted Taylor's official title was technical director and chief scientist. Unofficially, he was the leader of an expedition and began assembling his crew. "A lot of personal focus went on at General Atomic, on being a member of the crew of Orion, and on spending the next fifteen or twenty years walking on Ganymede," he remembers. "I didn't care about the ship, I was much more interested in what was out there, in poking around. It didn't matter what we built, as long as it would get us there."

"He wanted to make this a comfortable ship on which people could really live," Harris Mayer explains. "And with four thousand tons, which would have nearly a thousand tons payload, you could do all these things. It was the difference between something so stringent, like in the space program, a little capsule and no space to move, compared to a yacht. Orion was a big heavy thing, and used conventional engineering. This means steel, no fancy materials, and really no restrictions on the weight of things. And little by little it began to be, 'Now, let's do the engineering on it.' Ted Taylor's idea was low technology—make it out of standard parts. A grand concept, absolutely, but essentially no new technology."

Freeman's imagination was captured by Ted's determination to go into space quickly, comfortably, and large scale. "He is such a modest and ordinary-looking young man, it is hard to believe when I am chatting with him that this is the Columbus of the new age," Freeman wrote to his parents in June 1958, when the ARPA contract was first announced. "On Friday night I went around to their house with a bottle of good cognac, and the three of us, Ted and his wife Caro and I, looked at Jupiter and Saturn through Ted's 6-inch telescope. The seeing was good, and we drank to the moons of Jupiter, to our children, and to the success of our enterprise."

"I remember lying on picnic tables at our house in La Jolla, with Freeman, looking up in the sky, and he knew what everything was," says Ted. "The sense of being out there, physically, big time, not all huddled together in a little capsule, was unbearably exciting. You just couldn't stay sitting down when you start really thinking hard about that." Ted hoped to take some of his four children along. "What would I as father do about the family if I went off for three years?" he asks. "Quite often the expectation was that some of them would be on board." Freeman assumed he would be leaving his own children on the ground. "It was always a question, what about the family," he says. "You'd be leaving them behind for five years or so. That was a little bit of a problem. But at that time I was young and irresponsible so I didn't think that would be a fatal flaw."

Ted and Freeman saw Orion as a first step toward a space-faring society that would someday produce children on board. "One thing that always had a way of drifting in when we were talking about what it would be like when there were dozens of Orions flying about all over the place," remembers Ted, "was the whole matter of, in a big vehicle, where one wasn't at all cramped, what would lovemaking be like?" The ship's designers imagined a room shaped like a chambered nautilus, where the period of oscillation in zero-g could be varied by moving around. "The physical layout of the bedroom, if you want to call it that, was really interesting to think about," says Ted. "What can you do that you can't do on the ground? A whole lot of things. You would move around in a padded room which could be shaped like a snail or a funnel so that the timing of any emotionally charged contact could be slow and easy if you were in the big part, you could just push off gently from the wall, or you could get more and more high frequency."

A million dollars went a long way in 1958. General Atomic's support staff and infrastructure were already paid for on General Dynamics' account. Some of ARPA's money went into technical design and engineering, some went into computer time and experimental tests, but much of it went directly to people who were paid to think. Outside consultants were paid $50 to $200 per day. A senior design engineer was paid $16,000 a year. Many of the Orion team bought houses in Del Mar or Solana Beach, where beachfront living was inexpensive and within twenty minutes' drive from Torrey Pines. A two-bedroom house could be purchased even in La Jolla for $15,000, and $45,000 would buy a three-bedroom, 2.5-bath house on a half-acre lot on La Jolla Farms Road, above Black's Beach. Ted purchased an acre on top of Muirlands Drive, overlooking La Jolla, for $10,000, planning to build a house, but, when he left for the Pentagon in 1964, he sold it for $15,000 instead. Renting a car in San Diego cost $9 per day. A General Electric Low-boy black-and-white television cost $199. An IBM 704 computer with 16,000 words of core memory cost $205 per hour—more than one of its programmers earned in a week.

Project Orion was well under way before the first dollar of ARPA's money was spent. In October 1957, with *Sputnik* overhead, Ted spoke with Freddy de Hoffmann, who authorized spending whatever time and General Atomic resources were necessary to move the idea along. It was de Hoffmann who went to Princeton to recruit Freeman, the subject being too secret to discuss by mail or phone. "He came here and he said,

'Look, you've got to come to GA,'" says Freeman. "I said no, I have no intention of coming to GA, I've done my bit for GA. And he said no, you must come, we have something much bigger and much more exciting, and then he told me Ted had this wonderful scheme for getting around the solar system with bombs."

Charles Loomis, a mathematical physicist from Los Alamos, helped to germinate Ted's plan. "I was up all night and then I got alarmed that things were getting big," says Ted. "Energy divided by volume is giving pressure, so the pressures were out of sight, unless it was very big. It got easier as it got bigger. I was thinking of something that might carry a couple people, with shock absorbers. I went in to General Atomic the next morning and my office was right next to Chuck Loomis, who had come down from Los Alamos to work on bombs, and I told him about the sense of discouragement because it was so big. And he said, 'Well, think big! If it isn't big, it's the wrong concept. What's wrong with it being big?' In less than thirty seconds everything flipped. It was Chuck's call that if you were serious about exploring the solar system, why not use something the size of the *Queen Mary*? He understood that bombs could in principle do it. They could lift downtown Chicago into orbit."

The next person brought on board was Marshall Rosenbluth, a Los Alamos colleague of Ted's who had been hired by de Hoffmann in 1956. A plasma physicist who had played a key role in the development of the hydrogen bomb, he was well equipped to evaluate Ted's scheme. Orion's feasibility depended on how much pusher plate would be ablated with each shot. Ted had seen the effects of nuclear explosions, but to go any further with the idea required more than an intuitive guess. "This question about ablation, how thick a layer you would actually wind up with, I couldn't calculate, I didn't know how," says Ted. "I talked to Marshall, and he said, 'Well, I can model that.' Which he did right away, making sense out of those experiments where people picked up things that had been exposed to twenty kilotons twenty feet away. The order of magnitude of the ablated thickness of the pusher plate, whether it was a conducting material or not, was a few thousandths of an inch. And Marshall's stamp of approval in that was enormously important." Rosenbluth had

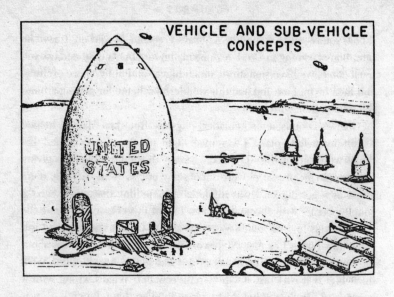

*Multiple-Orion Mars exploration mission: two 4,000-ton Orion ships
(not to scale) remain in Mars orbit in the background; the payload compartment of a third ship, separated from its propulsion module, has
been landed to serve as a surface base.*

worked on two similar problems. "I was quite familiar with this," he
says, "both from the reentry-vehicle nose cone work people had been
doing and also from looking at what happens when the radiation hits the
cases of bombs."

Rosenbluth then produced, as he describes it, some "real quick and
dirty calculations, the way a physicist would do the problem" concerning the capabilities of shock absorbers, and whether a bomb-driven ship
would be stable in flight. "Far from whether you could really engineer
it," he adds, "I could have proven it was utterly impossible, but it came
out that it was possible, but you would have to avoid goofs like the bomb
that didn't go off or unbalanced shock absorbers and things like that."
He saw that the worst thing for Orion, worse than a complete dud,
might be a bomb whose high explosive detonated without the bomb
going nuclear, throwing shrapnel rather than plasma at the ship.

"That remains a very serious question," says Ted. "What do you do? The answer we used to give was, 'We'll make damn sure they all go off.' Well, how do you do that if you are going to fire four thousand of them? Marshall wrote that one up, brought that question up enough so that in his mind it may have been a showstopper—the kind of thing that could have killed the project if left unresolved. It's peculiar that our biggest problem was if we *didn't* get an explosion."

Rosenbluth was listed as Ted's coauthor on the report that formed the basis of the proposal to ARPA, and he accompanied Ted, de Hoffmann, and Creutz to Washington to begin, as Ted remembers it, "the first probing as to what some of the fancy people in Washington thought about this." Roy Johnson, the new head of ARPA, responded, according to Ted, by saying that "people have been coming in here over and over and over again and telling me about the gigantic things required to put a small payload in orbit, and you're coming in here and saying you are going to put an honest to God spaceship up there."

"Marshall Rosenbluth had already done most of the theory," says Freeman of his visit to La Jolla over New Year's 1958. "So I spent a week or so, hearing what Ted and Marshall had done. Marshall would find out something and explain it to me and then it would take me a week to understand why he had done it right. He was amazingly quick. The basic theory was already done—essentially just calculating how much stuff would get ablated from the surface, that was the only real uncertainty. The rest of it was just mechanics."

For the first six months of the project, until the ARPA contract was announced, most of the work was done by Ted, Marshall Rosenbluth, Chuck Loomis, Burt Freeman, and other individuals already at General Atomic, supplemented by consulting agreements with people like Freeman Dyson, who visited regularly, and others who were consulted once or twice. The list of consultants included many notables in physics: Hans Bethe, Stan Ulam, Richard Courant, Harris Mayer, Wallace Birnbaum, Thomas Gold, Willem Malkus, Ken Watson, Murray Gell-Mann, Robert Christy, Keith Brueckner, Hans Liepmann, Arthur Kantrowitz, and more. Richard Feynman came down to General Atomic but declined the invitation to sign on. He called Orion "the pie in the sky."

He did not believe the idea was technically impossible, he just did not wish to have anything more to do with secret projects or nuclear bombs. "Feynman was determined after Los Alamos never to do anything like that again," says Freeman. "He got too addicted when he was at Los Alamos and didn't want to be involved."

"This summer we shall be running around cajoling all the best people we can think of to come and work with us," Freeman reported at the end of April 1958, after accepting Ted's invitation to move to La Jolla and work for the project full-time. "Money is no object. You cannot get people to drop everything, leave their jobs and move house, without giving them some idea of what it is you want them to do. For this reason we asked the government to allow us to make public the existence and general purpose of our project." It then became possible to recruit openly and the crew began to expand. On July 3, 1958, Freeman sent a one-line telegram to H. Pierre Noyes at the CERN High Energy Physical Conference in Geneva:

SPACE SHIP PROJECT OFFICIALLY BEGUN. JOB WAITING FOR YOU. DYSON.

Noyes was a physicist, then at Livermore, who had met Freeman through Hans Bethe and Rudolf Peierls during Freeman's two years at the University of Birmingham. Enthusiastic about space, Noyes had made a bet—for two bottles of scotch—with Brian Flowers, Her Majesty's advisor for atomic energy, that there would be a man on the moon by 1970. "When Flowers heard I was going to work on Orion," says Noyes, "he said, 'That's dirty pool. That wasn't included in the bet.'"

"Your bet with Flowers is quite safe," Freeman had assured Noyes in a letter from La Jolla shortly before the contract with ARPA was announced. "About what we are intending to do I cannot of course tell you anything. All I can say is, everything else in this field will be children's toys when we are finished. If no unforeseen breakthrough occurs, I think 1970 should see us on one of the satellites of Saturn. I would be surprised if the Russians are not several years ahead of us." It was never determined whether landing on one of the moons of Saturn would have allowed Pierre Noyes to collect on the scotch.

Keith Brueckner, who had already done some consulting on the project, was at the Geneva conference and was able to give Noyes a few more hints about what was up. "I knew that it would involve nuclear explosives," says Noyes. "But I didn't have a clue until I arrived how they were planning to use them. And then as soon as Freeman and Ted told me about throwing stuff at a pusher plate and having a shock absorber, I understood it. And then I started to think about what the problems would be."

Orion featured an international cast. Stan Ulam was Polish; de Hoff-mann was Austrian; Michael Treshow, Danish; Dennis ver Planck, Dutch; Jaromir Astl, Czech; Carlo Riparbelli, Italian; Ed Day, German-Scot; Ta Li, Chinese; Thomas Macken, British; Hans Amtmann, Ger-man. Constant David, who did endless shock absorber experiments and wrote a huge number of technical reports, was French. "There was some talk in the offices at General Atomic about the liberating aspects of being out there, and the solution of international tensions," remembers Ted. "I always dreamed a lot about a *Star Trek*–like crew."

The initial rate of progress suggested the ship might soon fly. "That was the best working environment and best working conditions that I have experienced in my life," remembers Jerry Astl. "And that's why we achieved what we did, because nobody worried whether it was your sphere or not, if you knew you could help you did help. Nobody worried about punching the clock. There was free exchange of information and opinions. And I believe that is what is necessary to formulate every-body's mind and push it forward. If you can bring together high theo-reticians and men with practical experience and ability to create, and if you can get them to work together, like brothers, then you have some-thing."

Most of the crew had worked on large, ambitious projects during and after the recent war. Besides the experience gained in the development of nuclear weapons, Orion benefited from the general wartime tradition of get the job done, fast. For the first year, almost everything went right. "I can't emphasize enough the fun we had in '58 and '59," says Bill Vul-liet. Most of the problems were minor complications arising from trying to reconcile the speed at which Orion was progressing with the slow pace of bureaucracy at the AEC and the Department of Defense. When the first twelve months were up, it turned out there was still money left—so the contract had to be extended for an extra month. "About the worst news you can give the source of the funds is that you've got money left over," says Ted. "We did not feel strapped for money that first year. It just didn't cost all that much."

Payload restrictions were also no obstacle. In 1958 and 1959, a crew cut was part of the uniform, both among the Air Force officers from Albuquerque and among the engineers and technicians at General Atomic. "I wanted to just be an ordinary member of the crew," says Ted. "I had a lot of fun making tallies of payload, and one thing I always saw to it that was on there, in scorn for the cost of payload weight, was an old-fashioned two-ton barber's chair." Some of Ted's more serious thoughts about "Uses of Large Payloads" were recorded on two hand-written pages of notes as follows: "Solar power . . . Electrical power beamed to earth by microwave . . . Visible light beamed to earth by mirrors . . . Local weather control . . . Deuteron accelerator . . . Solar powered orbital computers, information storage banks . . . Arbitrarily big communications system, ultra-many channel relay stations, house-to-house TV, coded conference linkups, etc., huge influence on education . . . Bomb power, BATS & MICE on moon or asteroid . . . Space exploration, Astronomy, Dyson's parallax measurement."

Dyson began to think about *really* large payloads. One of his ideas became known as Project Deluge, a plan for bringing water to Mars. "There was an old science-fiction novel with the title *Wasser fuer den Mars* with the theme of crashing a big ice comet into Mars," he explains. "We had talked of using Orion to do this on a more modest scale, bringing water from Enceladus to Mars." Such thinking was encouraged, as was the assumption that those working on Orion would be among those going along. "The importance of the large space ship is, of course, that it will be manned," wrote Bryce DeWitt, in *The Scientific Uses of Large Space Ships*, which catalogued the ideas of the General Atomic scientists during the summer of 1959. "Of all the complex and versatile devices in existence today, men are among the easiest to produce." One suggestion was the establishment of a permanent space observatory, occupied by "eight or ten families, including a number of bona fide astronomers and the equivalent of a 'night assistant' or two."

Ted's enthusiasm was infectious. "The morale and enthusiasm of the group is extraordinarily high," reported an Air Force official sent to check up on the project in early 1959. "I think these people are practically convinced that they can turn this dream into reality." Orion was going to fly, and Ted had gathered a group of fellow nonconformists who were ready to go along. "Ted put up with anything to keep good theorists within the organization," remembers Brian Dunne. "A group like that is like a ballet or an opera. Very talented but temperamental people. You never saw such diversity of personalities—and it was due to Ted. He attracted all these diverse characters. Completely different people, like Jerry Astl, would work for him, who wouldn't work for anybody else." Astl explains why: "He didn't play big shot. He played one of the guys. That gives you an incentive to pull all you can."

Ted's modesty and informality were incongruous for the leader of a big project, and he was an unlikely Columbus when it came to leaving Earth. He battled a deep, inner phobia about outer space. "I had a lot of dreams about being out there, some of them nightmares, like being in a big spaceship looking out a porthole and seeing an incredible, unbelievable display of stars. And the sense of motion through that under-surface sea of stars, a sense of wonderment, and then all of a sudden it would all go black, and I would look out and realize there was nothing there at all to see," he explains. "It was a terrible feeling—I get a little of it back right now—of being absolutely alone, not even conscious of being in a ship. Out there there's nothing. Inside there's nothing. There's nothing anywhere. I would wake up screaming and I mean screaming, yelling. I still do that every now and then. It seems to some extent to be connected to this terrible fear of a large spherical image of light color or mottled color on jet black, and I remember being terrified by that all the way back to when I was just a few years old, and I've never been able to explain that, this fear. I still cannot look through a pair of binoculars let alone a big telescope and see the full moon. It's like standing on a ledge on a tall building. I just refuse to do it."

These feelings haunted Ted long before Orion. "We had a book on astronomy at home in Mexico City when I was a little kid, and there was a full-page photograph of the full moon, and if I even glanced at that from across the room I began having the shudders, and I just could not look inside of it. I think my mother knew about this: 'Don't worry about it. Don't look at it.' I have never found anybody who has this fear of looking through a telescope. I want to know what's there. I can steel myself to look at a double star, but I cannot look at Saturn or Jupiter when the image is big. I wonder sometimes if everybody goes through a series of lives and whether the reason I'm terrified is I was up there somewhere in the past and crashed."

11

Noah's Ark

In what Kurd Lasswitz described (in 1901) as "The Universal Library," elaborated by Jorge Luis Borges as "The Library of Babel" (1941) and revisited by Kevin Kelly (1994) as "The Library of Form," all possible books, all possible creatures, and all possible technologies have a place somewhere on the shelf. "When it was proclaimed that the Library contained all books, the first impression was one of extravagant happiness," wrote Borges. "All men felt themselves to be the masters of an intact and secret treasure. There was no personal or world problem whose solution did not exist." It is the business of both evolution and invention to sift through the possibilities, cataloguing those combinations, however improbable, that make sense.

Nature and technology usually advance by increments, with sudden innovations appearing as the result of novel combinations or appropriations of features that already exist. The space of possibilities is infinite, but the library is not. It is finite but unbounded: if you do not find what you are looking for, you can always add one more book to the shelf. Ted Taylor sought to open a whole new wing at once.

"The variety of conceivable space engines is huge; we have so far worked hard on only a very small fraction of the possible ones," he explained in 1966. "I have made a morphological outline of possible space propulsion systems, classifying them according to whether the energy release is pulsed or continuous, the types of energy sources that are used, the numbers and types of energy conversion stages in the engine, and so on. If one randomly permutes the elements of this outline, one generates more than 10^{22} different space propulsion concepts, each of which makes logical sense! If each of these concepts were studied by one person for an hour, it would take a billion people a billion years to study them all!" Ted posted the outline on his refrigerator at home. "Random generation of propulsion concepts from Table III is practically guaranteed to produce a concept that no one has ever thought of before," he reported. "I have found it impossible to reject, as clearly nonsensical, any of the dozen or so concepts which I have seen derived that way, mostly by my children. But every one of them has been a strange idea indeed."

A universal library, whether of books, genotypes, or technologies, forms an expanding cloud of possibilities in a multidimensional space. The laws of nature form an outermost bound. A smaller cloud, condensed out of this atmosphere of possibilities, represents the organisms or technologies that can be assembled from available parts. Finally, a small central core—where we live—represents the books, organisms, or technologies that exist at the present time. Instead of building outward by small increments, Ted sought to develop Orion the other way around: start with the laws of nature; delineate the bounds first of possibility and then of practicality; finally, trace a path backward to existing technology so as to advance not by increments but by leaps and bounds.

We have an unusually detailed record, for a secret project, of how the requisite conceptual leaps were performed. De Hoffmann insisted, says Ted, that "anytime anybody had an idea, write it down. And put the GA logo on it." When an idea was written down, it was reviewed by General Atomic's technical document center, and, if approved for distribution, was released internally as a GAMD (General Atomic Manuscript Document) report. De Hoffmann applied academic standards to General Atomic's technical literature, both in deference to academic tradition and because clear thinking was aided by written reports. "Just in the process of writing it up, you refine your thoughts and often find that something that is not quite wrong was not quite right," says Burt Freeman. It was also a good way to build an institutional memory and benefit collectively from individual work. "Any informal report would come over with a distribution list," explains Bill Simpson. "Fred was hell on cross-fertilization of ideas—and the distribution lists were supposed to be constructed with that in mind."

F. W. (Bill) Simpson, director of the library and document center, had been a librarian at Furman University in Greenville, South Carolina, until hiring on in 1946 with the Manhattan District at Oak Ridge, Tennessee. "I thought we were getting in on the ground floor of atomic energy," he says, "but after being there a while, I decided we entered the basement!" He was assigned the job of organizing the documents belonging to the research division of the Manhattan Project, then in complete disarray—"an unindexed, uncatalogued, unabstracted mass of information"—with no coordination between the different installations being transferred to the newly established AEC. The huge number of classified documents presented a challenge, but what to do with the first *unclassified* document was even more of a problem for the Manhattan District. "The guys from the declassification branch brought this manuscript around to me one day and said, 'What can we do with it?' And it threw everybody into a tizzy. Heretofore, everything had been restricted, confidential, secret, and so on. What did we do with an unclassified report?"

Simpson helped organize the Manhattan District's (later the AEC's) collections, abstracting, indexing, and circulating them according to standard distribution lists. Freddy de Hoffmann noticed. Simpson was hired by General Atomic in April 1956 and began ordering books and journals out of the General Dynamics office in Washington, D.C. "Fred wanted very much to have a library, which he regarded as an inducement to the people from the universities and national labs," Simpson explains. "Everybody that came in, the new hires, he would ask to make recommendations for the library. And Fred spent a lot of time on that, himself." In addition to assembling a research library, Simpson established a team of editors and typists—consisting largely of English majors, not scientists—to produce General Atomic's own reports.

"I have one of the most unmathematical minds you have ever encountered," Simpson admits. "I enjoyed my associations with the scientists and always asked what they were working on. And they were always happy to talk about their work!" Simpson has no patience for scientists who say they cannot explain their work to someone who does not understand the math. "In my entire tenure at General Atomic, talking with aeronautical engineers, metallurgists, reactor physicists, fusion physicists, astrophysicists, I never had one instance of that. They all talked to me like I was an intelligent being." Project Orion produced an exceptionally lucid series of technical reports. No matter how mathematical in nature, the meaning is clear and the language understandable independent of the mathematical results. The title pages identify who did the work as well as who wrote the report.

The AEC's classification rules differentiated Orion's literature into two separate phyla—one branch that circulated freely (if internally) and one branch that was confined to a vault. Reports that mentioned "bombs," provided specific design details or dimensions of the ship, discussed or allowed inference as to either the yield of or fissionable material consumed by the individual pulse units, or discussed specific missions or military applications were classified—usually "Secret—Restricted Data," or S-RD. Any release of information was controlled not by the Air Force sponsors but directly by the AEC.

In this category were all the progress reports issued under the terms of the original ARPA contract and its Air Force successors. This includes a long series of preliminary, annual, and final reports, beginning with the *Feasibility Study of a Nuclear Bomb–Propelled Space Vehicle, Interim Annual Report, 1 July 1958–1 June 1959*, written by Brian Dunne, Freeman Dyson, and Michael Treshow, and edited by Ted Taylor, who remembers this as the document that "turned on the Air Force," including Mike May, later director of Livermore, who said "it was the best progress report he had ever seen." It remains classified S-RD. "It only covers the first year, but if I had to choose one document for declassification, that would be the one," says Ted. By the end of the project, Orion's final re-

Ted Taylor and the 135-foot-diameter library/cafeteria at General Atomics, November 1999.

ports were being issued in four volumes, totaling more than six hundred pages and constituting a cumulative handbook on the state of the art.

Hundreds of GAMD reports were issued covering every aspect of the feasibility, design, and possible operation of the ship. Some reports were two or three pages and some were two inches thick. A sampling of classified reports: *A Survey of the Shock Absorber Problem; Trips to Satellites of the Outer Planets; Random Walk of Trajectory Due to Bomb Misplacement; Flight Characteristics During Takeoff Through the Atmosphere; Radioactive Fall-out from Bomb-Propelled Spaceships; Multi-ICBM Weapon System; ORION Charge-Propellant Fire Control; ORION Parameter and Payload Study Based on 200- and 4,000-Ton Reference Design; Orion Fuel Requirements.*

De Hoffmann encouraged the publication of as much work as possible in unclassified form, distilling the underlying science and carefully removing any reference to specific dimensions, military applications, or bombs. The unclassified literature reveals who was thinking what during Project Orion's seven years of work (see the appendix for a more complete list): *The Absorption of X-Rays by Cold Materials; Flexural*

Vibrations and Stresses in a Flat Pusher; Shock Structure in a Medium of Finite Radiation Opacity; Optimal Programming for Vertical Ascent in Atmosphere; Minimum Energy Round Trips to Mars and Venus; Deformation Analysis of a Plate-like Structure Represented as a Grid of Beams; The Scientific Uses of Large Space Ships; Diffraction of a Shock Wave Around a Corner; Diffraction of Radiation Around an Opaque Disc; Minimum Energy Loss in a Two-Mass Spring System; Application of the Single-Scattering Approximation for Atmospheric Side-Scattering of Gamma Radiation into a Nuclear Space Vehicle; Viscous Flow of Ablating Grease Films; Hydrodynamics in the Interaction of X-Rays and Cold Iron; Preliminary Data on a Complete Life Support System for a Manned Space Vehicle; Preliminary Analysis of Meteoroid Protection for the 10-M Diameter Orion Engine; Study of the Effects of Using Lunar or Planetary Material for Propellant.

These reports develop Orion from first principles, defining the bounds of feasibility that the more classified reports, by adding engineering details, attempted to fill in. "It was all slide rules, and sometimes you used log tables," says Brian Dunne. "All the reports were typed up by hand." A large number of them end with the lowercase initials "br"—the mark of Betty Risberg, who "could type up equations without even stopping," according to Dunne. All this technical literature, establishing the theoretical framework for the ship, was both produced and collected in the document center that occupied the ground floor of the central building at General Atomic—which also formed a model of Orion, full scale.

This building was a trademark achievement for its architects, Pereira & Luckman, appearing as futuristic today as it did in 1959. A fluted, toroidal monument, with plate-glass windows, it is supported above a central courtyard on tapered, angled steel buttresses that give the impression it has either just landed or is ready to take off. As you ascend one of the curved steel staircases attached to the periphery of the central core, you do not feel you are entering a building; you feel you are climbing aboard. As a six-year-old, I watched my father head in through the classified security gate to work at General Atomic and thought the round building was the beginning of the spaceship. I was not completely wrong.

"To me, the library always was Orion, ready to take off," Ted recalls. "I saw it take off! I had repeated dreams about it. Imagine sitting up there, eating, on something rotating at about one-quarter g." The upper level is still the General Atomic cafeteria, and sitting near one of the peripheral windows you can imagine the ship rotating to produce enough artificial gravity to keep meals in place while passing through Saturn's rings. "We always imagined the ship with a big recreation area in the nose, and windows looking out forward and sideways, so we could see the rings of Saturn sweeping overhead as we passed through," says Freeman. "There would be heat shields covering the windows at take-off and landing and during thrust maneuvers, but most of the time we would be cruising in space with the windows uncovered."

No one was thinking about Orion when the library was designed. And no one was thinking about the library when the Orion group, still at the Barnard Street School, established the basic dimensions of the ship. "Something with a gross weight of 4,000 tons was the way all of us were thinking about Orion at the very beginning," Ted explains. "A 4,000-ton vehicle, how big is that? Well, about 100 to 150 feet across. How much does 150 feet mean to somebody—me in particular? Nothing without comparing it to something else. It turned out, when I went out and paced the distance, to be the diameter of the General Atomic library. This was after the general scale of the thing was determined, while we were still at the schoolhouse. How did the transfer of attention happen? The library was obviously something to point at if one wanted to say roughly how big the thing was—or could be. Once having done that it was easy to visualize shrinking down this dimension closer to a delivery shaft for warheads. The shock absorber distances were about right if you just went from floor to floor. It was easier to me than pointing at a blackboard to say here's this building and just imagine that there are nitrogen-filled shock absorbers directly attached to pneumatic tire-like things at one end. You get a sense of how the shock absorbers looked. Were they spindly? No, they weren't. The columns that are out there are roughly half the diameter they should be. It was a very helpful way to think about the project as a whole.

"I remember leaning on a rail and pondering the thing after going down to Torrey Pines beach and eating my lunch down by the water, among the birds," Ted continues. "It was an object for reflection about the project, in a lot of different ways. The setting was perfect. And there was a model! It was a way to deal with questions like what is the flight of something three feet in diameter compared with the flight of something like this, how can it be relevant? Is it just a waste of effort? It was easy to focus attention on different components, to separate, for instance, the shock absorbers from the rest of it. But then you could glance at the building and see it back where it was supposed to be, and not get carried away with things that did not make sense, for reasons that would occur to you if you looked at this thing that was the right size."

Before anyone was thinking about a building as Orion, Freeman was thinking about Orion as a building. According to Harris Mayer, early in the project Freeman sought to establish the dimensional and structural bounds of Orion-type vehicles, given as a foundation the acceleration of a bomb-driven plate in space. "We have a building, the Orion ship, and it's being accelerated," says Mayer. "Well, OK, we have buildings on Earth and they're accelerated, the acceleration of gravity. So he asked the question, 'What's the biggest building we can make?' And he carved out the whole field."

"He derived certain engineering parameters from physical first principles in an amazingly clear way," recalls Lew Allen. "He ended up showing that really the only number that mattered was the strength of materials. Once the strength of materials was set—as it was for, say, steel—all the other parameters of the vehicle naturally fell out. It was such a beautiful and simple way to look at that."

"Soon after we moved out to the new laboratory," remembers Ted, "I set for myself the task of doing some parameter studies, and I did them all graphically, and they were painfully slow. I showed them to Freeman and he said, 'That's a good idea,' and within a week he wrote down about a dozen simultaneous equations, solved, for the whole thing. He did analytically what I had been struggling to do graphically, with all the important parameters of the ship: total momentum transfer, shock absorbers one-stage, two-stage, and so on. That led him into his unfettered, no-limits study and within a couple weeks he was designing starships."

To begin with, Freeman limited his parametric studies to orbital and interplanetary ships capable of taking off from the ground—described in a report titled *Dimensional Study of Orion-type Spaceships*, issued on April 23, 1959. "The dimensional study was less serious," Freeman explains, "but it answers the question, 'Did you explore the outer limits of this technology?' The answer is yes."

"What range of variation can be allowed each of the design parameters without violating general principles of physics and engineering?" Freeman asked. "The general conclusion of the analysis is that ships able to take off from the ground and escape from the Earth's gravitational field are feasible with total masses ranging from a few hundred to a few million tons. The payloads also range from zero to a few million tons. The number of bombs to be carried is independent of the size. The total cost of each trip in fissionable material and in atmospheric contamination is also roughly independent of the size of the payload."

After defining the limiting parameters and establishing the algebraic inequalities that have to be mutually satisfied by any given design, Freeman presented the results as a series of graphs defining the boundaries of feasibility for three classes of ships:

> SATELLITE means a ship with propellant velocity 30 km/sec and propellant mass 100 kg intercepted by the ship. This is the smallest ship which can go into orbit around the earth with reasonably economical use of fissionable material.

> ORION means a ship with propellant velocity 60 km/sec and diameter 40 meters. It has a smaller mass than the nominal Orion M2 design, since the M2 was not optimized for minimum number of bombs. ORION is the smallest ship which appears economic for interplanetary missions.

> SUPER-ORION means a ship with propellant velocity 60 km/sec and diameter 400 meters. It is the largest interplanetary ship which can take off from the Earth's surface. It can be economically propelled by H-bombs.

The ship masses range from 300 to 8,000,000 tons. "It is clear that the larger sizes of the Orion system have immense promise for the future," Freeman explained. "A ship with a million-ton payload could escape from Earth with the expenditure of about a thousand H-bombs with yields of a few megatons. The fuel cost of such a mission would be about 5 cents per pound of payload at present prices. Each bomb would be surrounded by a thousand tons of inert propellant material, and it would be easy to load this material with boron to such an extent that practically no neutrons escape into the atmosphere. The atmospheric contamination would arise only from tritium and from fission products. Preliminary studies indicate that the tritium contamination from such a series of high-yield explosions would not approach biologically significant levels."

Once you start to imagine launching a million tons into orbit, it is no longer an impossible leap to start thinking about building *really* large vehicles that could operate in deep space but would never get off the ground. "Freeman gave a talk about what's the largest thing you can do, never mind the engineering details," remembers Harris Mayer. "So this was a spaceship propelled by megaton hydrogen bombs. The pusher was made of uranium, and the neutrons on the uranium would make plutonium, so when you got to Alpha Centauri's planet, if there was one, you would just take the pusher off and build a nuclear reactor so you could have a colony. We thought this was absolutely marvelous, even though we weren't going to do anything about it. But the atmosphere encouraged us to do things like this. And Freeman did not work in a vacuum, he was interacting with all the people, including Ted Taylor, who was saying, 'Calm down, calm down.'"

A dense, five-page handwritten General Atomic Calculation Sheet, titled "High-Velocity Ships," survives from 1959. It is filled with brief statements such as: "1,000 or 10,000 km/sec in principle obtainable in nuclear explosions. Such velocities necessary to cross solar system in a month. For 1,000 km/sec exhaust we can think of masses of 10^4 tons and $A \sim \frac{1}{2}$ g. Cannot take off from surface. Only 40% of mass used as propellant. So max ship velocity only ⅓ V. To get 100% need only scrape surface. Also possibly reuse fuel and even breed it. Ship in shape of hollow sphere with ¼ solid angle window. Propellant is shit and fission products. The ship velocity is ½ V. Type II reaches 500 and Type III 5,000. Right for energy sources. Type III with mass-ratio 10 could reach 10,000. Take colony of several thousand with amenities of civilization to Alpha Centauri in 150 years."

"This was just an informal talk I gave to the group rather early in the game, about wild extrapolations, just to give people a feeling for what the ultimate limits would be," Freeman remembers. The power source, however, was not science fiction, but hydrogen bombs such as those already sitting on U.S. and U.S.S.R. shelves. "Hydrogen bombs are the only way we know to burn the cheapest fuel we have, deuterium," Freeman explained. "I do not know exactly how efficient hydrogen bombs are, and if I did know I would not tell you. So I will put upper and lower limits on the numbers that we are not supposed to know exactly." Taking a conservative guess at the efficiency of one-megaton bombs, Freeman estimated what it would take to reach velocities of 1,000 and 10,000 km/sec, in each case examining two different kinds of ship: one optimized for maximum acceleration, the other for minimum size.

The outer limits are constrained by the velocity of the bomb debris, the strength of materials, and the maximum temperature—1,000 degrees Kelvin—the ship's surface can withstand. "That's just so the pusher won't evaporate," Freeman says. "With hydrogen bombs you have much higher temperatures of the gas coming in but much lower density so the gas remains transparent. As soon as it hits the surface it radiates away the heat, as long as the kinetic energy of the stuff coming in is not greater than the heat capacity of the pusher. It just says, 'Thou shan't melt the pusher.'"

The 1,000 km/sec ship has a total mass of 24,000 tons. "The difficulty with space ships in the 1,000-km/sec class is not the high cost per pound but the large size of the smallest feasible ship," explained Freeman in 1968. The small-size 10,000 km/sec ship, with a pusher 150 km in diameter and a mass of 240 million tons, would take 30 years to accelerate to full speed, and 150 years to cover the four light years to Alpha and Proxima Centauri, our nearest neighboring stars. To reach 10,000 km/sec, 90 percent of the original mass has to be used as propellant, requiring either an extremely light structure, unfolded in space like a spinnaker or a parachute, or the jettisoning or consumption of part of the ship during the voyage, like a steamship burning its furniture as it nears the end of a trip. The fourth page of Freeman's notes is a table showing how the numbers work out for six different ships. The parameters are V, velocity; M, propellant mass per bomb; μ, mass of ship; N, number of bombs; A, acceleration; L, pusher diameter; b, shell thickness; τ, bomb period. The interval between explosions varies from 0.4 seconds to 50 seconds across the different designs. "For the small-size ship the times are long enough," says Freeman, "but for the high-thrust version it is too short. Four-tenths of a second is certainly not easy. Thirty seconds, then you can imagine opening and shutting a door, pushing the bomb out by hand."

However implausible—to reach 10,000 km/sec requires 25 million bombs—nothing beyond existing materials and technology is assumed. Cost is no constraint, since the project is envisioned as at least 200 years out, when, if the economy keeps growing at 4 percent per year, "the building of a ship for $100 billion will seem like building a ship for $100 million today." The ultimate question raised by super-Orion is not how or when but why. "These numbers represent the absolute lower limit of what could be done with our present resources and technology if we were forced by some astronomical catastrophe to send a Noah's ark out of the wreckage of the solar system," Freeman explained in 1968.

"By the time the first interstellar colonists go out they will know a great deal that we do not know about the places to which they are going, about their own biological makeup, about the art of living in strange environments," he says. Echoing his 1958 manifesto, he listed two goals for such a voyage: "assurance of the survival of the human species against even the worst imaginable natural or man-made catastrophes" and "total independence from any possible interference by the home government."

Freeman emphasizes that Orion was never intended for travel beyond the outer planets. "It's a very poor system for this kind of interstellar trip. 10,000 km/sec is only $\frac{1}{30}$ of light speed, it's just far too slow to be interesting." Interstellar travel, if and when we get to it, will be found on a different shelf in the universal library, where, as Ted sees it, there are $10^{22}-1$ other propulsion concepts left to explore.

12

Free Expansion of a Gas

Physicists love explosions. Twelve years after the end of Project Orion I was cooking breakfast for my father, in British Columbia, on a pressurized kerosene stove that sprung a leak and became engulfed in flames. As I dropped everything and turned to run, there stood Freeman. "Oh good! An explosion!" he exclaimed.

Physicists also love simplified, abstract models. A mathematical model need not correspond exactly to actual physics to provide insight into the real world, and a physical experiment that does not correspond exactly to a mathematical model may still indicate whether the model is on the right theoretical track or not. The development of nuclear weapons, ever since the first test at Alamogordo, was driven by this interplay between theory and experiment: numerical models advanced the design of test devices that advanced the design of numerical models leading to new generations of bombs. "Nine times out of ten we got about three-quarters of the way with computing, but we always had rude surprises when we did experiments," says physicist Bud Pyatt, still engaged today in weapons-effects work descended from Project Orion.

In early 1958, Ted Taylor and his colleagues faced the same challenge that had faced the pioneers at Los Alamos: how to combine numerical modeling, intuition, and limited experimental evidence into a design that stood the best chance of working on the first try. They were operating in a vacuum, propelled by a million dollars from ARPA, without precedent or constraint. Until August 1958 physicists had no firsthand experience with nuclear explosions in space. The behavior of a nuclear explosion in a vacuum should be easier to predict than the behavior of a nuclear explosion in the atmosphere, yet, when the AEC and DOD did conduct high-altitude nuclear tests at the edge of space, many people—if not the Orion physicists—were quite surprised. "Setting off explosions in space is so complex you just can't understand it," says Ted. "Nobody can understand it. All you have to do to prove that is set somebody down and ask them questions until you ask them something where they say, 'I don't know.' You don't have to go very far."

A nuclear explosion in a vacuum instantaneously transforms a certain amount of cold matter into an extremely hot, unconstrained gas. How does the initial shape and density of the cold material affect the distribution of high-temperature, high-velocity material that results? This was one of the first questions that Freeman examined in 1958. Assuming Orion to be a sequence of events leading to Mars or Jupiter and back, the initial expansion of the propellant—material placed around, or near, the bomb—was a good place to start.

This did not mean designing bombs. That was the domain of Livermore and Los Alamos, the AEC's two authorized bomb-designing labs. Ted and his colleagues might have ideas about what kind of bombs to use for Orion, but it was none of General Atomic's business to specify their design. "What was finally agreed on," says Moe Scharff, "is that only the labs should work on weapons design, but other entities could work on weapons effects. The labs—Livermore, Los Alamos, Sandia—were willing to have outside companies work on the effects of their products, as long as they didn't dabble in the products themselves. In the end the position was taken that the weapon ends with its outer skin or envelope, so if you then put something around it, to utilize the output, OK, even if that something was less than a meter away. That's the way it finally worked out. Don't try to fiddle around inside this energy-producing mechanism, but once the energy is produced, if you want to transform it into some other kind of energy, be our guest. As long as you check carefully with us, regularly."

Freeman Dyson had learned most of what he knew about nuclear weapons in one day at the end of the summer of 1956. Not yet an American citizen, he could work on a civilian fission reactor like TRIGA, but not on civilian fusion power ("Project Sherwood") or anything to do with bombs. Toward the end of the summer, after the design of TRIGA had been completed, the AEC, in a panic over a perceived shortage of tritium, assigned General Atomic to design a tritium-producing reactor, code-named "Project August" because the design had to be completed within three weeks. To enlist Freeman's help required a special clearance from the AEC. "The AEC of course has a logical explanation for this absurd situation," Freeman reported on August 26. "Their regulations say that secret information may be given to a foreigner only when this is necessary to the national defense. Obviously, if the information is not vital military information, it cannot be necessary to the national defense to give it to me. Therefore I can have the important military secrets but not the unimportant civilian secrets. It is the craziest joke I ever heard."

Within a few days of receiving his temporary clearance, Freeman received an invitation to stop by Los Alamos on his way home to Princeton in September, for which the necessary additional clearances were being arranged. "I finally managed to get here," he wrote from the Lodge at Los Alamos on September 20. "Yesterday came the news that my clearance has been approved. So I flew to Albuquerque in the evening and this morning took the little 5-seater plane which comes up here and lands on a little mesa not much wider than the runway, perfectly flat on top and with a deep canyon on each side." Freeman had only two days in Los Alamos before flying to New York. "I took the last of my 14 rabies injections in La Jolla yesterday," he added, the result of a trip to Tijuana where he had been bitten by a rabid-looking dog. "Today I spent absorbing all the information I could at tremendous speed. My clearance is good for everything, Sherwood machines and all kinds of bombs."

"To my amazement they simply stuffed me with all their information about bombs," says Freeman. "I hadn't asked for that, I wasn't particularly interested in bombs. They wanted to tell me everything they'd been doing, as if they'd just been burning to talk about this to somebody—all the designs that they had done and what they were planning to do. So I listened to all this, I didn't do anything, and came back here to Princeton and resumed the normal life. But it was very useful when it came to Orion." Freeman now believes the mysterious invitation to Los Alamos was organized out of a concern that Livermore might get to him first.

Freeman's analysis of nuclear explosions in a vacuum, resulting in a series of three short papers titled *Free Expansion of a Gas*, was central to the feasibility of Orion. It was also central to the feasibility of directed-energy nuclear weapons, and led directly from Orion to a project code-named "Casaba-Howitzer," described as "a one-shot version of Orion, like Orion except without any ship." Casaba-Howitzer, conceived by Moe Scharff while still at Livermore, would be resurrected many years later as the basis for the "Star Wars" space-weapons program, known as the Strategic Defense Initiative or SDI. "Whereas Orion directed a dense plasma at relatively low velocity at a wide angle, this was to direct a lower-density plasma at a higher velocity and a narrower angle," Scharff explains. "Orion was a space vehicle. Casaba-Howitzer could be considered space weaponry. It could even have been things carried aboard an Orion, for example, if Orion was a battleship."

Casaba-Howitzer's descendants remain under active investigation and Scharff is unable to give any further details beyond the origins of the name. "They had been naming things after melons and the good ones were gone already. They were on a melon kick that year. The one connection was seeds—many of those melons have seeds, like the particles we were projecting." Casaba-Howitzer was derived directly from Orion, and later versions of Orion drew heavily on Casaba-Howitzer's experimental and theoretical results. Funding for Casaba-Howitzer kept the Orion team going after funding for Orion dwindled out. But there was a costly side to the bargain—a shroud of secrecy that has lingered long after any plans for battleship Orion were shelved. Conversely, if we ever decide to build something like Orion, it will be the continued work on directed-energy weapons—and how to protect surfaces against them—that will allow us to pick up where Project Orion left off.

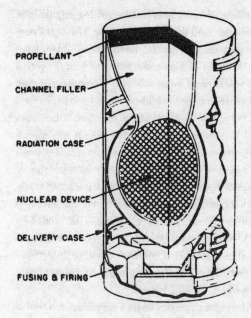

PROPELLANT

CHANNEL FILLER

RADIATION CASE

NUCLEAR DEVICE

DELIVERY CASE

FUSING & FIRING

Pulse unit for a 10-meter-diameter Orion vehicle: yield approximately 1 kiloton, weight 311 pounds, with between 2,000 and 3,000 charges required for a voyage to Mars and back. As the nuclear device explodes, the initial burst of energy is confined by the radiation case and channeled toward the propellant slab.

Anything in the near vicinity of a nuclear explosion gets vaporized into a plasma—a cloud of material so hot that its atoms are stripped of their electrons—that cools as it expands. It was a simple mathematical problem to draw some conclusions relating the shape and density of the initial object that gets vaporized to the shape and density of the resulting cloud of gas. "The model should be simple enough so that the hydrodynamical equations can be integrated exactly," Freeman explained. "A real cloud of gas will not have precisely the density-distribution of the model, but still one may expect the behavior of a real cloud to be qualitatively similar to that of the model." Freeman set up the equations and the numbers were run on General Atomic's IBM 650 card-programmed calculator, one of the workhorse machines that had handled many of the early bomb and blast-wave calculations at Los Alamos and had not yet been superseded by the IBM 704 that General Atomic acquired in 1959.

According to Freeman's model, something originally in the shape of a cigar expands into the shape of a pancake, and something originally in the shape of a pancake expands into the shape of a cigar. This was "very directly relevant to the expansion of a bomb," he explains. "If you have something that starts in the form of a pancake and you heat it up to a very high temperature it will expand more sideways along the axis, and less at the edges. The pressure gradient is highest along the axis, so then after a while, since the velocity is highest along the axis, it becomes cigar-shaped. So you get inversion, something that begins like a pancake becomes like a cigar, and something that begins as a cigar becomes a pancake, if you just let it expand freely. It goes roughly with the square root, if you start with a pancake where the ratio of the diameter to thickness is ten, then it will end up as a cigar where the ratio of the length to the diameter is square root of ten, roughly speaking. That would be quite helpful, of course, if you had a real Orion, to start out with a pancake and it will produce then a jet that is collimated within 20 degrees or so quite nicely. The fact that it's so easy to make an asymmetrical explosion may still be classified, for all I know."

The right pancake in the right place can focus a significant fraction of the bomb's output into a narrow jet of kinetic energy, directed constructively at the pusher plate of a nearby spaceship—or destructively at something else. The thinner the pancake, the narrower the jet. In the early days of Orion, with a huge pusher plate as the target, the propellant was assumed to be a thick slab of something light and cheap like polyethylene; later versions of Orion, with smaller pusher plates, required a thinner slab of higher-density material, such as tungsten, to focus the bomb's energy into a narrower cone. Exactly how narrow remains a secret, though a look at the later configurations of Orion permits a guess. This is one of the reasons that detailed design information about Orion, such as the exact standoff distance between the pulse unit and the pusher plate, remains classified, even after forty years have passed.

As the jet of propellant is targeted more narrowly in space, its impact against the pusher plate is spread out more widely in time. The result is more effective horsepower and a softer ride. "In the end we did come up with some designs that were very tight in their angular distribution of momentum," says Bud Pyatt, without mentioning specific numbers, but revealing that "you had to have it pointing at the center of the pusher plate, it couldn't even be five degrees off without stressing the shock absorber too much."

Pyatt, then twenty-six years old, arrived at General Atomic just as Freeman was leaving in September 1959. "It was an exciting period," he says. "When people asked, 'What are you doing?'—'Well, I'm working on a spaceship propelled by nuclear weapons exploding a few hundred meters away.' They would look at you with this very strange look." Pyatt spent his first eighteen months assisting astrophysicist John C. Stewart in a detailed study of opacities of light elements and then began to focus, under the guidance of Burt Freeman, on improving the pulse unit design.

Adapting weapons-design codes from Livermore and Los Alamos, Pyatt and his colleagues explored a series of refinements to Orion, in far more detail than the first approximations made in 1958 and 1959. "A typical complete calculation for a given pulse system and the subsequent interaction with the pusher requires about two man-years of effort and 50 hours of computer time on an IBM 7090," he explained in 1963. As new computers, improved computer codes, and experimental data came in, confidence increased that the pulse units could be made to perform better than had been hoped for in the original design. "No one had really looked into this with the detail that we examined the design of the pulse propulsion system," Pyatt explains. "The weapons lab people were perfectly happy to stop once they figured out that the bomb worked. All the emphasis had been on bomb physics, not on the analysis of what the emanations of the bomb might do, particularly the hydrodynamics. Some of the stuff Freeman Dyson did, that I followed up on, was very exciting.

"The idea was to have a variable density in the pulse propulsion system. In the same way that one designed two-stage bombs, we had a radiation channel and then a plate was accelerated by the radiation pulse." In cross section, the Orion pulse units resemble an old-fashioned television: the bomb sits at the neck of the picture tube, surrounded by a melon-shaped radiation case; the conical picture tube contains the channel filler; the face of the picture tube is the pancake of propellant. "And now one can go in here," says Pyatt, pointing to the pancake, "and start shaping this and controlling its density in such a way that as it expands outward it's going to have the right density."

The load on the pusher—which for the sake of shock absorbers and passengers should be spread out as widely as possible in time—is governed by the local density of the propellant cloud multiplied by the square of its velocity. "Freeman Dyson wrote a beautiful report on that the summer he was here before I came, and it proved perfectly correct," Pyatt continues. "The velocity is the velocity; you can affect the average and the peak, but you cannot affect the distribution. But you can affect the density distribution, greatly, by controlling the initial density in the propellant slab. Not only does a flat plate expand as a long cigar, if you build in a density profile through the flat plate, that is, a lower density in the front or a higher density and then a lower density in the middle or something, it remembers this. The idea was to mitigate the shock. You didn't want to change the total impulse. The impulse was the impulse; you had to have that to make the whole concept work. But you could certainly control the pressure, if you could stretch it out, spread it out over time, but first of all just direct it—within a half angle of ten degrees or so. And that was highly classified at the time."

Any detailed discussion of how to direct the propellant comes dangerously close to certain details concerning the design of hydrogen bombs. "The technology associated with two-stage devices—radiation channels driving the implosion of secondary devices and bombs—was the technology that we exploited to get the momentum direction," Pyatt explains. "And I'm sure there could have been much more done with this. We never went as far as we could have in designing the pulse system so that it controlled the delivery of the impulse in such a way that it was complementary to the shock absorber. And that would have made the shock absorber problem a heck of a lot easier than just living with a rapid rise and almost exponential decay.

"Later, in the very early days of the first Apple Macintosh I ever owned," says Pyatt, "I ran a design program that let me play with that in my spare time." In 1959, General Atomic owned less computing power than $300 will buy today. "Most of the work that we did on the pulse propulsion system was a full-up, two-dimensional hydrodynamics," says Pyatt. "General Atomic never had a machine that was fast enough, but there were machines that the Air Force made available. I remember endless nights of traveling, and this was before I-5, you still had a lot of

Highway 101 to go up to Hughes Aircraft in Los Angeles. We would get time there, on an IBM 7090. That was a fairly big machine, it probably had 64,000 words of storage on it." This is the memory of the first IBM PC introduced in 1981, and half the memory of the first Apple Macintosh introduced in 1984. "On my desk today I have far more computing power than I ever had when I was working on Orion," adds Pyatt, "with machines that filled the whole basement of the big building at Convair."

There are three surviving legacies of Project Orion: people, documents, and codes. Many of Orion's people came from Livermore and Los Alamos, and so did the codes. "In a moment of weakness, Johnny Foster had agreed with Ted that if they would send someone up to Livermore for a couple months to work with one of their design groups he would let them have one of the big two-dimensional codes that they had developed," Pyatt recalls. "I was elected to do that and I spent a couple of months up at Livermore working with Bill Schultz and brought down the so-called Coronet code. Coronet was the two-dimensional radiation transport code that allowed Livermore to put Los Alamos to shame for ten years in the efficiency of the design of their two-stage devices. We converted that to be a design tool for calculating the behavior of the pulse propulsion system." The Orion version, named MOTET, incorporated improvements that have remained at the heart of the weapons design and verification business ever since.

On July 9, 1962, a 1.4-megaton thermonuclear bomb was exploded 400 km above Johnston Island in the South Pacific. AEC and DOD officials were caught off guard by the spectacular and unexpected after-effects of the Starfish "event," including eye damage to observers within the exclusion zone, illumination of the nighttime sky 1,400 miles away, and a major disturbance of the Van Allen radiation belts. The Orion group was able to model what had happened, after the fact, using MOTET, concluding that "its close prediction of what was actually observed in the test provided strong verification of the code." This was viewed as a milestone for Orion, even though Starfish was not an Orion test.

In addition to MOTET for expansion and SPUTTER for ablation, the mathematical group at General Atomic came up with codes such as BUMP, for impulse; BAMM, for dynamic response; PRESS, for pusher plate stress; BETELGEUSE, for pusher plate vibration; POGO, for shock absorber behavior; HAYO, for computing propellant mass and number of charges per given maneuver; TRIP, for estimating fuel requirements; and OROP and OROPLE, the Orion Optimization codes. Completed in December 1964, OROP and OROPLE embodied the mathematical relationships among 106 different design and performance parameters defining any given Orion vehicle. The accumulated wisdom of six years of work on all aspects of Orion was distilled into sixty-one pages of Fortran code written for the IBM 7044.

OROP and OROPLE were evolutionary dead ends, codes so specialized that they went extinct when their host project came to an end. More adaptable Orion codes are still going strong. Soon after Project Orion was terminated in 1965, Pyatt and a core group of Orion physicists left General Atomic to form their own independent company, Systems, Science, and Software, or "S-Cubed." The new group included Burt Freeman, Charles Loomis, and Moe Scharff, who brought with them the latest generations of programs descended from those first brought to General Atomic from Livermore and Los Alamos in 1958 and 1959. S-Cubed was subsequently merged into Maxwell Technologies in San Diego and recently transferred to SAIC (Science Applications International Corporation), where questions first raised by Orion are still under investigation, using the latest versions of computational tools developed forty years ago, such as the Sputter ablation code. Originally constructed by Charles Loomis and Burt Freeman, Sputter can be applied to questions ranging from whether an Orion ship can survive repeated explosions to whether directed-energy weapons can be counted on to cause hostile mechanisms to fail. "Sputter became the Zeus code, which became—I can't even give you all of the legacy," says Pyatt. "That basic code was really the heritage of Orion that S-Cubed exploited, in all of the work that we've done on the ablation problem. I used it extensively on the earliest laser weapon effects calculations. We're using it today."

Orion, with its unanswered questions about ablation and how to fine-tune the free expansion of a gas, has always remained in the back of Pyatt's mind. "I don't think there's anything I've seen that would raise any questions about what we were saying forty years ago," he says. "As to precise details, we'd probably come up with different answers today."

He remains convinced that the optimism of 1959 was technically sound. "It would have worked. Even in my dotage, I'm a true believer." When asked about a specific aspect of the pulse unit design, he answers: "The answer is yes, but I can't go into any details on it. It works." So at the time of Orion, I suggest, it was a guess, and then later it was tested? "Yes, for other reasons. It wasn't an Orion test."

In answer to a less specific question, he elaborates: "I think there is absolutely no doubt—and we did some experiments later; still quasi-classified, related to Casaba-Howitzer—that the propulsion system would have worked. We knew what we were doing in designing it. We could send 85 percent of the momentum in one direction that we wanted it to go in, and there were enough experiments—and there have been enough experiments—done on the protection of the pusher plate, to have no doubt that it would have worked. Between those two things there is a tremendous amount of engineering detail to be worked out, but I think it was engineering detail. It could have worked. Now, could it have been done economically, could it have been done in time? Those were all different questions, but I think all of those things could have been solved. Today, people ask me, 'Was it really a joke, Pyatt, or was it serious?' It was dead serious. If we wanted to do it, if there were any good reason for wanting to have high specific impulse and high thrust at the same time, we could go out and build Orion right now. And I think it would make a lot of sense."

13

Hotter Than the Sun, Cooler Than a Bomb

"When the nuclear device is exploded, the channel filler absorbs the radiation emitted and rises to a high temperature," explained Bud Pyatt in one of Project Orion's later reports. "The radiation case serves to contain the energy released by the explosion so that more energy is absorbed by the channel filler than is emitted into the solid angle it subtends relative to the source. The high pressure achieved in the heated channel filler then drives a strong shock into the propellant, which vaporizes the propellant material and accelerates it toward the pusher." By this time—1963—tungsten had been chosen for the propellant, beryllium oxide for the channel filler, and uranium for the radiation case. Tungsten—2.5 times heavier than steel—allows for a very thin pancake, producing an optimally narrow jet; beryllium, a strong absorber of neutrons, captures maximum energy from the bomb; uranium is highly opaque to X rays, making it difficult for the bomb's initial burst of radiation to escape.

The expansion of the bomb and subsequent compression of the tungsten pancake takes a few millionths of a second. During this time, the channel filler and propellant absorb neutrons and X rays emitted by the bomb. This reduces the shielding required to protect the Orion crew, and transforms as much as possible of the bomb's output into kinetic energy that can be intercepted to drive the ship. The re-expansion of the propellant gives the pusher a brief but intense kick. "It's like what happens down at the ocean on a very, very stormy day, and suddenly a lot of churned-up sand hits against you," says Pyatt. "Or if you are suddenly hit with a very strong firehose." For the original 4,000-ton, 135-foot-diameter Orion design, there was almost one-third of an acre of pusher plate. All this pressure—on the order of 50,000 pounds per square inch—adds up.

The propellant slab, after being compressed to about one-quarter of its original thickness, expands as a jet of plasma moving at some 150 km/sec (300,000 mph) toward the ship. It takes about 300 microseconds to make the trip. During this time the expanding propellant cools to about 10,000 degrees—a temperature described by physicists as roughly one electron volt. Within another few hundred microseconds the propellant cloud hits the pusher (or the advancing front of the reflected shock wave produced by the initial collision) and is suddenly recompressed. For less than a millisecond the stagnating propellant reaches a temperature of between 100,000 and 120,000 degrees—about ten times the temperature of the visible surface of the sun, but only a small fraction of the temperature of a bomb. In space, with no atmosphere to produce a fireball, the explosion would appear quite different from what we usually picture as an atomic bomb. "The debris goes out from the bomb essentially invisibly," explains Freeman Dyson. "You don't see anything until the stuff is stopped. Around the bomb you have a lot of cold stuff, which absorbs the energy so the debris comes out forwards and backwards and that won't produce anything very spectacular in the way of a flash until it hits the ship. Then all its energy is converted into heat and so you get about a millisecond or so of intense white flash. And very little else."

Orion's feasibility depends on what happens during those few hundred microseconds as the hot plasma piles up against the plate. After two or three thousand impacts would there be any spaceship left? It was the amount of ablation, or eroding away, of the pusher's surface that placed Orion in a regime that was completely unexplored. Later in the project, jets of high-speed plasma were fired at sample targets, attempting to validate the predictions of successive generations of computer codes. But in making the proposal to ARPA in 1958 optimism rested precariously on untested theory and the one-shot evidence from Lew Allen's Balls.

"To calculate the ablation you needed some pretty good physics, and that Rosenbluth was able to do," Freeman explains. "The most important thing is how opaque the stuff is. This whole business of opacity is the central problem both in stars and in bombs. The opacity is like the resistivity of a metal except you are dealing with radiation instead of electrons. It tells you how hard it is for the radiation to get through." Opacity is where Orion either succeeds or fails. "It just kept coming up," says Ted Taylor. "Opacity was repeated ten times a day." The benefits of high opacity are manifold. If the material is opaque, it prevents harmful radiation from reaching the surface of the pusher. It also blocks secondary radiation produced by the collision between the plasma and the pusher from escaping back through the layer of stagnating propellant, thus doubling the kick. "If it is sufficiently opaque so you don't lose that energy by radiation, then it bounces back and you get the momentum doubled. If it is transparent the heat radiates away and you lose it; it is just like a slab of mud being thrown against something and you get the momentum it had originally, nothing more." The initial estimates were rough. "I just did some more opacity calculations and got results differing from Marshall by a factor 4 (which is not significant) in the pessimistic direction," Freeman reported to Ted on May 2, 1958.

Nature appeared to be on the side of Orion. "If you have, roughly speaking, a bomb that is a hundred meters away from the ship with a yield of a kiloton, the temperature works out at a hundred thousand degrees," Freeman explains. "This was an unusual temperature, which had never been thought about much because stars are generally cooler and bombs are usually hotter. So this was an intermediate range. What Rosenbluth understood was that this is a good range for getting high opacity. It's essentially just ultraviolet radiation, soft X rays, which is easily absorbed. Almost anything you put there is opaque. And that's why the thing works, because the more opaque it is then the less the radiation eats into the surface."

Opacity increases as the plasma piles up. "The densities we were talking about were, roughly speaking, one gram per liter, or normal air density, which is unusual for something that hot. The more dense it is the more opaque it gets; if you squeeze the stuff together it gets blacker. Nobody had calculated this before." Opacities had been studied intensively and in secret at both Los Alamos and at RAND. The opacity of heavy elements like uranium at high temperatures was essential to hydrogen-bomb design, and the opacity of air at lower temperatures was critical to an understanding of fireball development in order to either survive or maximize the effects of nuclear bombs. The domain in question for Orion—a hydrocarbon plasma hitting an iron pusher plate at a temperature of 10 electron volts—fell somewhere in between. The Orion physicists were unsure at first whether these numbers would be classified or not. "The question came up very quickly after we started doing this work at General Atomic, what's classified and what isn't in this field, because all during the war the work on opacity was as dark as it could be, it was kept hush-hush," says Pyatt. "So there was an arbitrary decision made that if it was lighter than iron it was not classified. If it was heavier than iron it was classified, at temperatures above 10 electron volts. And to this day that pretty much still holds."

Orion depended on how the numbers turned out. "If the opacity of the propellant is not sufficiently high to contain the radiation near the pusher then one loses the factor of 2 from reflected momentum and this hurts the whole scheme very seriously," Don Mixson and Lew Allen reported after a visit to General Atomic in July 1958. Harris Mayer, the leading authority on opacity, was brought in as a consultant; Dyson and Rosenbluth went to meet with Arthur Kantrowitz at a company called AVCO, which was at the forefront of designing ablative nose cones for ICBMs; the computer programmers started adapting weaponeering codes. Mayer remembers Dyson taking an approach that "was more than mathematical," looking at maximum possible opacity to start things off. "He said, never mind calculating opacities, let's see what the largest opacities could be. And he had a very simple theorem for this, which was well based. Now I'd worked many years on opacities. I never thought in that way."

The opacity of a material across a radiation spectrum is characterized by lines and windows. Lines are where the radiation is absorbed and windows are where the radiation gets through. "To describe where the lines were, how broad they were and how much of the window regions would be obscured by the lines—how much they overlapped, how much they were split by various interactions—was a very, very messy quantitative problem," says Burt Freeman. Astrophysicist John C. Stewart was brought in to focus on the opacities of light elements at relatively low temperature, which, with ingenuity, would eventually intersect with enough computer power to perform a calculation rather than a guess. "What was unique about John Stewart's work," says Burt Freeman, "is that it was a detailed description of a region where the electronic structure was sufficiently simple so that you could do a quantitative calculation."

Opacity was a perfect exercise for someone fluent in QED. "We started doing a much better job than anyone had done before, doing it atom by atom, not just using averages," says Freeman Dyson. "These atoms all have very complicated spectra and everything depends on windows because it's where the atom doesn't absorb that the radiation gets through. The important thing is to get the exact shape of the windows right. It's a delicate calculation. And to fill in the windows it's important to have a mixture of things: carbon and nitrogen and oxygen, which have windows in different places so they fill in each other's windows. And you need the hydrogen just in order to have the chemical compounds that are easy to handle, like polyethylene, which is good stuff physically and also reasonably opaque. You prefer to have something with nitrogen and oxygen as well. But we generally thought of polyethylene as being good enough. It turned out the opacities were pretty high, even just for carbon by itself. The results always turned out to be rather good from the point of view of feasibility."

The results also turned out well from the point of view of economy—and at that time large-scale commercialization of Orion was what Ted and Freeman had in mind. "The best propellant worked out being something like equal amounts of hydrogen, carbon, nitrogen, and oxygen," says Freeman. "Urea would be the ideal substance, it has just about the right proportions." This had two implications for extended interplanetary voyages: 1) ordinary nitrogen-based high explosive, minimizing consumption of expensive plutonium by reducing the critical mass of fissile material required for each bomb, would become excellent propellant when its ionized remnants hit the ship, and 2) shipboard waste could be recycled as propellant instead of as drinking water, an alternative cited in General Dynamics mission studies as a factor affecting crew morale.

The next step was to execute numerical simulations of a cloud of propellant hitting a plate, following the process step by step in time, first as a one-dimensional calculation and then in two dimensions, looking at what happens at a surface being ablated not only by a vertical impact but also by a horizontal wind. The initial shock wave and rarefaction wave were followed by complex interactions as the incoming plasma begins to mix with material being evaporated from the surface of the plate. "The question is, when is that stable and when is it unstable," says Freeman. "The answer was that it was generally stable, but you couldn't be sure."

Convection or turbulence between the layers of stagnating propellant and ablating pusher might defeat the self-protection of the pusher, with disastrous results. "I did a calculation looking at the worst case," says Freeman. "If the thing was totally unstable and convective then how bad would the ablation be? And it turned out even in that case it wasn't terribly bad. Because the time is so short, convection only has time to go around once or twice, so even in the worst case the stuff doesn't ablate more than is tolerable. It was on the whole quite encouraging." Turbulent ablation remained one of the unknowns that could be decided only by a nuclear test. "We just said, 'We'll see when we do the trials whether that happens or not.'"

In 1958, the pusher plate was envisioned as a heavily reinforced 1,000-ton steel or aluminum disk about 120 feet in diameter, lens-shaped so that its mass distribution matched the momentum distribution from the bomb. Fiberglass was also considered and given preliminary tests. "General Atomic may require fiberglass impregnated plastics to be subjected to extremes of temperature and stress," one of Orion's project officers wrote to the Air Force materials laboratory in September 1958. "The material may have a very important application. We are interested in manufacturing methods and techniques for the production of massive slabs weighing up to 1,000 tons. The need for this information is urgent."

After receiving an ambivalent reply—"We are not familiar with any work that has been conducted on molding massive slabs of the size mentioned"—Carroll Walsh, the project's all-around logistical troubleshooter, enlisted a local surfboard maker willing to help. "We got them to make us a big piece, three-inch-thick fiberglass that had never been done before, but they did it. And then we busted the hell out of that." After the expenditure of considerable high explosives, adds Ted, "fiberglass was abandoned on the grounds that it was hard to ensure it would be in the same state after a few shots that it was at the beginning." A good way to envision Orion is as a ship that surfs through space on waves of plasma generated by atomic bombs.

Pusher tests were first performed by detonating a few pounds of high explosive a short distance from target plates. This approximated the mechanical stress on the pusher but did not get anywhere near either the velocity or temperature of the bomb debris that would hit the ship. Brian Dunne thought that they should see how close they could get. Having worked with Ted and Freeman on building the TRIGA reactor, Dunne joined Orion almost from the start. "Ted Taylor called me down to Barnard Street shortly after *Sputnik* and asked me to contribute to this proposal that he and Rosenbluth and Loomis were haranguing over," remembers Dunne, who had a knack for bridging the gaps between theorists and experimentalists, turning this to his advantage early on. "When I wrote proposals, I learned to include both theory and experiments. When those proposals go before the committee, there are going to be both experimentalists and theorists. And the theorists are impressed with the experiments, while the experimentalists are impressed with the theory. This almost always works." Dunne became Project Orion's chief experimentalist, but he is a theorist in disguise. "Experimentally that's what I do—I picture things," he says. "You picture things and then go work with the thing that is most soothing to the nerves."

Dunne knew that you could never duplicate the effects of a nuclear explosion with chemical explosives, but if you began heading, experimentally, in that direction you could check whether the mathematical

PULSE SYSTEM EXPLOSION AND EXPANSION

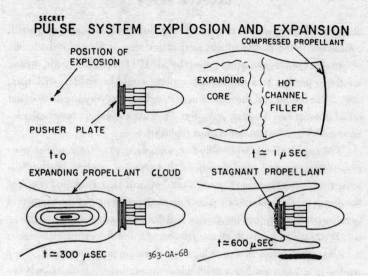

Within one microsecond of the bomb's explosion, the propellant is compressed to a high temperature and density before expanding as a jet of plasma that takes about 300 microseconds to reach the ship. Within another 300 microseconds, the propellant cloud has stagnated against the pusher plate, giving the vehicle a kick.

models of the plasma hitting the pusher were on the right track or not. As a graduate student, he had worked with shock tubes—evacuated cylinders in which a high-speed shock wave is propagated from end to end—and was also familiar, from Los Alamos, with shaped high-explosive charges whereby a jet of material can be accelerated intensely enough to penetrate an armored tank. He put the two concepts together and came up with high-explosive-driven plasma guns—lead-lined evacuated cylinders encased in a thick sleeve of high explosive, up to 40 pounds per shot. The implosion produces effects similar to squeezing a ripe banana out of its skin—with 50,000 mph banana plasma as the result. Dunne remembers trying everything to get to 10^7 cm/sec but the best they could do was 1 or 2 x 10^6. "That's just the kind of problem I wanted to be working on," he explains. These velocities were lower than an Orion plasma but the densities were higher, producing conditions at the target that were close enough to keep the theorists honest and instill confidence in the mathematical models that were evolving, at the hands of Charles Loomis and others, into the SPUTTER ablation code, which sought to predict how much pusher plate would be ablated with each shot. "The theory and the experiment coupling was very similar to what it had been at Los Alamos," says Ted. "You use these very fancy calculations to bridge the gap between actual tests."

"The explosive jets were able to cover only part of the range of temperatures, pressures, and durations that were of interest for the full-scale ship," says Freeman Dyson, "but they provided a detailed check of the theoretical calculations within the overlapping part of the range and gave us confidence that the theory had not overlooked anything essential. You couldn't really fit all the parameters, but the experiments gave a feeling that some of the things we were saying were right. They tended to ablate a tenth of a millimeter or something, which looked very much like what we had in mind for the full-scale ship. It couldn't be much more than that." During the course of the project, with hundreds of charges fired, there was only one accident. "We were working at night on shaped charges, measuring the speed of the jet, doing it optically with a two-spark camera," remembers Dunne. "Somebody pushed the firing switch and nothing happened. Perry Ritter went over the revetment to see what happened and tripped over a wire and the thing went off. He was completely dazed. He gradually came back into focus, with a punctured eardrum and a concussion to one side of his head."

The ablation problem remained under active investigation long after the termination of Project Orion in 1965. In the early 1970s, Los Alamos investigated a possible reincarnation of Orion based on tiny laser-ignited fusion bombs. When the problem of pusher-plate ablation came up, the Los Alamos team dug out the old Orion research, reconstructed the SPUTTER code, and consulted with Brian Dunne. This time, they were able to build an electrically driven plasma gun that produced velocities as high as 1.6×10^7 cm/sec (350,000 mph) and pressures of 2.8 kbar (40,000 psi). The effects on targets of aluminum, polyethylene, phenolic, and greasy coatings were encouraging and indicated "that even much higher energy pulses would not cause ablation severe enough to significantly degrade the performance of a pulsed-propulsion space vehicle." The tests reached energy densities where the self-protection that the Ori-oneers had hoped for started to take effect. "In the ORION experiments the energy fluxes were insufficient to evaporate an optically thick layer of ablative material, and the radiation diffusion phase was never reached," the study concluded. "Relying solely on experimental results, one would conclude that the amount of material ablated scales as the energy flux and would extrapolate accordingly to the conditions of the actual devices. The results of such an extrapolation would probably be much too high because calculations indicate that 70 to 80% of the ablation actually occurs during the radiation diffusion-dominated phase where the rates are small."

Early in the project it was recognized that a sacrificial, ablative coat-ing—known as "anti-ablation oil" or "anti-ablation grease"—could be applied either to or through the pusher plate. According to Harris Mayer, "Sometime during 1958 it was apparent that you could have a transpiration layer of oil coming off, coating the surface, and this would ablate away. And that meant that the structure of the plate was inde-pendent of the wear and tear on it. That was one of the key ideas."

This was discovered experimentally when it was noted that a target plate was protected from ablation by the imprint of a greasy thumb. "I was helping Brian Dunne set up an experiment with an aluminum plate," says Pyatt, "and unbeknownst to both of us I had left my thumbprint on it from some oil. So when we did the experiment, lo and behold the rest of the plate was ablated, but underneath the oil it was perfectly pro-tected. I still have that plate. That led to a large amount of both analysis and further experiments, using a light carbonaceous material, which was light because it had relatively low energy of reaction, and carbonaceous because it turned out that, at the temperatures that we were creating, carbon has very broad lines and becomes opaque very quickly to the radiation created by the stagnating plasma. So you block any radiation from reaching the surface of the metal."

As Jerry Astl remembers it, "Brian Dunne proudly showed me his tests of multiple shock waves impinging on the pusher plate and it was beautiful. But what I saw were three human fingerprints in the middle of an ablated, shiny surface—they were carbonized but intact. You could preserve them as a criminal record. And I talked with Ted about it and I said, 'Ted, it will be very easy—as the pusher plate moves up we will have to have some structural pylons to guide it, so we can put nozzles there and spray a coat of oil on it as it comes down to minimize ablation.' And lo and behold the indication was that you could control ablation completely."

Later Orion designs included tanks, plumbing, and nozzles for applying a coating of heavy oil, about 6 mils in thickness, to the pusher plate between shots. "A specially selected layer of carbonaceous material is placed below the pusher before each explosion," Pyatt and colleagues explained during a presentation to NASA officials in 1963. "*No* pusher material is ablated."

Everyone familiar with the technical details of Orion agrees that pusher-plate ablation was *the* critical unknown. They may have doubts about something else—shock absorbers, bomb-ejection mechanisms, radiation shielding—but those were engineering problems that could eventually have been solved. Could a film of anything, spread as thin as paper, have protected Orion from nuclear bombs? Was anti-ablation grease realistic, or was it the 1950s equivalent of the "ghost shirts" that the last of the Sioux warriors wore into battle in 1890 before the massacre at Wounded Knee? The prophet-dreamer Wovoka had assured the Sioux they would be protected from harm. Was Orion a Ghost Dance?

Of all the original Orioneers, the physicist most familiar with ablation and anti-ablation is Moe Scharff. "There's a lot of ways to skin a cat, and sometimes the cat doesn't get skinned," he says. "I don't know what the outcome of that would have been. I can only say that subsequent experience of energy in various forms being directed at surfaces has indicated that these issues are more complicated than we were able to deal with, but that isn't to say incapable of solution. My gut reaction would be that it would have to be a lot fancier or more capable grease than we knew at the time.

"On the other hand," Scharff continues, "I think there's good news, generally speaking, in subsequent experience, not necessarily with Orion-like plasmas, but other things that are first, second, or third cousins. It is very important to choose the properties of the grease in dealing with that radiation. Do you absorb it all? Maybe. Do you try to transmit some of it? Maybe. Do you try to do something in between?

Maybe. You look at all these things and you would try and choose the right opacities for that impinging material. We are interested in the conditions at high pressure, so can one take advantage of the properties of the grease under those conditions, not under ordinary conditions? Things cut both ways. Certainly what Ted tried to do was to take advantage of those features rather than succumbing to them. 'OK, we have high pressures, let's see what we can do with them.'"

14

C-4

"Ted was not yet convinced that you can detonate a high-explosive charge in close proximity to a structure without causing substantial damage to it," remembers Jaromir (Jerry) Astl, born in Czechoslovakia in 1922, who joined General Atomic in late 1958 from Ryan Aeronautical's office for advanced design. "We were after a quick, easy test to settle the dispute. After many ideas were discussed in a staff meeting one afternoon, we piled into a car and went shopping—to a nearby supermarket—for a suitable spaceship model we could blow up. Within minutes we found a set of three matching mixing bowls made out of fifteen-mils-thick stainless steel. The next day I assembled the 'Spaceship Number One'—an aluminum pusher plate with three mixing bowls sitting on top of each other and all components held together by a long bolt anchored to the pusher. The assembly looked more like a beehive than a spaceship."

The first flying model of spaceship Orion was launched that night shortly after 7 P.M. "I detonated the approximately 60 grams of C-4, suspended 10 inches under the center of the pusher plate," says Astl. "A few coyotes and some deer got scared, a skunk in the nearby bush fired back, but 'Spaceship Number One' was unharmed."

The active ingredient in C-4 is RDX, or cyclotrimethylenetri-nitramine, bound by wax, oil, and polyisobutylene plasticizer into a stiff dough. C-4 resists detonation under all but severe impact and will burn harmlessly if ignited with a match. RDX, first widely used in World War II, detonates (or goes "high order") at 8,700 m/sec (20,000 mph), producing pressures of over 300 kilobars, or about 5 million pounds per square inch. Besides its application, in plastic form, to sabotage and demolition, it can be formed into precise, stable castings used in fabricating implosion assemblies for nuclear bombs.

The trade secrets of nuclear weapon design are in large part the details of how to shape and detonate conventional high explosives so that a convergent shock wave produces the pressures required to turn an otherwise subcritical mass of fissile material into a bomb. Project Orion's physicists were quick to apply their knowledge of high explosives to nonnuclear experiments aimed at gaining a sense of how Orion would perform. Flying models were propelled with high explosives; one-shot explosive-driven plasma guns were used to test ablation; spherical high-explosive charges were used to simulate pusher-plate and shock absorber stress; sheet explosive was used to model the pusher-plate pressure pulse. "It was at least as important to find out what not to do as what to do," says Ted. "So we tried a lot of different things, some of which just blew all to pieces."

Small quantities of explosives were obtained informally by Carroll Walsh, a retired Navy electronics technician hired by Ted in August 1958. Walsh had worked at the Navy Electronics Laboratory at Point Loma, where C-4 was used for sonar tests. "Commander Walsh could get anything, because he knew everybody," says Astl. "When I needed those high-resistance detonators with long leads, he said, 'Well, I know they have them there but they are guarding them like hawks because they are expensive.' Half an hour later he was back and I had six of them." Larger quantities of C-4 were requisitioned through Walsh's contacts in the Navy and delivered by barge from the regional explosives depot at Seal Beach. "We would get in there and take this dough and mix it up," says

Walsh. De Hoffmann wanted to use unmarked trucks to transport explosives among the different General Atomic test sites, but, says Walsh, "the highway department insisted that we paint the damned things yellow. And de Hoffmann raised hell because people would see General Atomic, and then see the explosive truck coming back and forth, so he said, 'You can't do that!'" Walsh, who knew when to bend the rules and when to follow them, made sure the explosives were carried in yellow trucks.

Jerry Astl owed his expertise with high explosives not to Los Alamos but to the Czechoslovakian underground. Upon receiving his degree in aeronautics during the German occupation of Czechoslovakia, he was assigned to the A.T.G. Leipzig (Messerschmitt) aircraft design bureau, overseeing work at a nearby factory that was building and upgrading sections of German warplanes, initially piston-driven fighters and later the Messerschmitt 262 twin-engine jet. The limits of aerodynamics, engineering, and armament were being pushed to the point of failure, with safety margins suspended for the duration of the war. "On takeoff you were loaded so heavily that if anything went wrong, you wrote not just the airplane off but the pilot as well," he recalls. "There were no ejection seats." Airframes and control systems had to withstand accelerations in the same range as the early Orion vehicles designed to lift off at two-bombs-per-second from the ground. "The fighter planes we were designing were for around 7 to 8 g's, and some of them were designed to 10 g's standard, when you expected high-speed dive-bombing and you had maximum loads. And they worked—no problem. So you can build a structure that will not weigh too much to fly, yet it can take a pretty damn good shocking."

Astl worked for the Germans during the day and against them during the night. "Nobody knew more than two other associates," he explains. "That way if you get caught you can divulge no more than two names in torture and there was hope that sooner or later you get somebody in that chain who will simply not talk." The saboteurs concentrated on communication lines and railway switches, where small amounts of high explosive had maximum effect. "You learned it by hard knocks," Astl says. "But I must have been good at it because I survived. A lot of people didn't, because we were working with explosives we didn't know.

Jerry Astl (foreground) and Jim Morris inspect the pusher plate of an early 1-meter tethered model, in front of a high-explosive storage bunker at the Point Loma test site.

We had to steal them from the Germans. And especially the plastic explosives, they were guarding it pretty tight." In mid-1944 Astl's moon-lighting was found out. "They finally traced down that this group was being managed from the A.T.G. Messerschmitt design office," he explains. "The Gestapo caught up with our group and started eliminating them, brutally." A German supervisor, risking his own life, gave Jerry fifteen minutes' warning and he disappeared into the full-time underground. "At the peak of power our group had five hundred fifty to six hundred people we could put in the field. When we laid down our weapons there were thirty-two left. And two in hospital who didn't survive."

Astl learned about convergent shock waves by forming shaped charges with his own hands. He also discovered, long in advance of Orion, that it was possible to blow something *up* without blowing it *apart*. "We once tried to blow up a bridge—it was near the end of the war when the Germans were retreating, just running from the Russian army," he explains. "It was a bridge that would have stopped probably half of that retreating army, and it was built in the old professional Czech way. We put all the explosives we had on the damn sucker, and we lighted it up. Biggest boom we ever created. I saw the whole bridge jump up and drop back, and you could drive over it again. It was incredible. We couldn't have put one ounce more explosive because we didn't have any. And the Germans didn't even know we tried to blow up that bridge, because it came right back down where it started from. There was a crack in the pavement on both sides. When I was there in 1992, I went back to see what happened. That bridge is still there. Nothing happened!"

After the Nazi exit from Czechoslovakia, Astl became a county secretary of the Union of National Revolution. He began arguing with Rudolf Slansky, secretary of the Communist Party, who warned him (not long before his own execution) that he had better watch his step. Astl escaped to Vienna. The American embassy turned him away but the British embassy provided shelter, and, when they saw that he had maps of the border region, asked him to guide a group of other refugees, including a Hungarian whose legs had been shot off at the knees by the Russians, in the next stage of his escape. "It was bad enough to get through the guards on our border, but to cross from Russian-occupied Austria to Western-occupied Austria was ten times worse." They reached the demarcation line and waited in the forest for nightfall to try to get across. Every time Astl probed between the Russian watchtowers, "there would be suddenly a burst of machine-gun fire, the floodlights will zero on the spot when they were shooting, and there will be four or five Russian soldiers with burp guns going to see what they shot." Things looked bad, especially for the Hungarian amputee. Astl saw that the Russian firepower offered them a chance. "When you fire machine guns during the night, you are not going to hear anything for half an hour later. When you look in these searchlights, you are not going to see much. So the next night I got everybody positioned and before long, there was gunfire and searchlights. I said, everybody, get going, forget about noise, forget about being seen, we have to cross in a few seconds. We dragged that guy by his hands and we got beautifully across."

Astl spent a year in a refugee camp in Ludwigsbourg, where his weight dropped to 96 pounds before the International Refugee Organization took over and the food allowance was boosted from 900 to 1,400 calories a day. Using a 24mm x 24mm "Robot" gun camera salvaged from a Messerschmitt fighter and film secured in trade for American soap, he went into business taking ID photos of fellow refugees so they could apply to foreign embassies for immigration papers allowing them to leave the camp. In April 1949 Astl sailed for Boston on the SS *Mercy*, a converted hospital ship, arriving with one dollar, a few words of English, an extreme distrust of Communists, and the name of an uncle in Baltimore who had sponsored his entry to the United States. He worked first at a printing plant and then at a shoe factory where he was paid $32 a week—"But boy, I was happy like a flea on a fat dog!" When the projectionist at the employee cinema got sick, Astl took over the after-hours job and kept it for two years. "I learned the English by showing movies," he says. "I usually grabbed somebody who spoke Czech. I said, 'Look, you are going to find out now how beautiful it is inside the projectionist room, and all you have to do is tell me what they are talking about!' You learn very quickly if you see and hear it three or four times in a row."

After saving enough money to buy a used 1950 Mercury, Astl left the shoe factory for a tool-and-die-making job, quickly advancing to a position as engineer. He took up recreational flying and joined the local sailplane fraternity, in which Czechs had long excelled. After three more years he became an American citizen, bought a brand-new 1955 Mercury, and, encouraged by a glider pilot who worked for Convair in San Diego, piled his belongings in it and headed west. "I said I'm not going to stop until I hit the Pacific Ocean, and that's what I did." After two weeks living in a trailer in El Cajon, he found work as an aeronautical engineer, first with Rohr Aircraft (on the Lockheed Electra), then with Ryan and Douglas (on the DC-8). When Project Orion received its initial funding from ARPA, he obtained an interview with Ted and was hired by General Atomic, where he gained a reputation for solving problems when the engineering got tough. "I was always asked to do the impossible," he says.

During Project Orion, Astl published only a few reports. "I didn't have time to write," he explains. "There are a type of people who thrive on writing reports and there are people who can do miracles with their hands and with their ingenuity but they see writing as a waste of time." Astl's *Multi-ICBM Weapon System* (November 1959) anticipated the MIRV (multiple independently-targeted reentry vehicle) missiles that began to shift the strategic nuclear landscape in the 1970s. In 1959 the challenge was how to get a single thermonuclear warhead launched by a single intercontinental ballistic missile. Astl saw that Orion offered the possibility of launching multiple warheads at once.

"The Air Force needed some justification to give us more money and sent a request for us to come up with ideas of what Orion can be used for, military applications," Astl recalls. "To me it was obvious that the best use would be to make smaller Orion vehicles, and put aboard maybe 15, 20, or 50 individually targeted nuclear warheads together with maybe 150, 200 decoy 'warheads.' You launch that, they will pick it up on radar, and until you reach apogee they will see one missile coming at them. Then you launch your decoys, and suddenly they see swarms of them. There is no way they could handle that. After the defenders deploy their defense missiles, then you sublaunch your real warheads. They will be very small, because all you need is just to change a few degrees of the trajectory to route them to their targets. There would be no defense against an approach like that."

Astl saw the potential military applications of Orion not just as an excuse for supporting space exploration, but as a necessary show of strength. "Russian people, if you get them sober, will split their heart with you," he says, "but you get them in a bunch, give them a bottle of vodka, and you don't know if they are going to cut your throat, or what." He got along especially well with Captain Donald M. Mixson, the project officer assigned to Orion by the Air Force Special Weapons Center, who, among his other duties, had to sell the project to the generals at the Strategic Air Command. "I wrote a small proposal," Astl remembers, referring to the multiple-warhead plan, "and Mixson said, 'This is really something!'" If the prospect of incinerating fifty Russian targets at once was more than SAC was comfortable with, Astl had another suggestion. "I said, if this is not acceptable, why don't we put aboard Orion

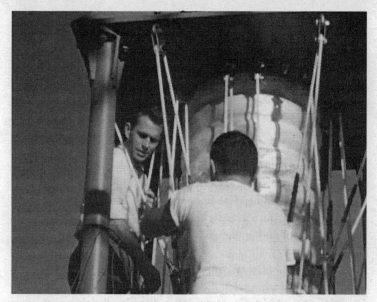

Ed Day (left) and Reed Watson preparing a pneumatic shock absorber test at Torrey Pines, early 1959.

a hundred tons or so of tranquilizer powder, and spread it all over Russia. Later we can have a tea party with them instead of war." According to Astl, Mixson liked the idea. "He was probably ready to spray it over Washington!"

Astl's *Nuclear-Pulse Propelled Vehicle Launching System* (May 1960) suggested how Orion vehicles could be boosted to a certain initial velocity out of a shallow launching silo. The meter-diameter model had refused to fly until boosted by a small initial charge of slow-burning gunpowder, as Freeman Dyson had predicted in his December 1958 study, *Optimal Programming for Vertical Ascent in Atmosphere*, where he concluded that "in particular, the starting velocity $V(0)$ at height zero is not zero." As Astl explains it, "Where do you consume most of the fuel? At the start point!" He envisioned a fleet of small, silo-launched Orions as a retaliatory force. The underground silos would serve as launching tubs, protect the ships against surprise prelaunch attack, and provide for convenient burial of any launchpad mistakes. "If it is for defense you don't need to worry one hundred percent about safety, and if you have it underground and something goes wrong—nothing happens. You just bring in bulldozers and smooth off the top after an explosion. You leave it right there."

Astl's third Orion paper, *Split-Cylinder Long-Stroke Shock Absorber System*, was issued in February 1961. The original idea for Orion's shock absorbers was to use inflated tubes, layered in concentric rings. This was simple and lightweight but had serious drawbacks, notably, as Don Mixson put it after a visit to General Atomic in July 1958, "a very serious problem is what happens in event of a dud. In this case the shock absorber is flying out and must be built to take this back motion." One thousand tons of pusher plate rebounding off into space is not an easy thing to stop.

As the design of Orion evolved, more and more of the pusher-plate acceleration (and rebound in the event of a misfire) was expected to be handled by longer piston-type shock absorbers, but the pneumatic rings remained the first line of defense. Astl worked on a series of tests of this concept that went on for seven years—beginning with the first tests at Torrey Pines in 1958 using inner tubes wrapped in duct tape to a final high-speed photographic analysis of the behavior of pneumatic shock absorbers under high-explosive loads, which continued into 1965, after all other experimental work on Orion had stopped.

"The whole exercise with the tubes, to me, was futile," says Astl in retrospect. "You know darn well you cannot apply this principle of supporting the pusher plate like this in space. It's absurd, you could never get it to work there. All materials lose elasticity in the cold. You're going to fire once and you are going to have it all over the stratosphere. Two shots and it will be all over space." The requisite elasticity would be in the gas, not the walls of the tubes, which would have been built like steel-belted radials, but Astl may be right. Six officials from Firestone, all with secret clearance, attended a briefing on Project Orion held for prospective contractors in Los Angeles on July 23, 1959.

"Have you ever seen a steam catapult?" asks Astl when asked to explain his split-cylinder shock absorber plan. "Like for an aircraft carrier—but in reverse. You use the same principle; a steam catapult is actually a split-cylinder shock absorber or actuator. If you have a split cylinder you cut the stroke to half of what you need with a conventional one. I was amazed when I found out they actually had something like this. I had never been on an aircraft carrier, and I had not the slightest idea how the thing operates. I mentioned the idea to Carroll Walsh, and he said, 'This is a steam catapult!' He made it possible for me to visit an aircraft carrier and we looked it over and sure enough, there it was. So the technology is pretty highly developed and could be adapted.

"They assumed very dangerous stuff—they assumed that they licked the shock absorber problem," Astl warns. He envisions a completely different approach. "You have two masses," he explains. "You have to absorb the major shock from the explosion, by pusher plate. The biggest mass sits on top of it. I would reverse that. I would use shock absorbers to just protect the payload, then you can design something much more reasonable. I prefer the pusher plate, the motor, to be a structural unit that stays together. You are going to take impulse without shock absorbers and you are only going to protect, with the shock absorbers,

Ed Day loading canister #4, containing 2.3 pounds of C-4 high explosive, into position on the 1-meter-model charge ejection stack.

certain defined parts of the ship, inside the major structure. You can make the travel longer. You can adjust the acceleration as you want it." Astl arrived at this idea through discussions with Ted. "I pried out of him information as to how closely he thinks he can control the size of the acceleration he can give to the pusher, with his little tiny nuclear bombs. He said, 'Well, in future we can probably do much better.' And that's what gave me the idea that you build a structure that can take it, and let just the payload move."

The final part of Project Orion that Astl worked on—with experimentalist Ed Day, who had initiated the Orion testing program six years earlier at Torrey Pines—was a proposed high-explosive test facility for conducting full-size tests of a 10-meter-diameter Orion engine, upside down. This was invoked as General Atomic's answer to NASA's question, "How can NASA develop a space vehicle that cannot be tested on the ground?" NASA administrators were reluctant to support anything that had to be launched full-fledged, as a bird is pushed for the first time out of its nest. In the final two years of Orion, General Atomic countered with a "Ground Development Plan." Part of this plan was a "Repetitive-HE-Pulse Test Facility" designed to test a full-size Orion engine by mounting it upside down next to a 100-disc jukebox delivering 32-foot-diameter, ¾-ton disks of PETN high explosive, detonated at one-second intervals above the pusher plate.

"With this test facility the nuclear-pulse engine can be tested, developed, and qualified for flight testing and then brought to a preliminary flight rating (PFR) on the ground," it was argued. "Two different HE-pulse unit delivery systems are considered. A fully mechanical system to move the HE pulse unit from a storage silo to the final detonation position directly above the pusher of the engine is described in considerable detail, and a system using rocket thrusters to provide the required driving force is briefly discussed." Coauthor and lead engineer on this proposal was German aeronautical engineer Hans Amtmann, who had begun his career in the shipyard that built the *Bismarck*, where he helped design the Blohm & Voss BV-238, a long-range flying boat powered by six 1,800-hp Daimler-Benz engines and, at 100 tons, the heaviest airplane of its time. Amtmann had worked on top-secret German design projects during the war, some relying on rocket thrusters to take off. Moving 1,500-pound disks of high explosives around with rocket thrusters might not have occurred to anyone else. "A test stand of this type, because of the character of its operation, will have to be erected in an area remote from densely populated areas," Amtmann advised.

Astl, however, thought it a waste to expend so much high explosive on test-firing Orion upside down. "To hell with that, let's build it so that we could put a cabin inside," he argues. "If we have to fire so many damn charges on it, let's take it for a free flight. Just have parachute with a spare, then on top of the trajectory the pilot bails out. Ed Day was horrified. Of course, he was not a flier. I was tempted. If I would have stayed there some crazy ideas would have popped up."

15

Point Loma

"We got chased out of there," says Jerry Astl, describing the abandonment of Project Orion's first experimental test facility on the mesa above La Jolla at Torrey Pines. "Because every time we made a few shots the other employees got upset and began to squawk." Thanks to Carroll Walsh, the Orion group soon found another site. Walsh, the project's internal technical ombudsman, could find anything—from high explosives to transportation for Queen Juliana of the Netherlands, who accepted an invitation to visit General Atomic to view a TRIGA reactor but requested a four-engine plane be made available for her flight. "I called the Navy at the air base, and I said, 'The Queen needs a four-engine plane. You set it up, we need to have it; she won't fly in anything else.' And they said, 'Let me think about this.' I had to talk to an admiral. Damned if he didn't arrange it! And he had the plane sitting there and he had written orders for about fifty captains and so forth to justify taking this big plane."

Whatever needed doing, Walsh could get it done. "Freddy asked me to write three pages about the Saturn-boosted Orion vehicle, and get someone to fly it out to Gardner on the night plane," Ted noted in his journal at the end of October 1960, when Trevor Gardner, chairman of the Air Force committee preparing to advise the incoming administration in Washington on space, decided to include a small version of Orion in the options from which it was hoped the new president would choose something to announce. "Felt like a heel when Wild and I asked Carroll Walsh to take it out."

Walsh, born in 1915, grew up in Oakland, California, just before the depression and was making his own gunpowder and launching homemade rockets by the age of twelve. He joined the Civilian Conservation Corps in 1933, building fire trails in Yosemite and learning to work with dynamite while earning one dollar a day—keeping five dollars a month and sending his mother and father the rest. After eighteen months in the CCC he enlisted in the Navy, starting as a second-class electrician's mate and advancing to become an officer during World War II. He had a knack for electronics and was comfortable around high explosives and nuclear bombs. "Guess who had charge of taking an atomic bomb and giving it a hammer test? Have these big weights hit it and see what happened? I did," he says. "I had Q clearance before I ever came to General Atomic. And remember the big experiment where they took all the ships out to sea out there in the Pacific, and they had the Big One and were going to see what happened to all those ships? Who was in charge of that stupid bomb? It was an enormous thing—as big as this room! I was." Walsh spent eight years working at the Navy Electronics Laboratory at Point Loma, developing an uncanny knowledge of who, among the network of San Diego military bases, had what. "Out at the test site, we needed an automobile. I could get one from the Navy for nothing. All of a sudden they needed a forklift. I knew right where to go get one. For nothing."

Point Loma is a steep, narrow, three-mile-long peninsula that guards the entrance to San Diego harbor and had been fortified with a series of gun batteries during the war. When the guns were decommissioned the area remained a naval reserve, adopted by the Navy Electronics Laboratory for radar experiments and other secret tests. One of the guards had been Lieutenant Commander Walsh. "There were all these big sixteen-inch gun emplacements—cement walls six-foot thick. I knew all about those places because I used to have to patrol those on my night duty. We had a lot of work going on that was secret and nobody was supposed to be there." Walsh persuaded his former colleagues to grant General Atomic the use of Battery Woodward and Battery Ashby, overlooking the Pacific Ocean on the west side of the peninsula—complete with ammunition bunkers and abandoned gun emplacements that were ideal for blowing things up. There was also a 75-foot-high steel tower that had been built for ¼-scale static tests of Atlas missiles, with a blockhouse that had been used for monitoring the tests.

"When we got to Point Loma, the Navy treated us so well, it was just like home," explains Jerry Astl. "Those bunkers! They had held sixteen-inch guns. We got whatever we wanted. But the launch test tower had huge steel platforms on three sides, so that they could shoot off the missiles at different angles. We asked the Navy about taking them down, and they said sure, they also wanted them down—but it would take two or three months before they could bring in a big crane to do the job. But we didn't have two months, we needed them down yesterday! So I said I could do it. And Carroll Walsh gave me just enough C-4, and long lead detonators, to do the job. And we had it down in two hours! It was just like if I was back in World War II."

Astl insisted on long lead detonators, resistant to radar-induced currents that might make regular detonators explode. "Detonators with long leads shall be used whenever possible," it was stipulated in General Atomic's *Safety Procedures at Point Loma Experimental Site*, compiled by Brian Dunne and issued on July 17, 1959. "Detonators shall at no time be carried about or placed in pockets of clothing," and anyone attaching a detonator to an explosive charge, long lead or not, "shall short the firing line to check for sparks from possible stray current and shall then touch the ends of the line simultaneously to his tongue for small currents." No experiments involving high explosives were to be conducted except under the supervision of a designated "physicist-in-charge." During the entire project, there were only a few minor accidents with high explosives and no serious injuries as a result.

"They were killing people at Los Alamos," says Dunne, referring to the mishaps with ordinary high explosives that far outnumbered mishaps with fissionable material in fabricating nuclear bombs. "I studied the accidents that had happened at Los Alamos, and you come away chastened from that." Dunne limited the amount of high explosives that could be stored in the General Atomic magazine at Point Loma to 400 pounds. "For charges involving shrapnel and/or charges of one-half pound or more, and for all tests in the tower," he ordered, "GA men shall be sent to block the access roads on each side of the experimental site." One of the access roads was within view of Point Loma College. "The real attraction there was a college for girls, that's why everybody, especially the young technicians, wanted to work on Point Loma," Astl explains.

In formalizing Walsh's arrangement for use of the Point Loma site, General Atomic explained to the Navy that "the tests involve the effects of small explosions, of the order of 10 grams to perhaps a kilogram, on certain materials." Besides building mock-ups of gas-bag shock absorbers and developing explosive-driven plasma jets, the initial tests included hanging pusher-plate test specimens from the tower, restrained by flexible cables to keep them from flying off into the distance with every shot. It did not take long for the Point Loma crew to start wondering what would happen to a pusher plate, attached to a rudimentary payload, when a small explosive charge propelled it *up*.

There are two surviving flying models of Orion. One of them, one meter in diameter, is in the Smithsonian Institution's National Air and Space Museum in Washington, D.C. The other model, one foot in diameter, is in Jerry Astl's garage in Solana Beach. "We started out very slowly with a one-foot-diameter model, with pressure gauges all around," explains Dunne. "The charges were tiny—about golf-ball size. We did Fastax film and got some idea of the shock wave scaling laws." It is this model—intermediate between the mixing-bowl experiment and the one-meter-diameter model now in the Smithsonian—that Jerry Astl has kept above the rafters in his garage for thirty-two years, rescuing it from destruction, thanks to security guard John Iles, when General Atomic, following its purchase by Gulf Oil, was cleaning house. Its fiberglass shell is a beat-up, faded Air Force blue, in the shape of a squat bullet (or "Anita Ekberg Maidenform bra," as Astl says it was known among the technicians) modeled at 1:130 scale after one of the original 4,000-ton designs. Its aluminum pusher plate is scarred from repeated blasts, and the polyurethane foam shock absorber has crumbled almost entirely to dust.

"I made it in three or four days," says Astl. "I found a guy in National City who was an absolute artist in fiberglass. Old man, grouchy like hell, but you go with hand sketches, you tell him something that will stimulate his interest and he will drop everything, all his customers have to wait, because he is going to make this bullet for me, and for a few dollars." The fiberglass shell is perforated from top to bottom with a series of holes for pressure gauges to measure how the shock wave refracting around the edge of the pusher plate impacted the hull. "It's good to know about shock wave scaling in this business," says Dunne. Another series of holes was situated to measure stress within the shell. "We were trying to get some idea if the charge is slightly out of line, how much torque is generated," says Astl. "It looks stupid, but it generated a lot of good information."

By February 1959, the one-foot-model had been followed by the first of a series of one-meter tethered models, which were subjected to single shots. "I was shown a number of interesting movies of the ¼₀-scale model which they are testing," reported Don Mixson after a visit to General Atomic on February 25, 1959. "The model weighs about 160 lbs. and employs a steel pusher plate. The scaled explosive charge is 2 lbs. of Composition C-3 molded into a roughly spherical shape. The model has also been overtested with a three-pound charge." The purpose of the tethered models was to investigate structural design, not ablation, yet Mixson noted that "no evidence of any pusher ablation has been observed. This also applies to the ⅟₃₀ model which shows no ablation after more than 50 shots." One month later, AFSWC project officer Ron Prater made another visit and reported somewhat less optimistically that "testing of the 3-foot model is continuing at the Point Loma facility. It is doubtful if further testing of this model will yield significant results."

Under General Atomic's original contract with ARPA, the construction of a free-flying model was out of bounds. But by 1959 the Orion physicists had convinced themselves of Orion's theoretical feasibility and wanted to get the next stage of the project off the ground. According to Brian Dunne, it was Carroll Walsh, watching tests of the tethered models, who observed: "You ought to fly this machine, then we'll get this program going." Building a flying model was brought up with Don Mixson, who gave enthusiastic support. "Yup, he approved it," says Astl. "He said, doggone it, we have to somehow convince people that indeed this does have feasibility, because every time I approach some higher-ups I hear stereotype answer: we use bombs to blow things to pieces, not to make them fly. So that was why there was so much emphasis put on making the damn thing fly, so they can show them it is not necessary to blow everything to pieces with bombs, they can be used for good, practical purposes. And I believe we succeeded in that."

According to Mixson, "It was ARPA that originally decreed no modeling. However, I strongly believed in it and risked a court-martial for direct disobedience of orders by telling de Hoffmann that I would authorize the model program personally provided he used General Atomic's first-year 'profit' to pay for it." Official authorization slowly followed. "There was some controversy over whether money should be spent on a flying model," remembers Don Prickett. "But we stuck our neck out and gave General Atomic the green light to spend the money, some of which we didn't even have programmed yet. But we had a lot of friends up through ARDC and into the Pentagon, that we felt we could bank on to give us some protection."

On June 19, 1959, Amendment No. 1 was added to the original contract's statement of work: "The contractor shall use its best efforts to construct, static test, and free-flight test a three-foot-diameter model of the device which shall be capable of free-flight using a small number of high explosives for propulsion." For the Point Loma experimentalists, led by Brian Dunne, it was now full speed ahead. "We did the whole thing in five months—from the glimmer of an idea to flying model," says Dunne. "To maintain the flow in the group, we had to increase the speed; it keeps people more focused. I was trying to get it finished before the theorists woke up and decided to get involved in the design." In addition to Dunne, Astl, and Taylor, the group responsible for the meter model included Ed Day, Michael Feeney, Rudy Cesena, Perry

Ritter, Michael Ames, Richard Morton, Reed Watson, Richard Goddard, Menley Young, Jim Morris, R. N. House, Leon Dial, W. B. McKinney, Charles Loomis, and Fred Ross.

The final flying model weighed 270 pounds with its ballistic envelope and 230 pounds (dubbed the "hot-rod") without. There was a narrow window between charges powerful enough to lift the model and charges so powerful they blew it apart. "Three-pound charges were found to be too damaging, and 2.7-lb charges also proved to be too potent. As a result, 2.3-lb charges were used in all the tests." There were many spectacular failures in the course of finding this out. There was also some tension between the need for safety precautions and the pressure to get things done. Dunne appointed Perry Ritter as the lead man at the Point Loma site. "Jerry's a daredevil, not the kind of guy you want setting detonators," he explains. "I believe my safety procedures were good because I am still kicking around," counters Astl, citing his accident-free record. "Here you have to have procedures because you are not at war with anybody. During the war I was probably violating them left and right."

The main challenge in building a flying model—which did not have to withstand ablation by nuclear explosions or provide shock absorption for a human crew—was a problem that plagued the full-size design: how to eject the bombs. "All you would see is a picture of this pristine pusher plate," says Dunne of the early conceptual sketches of Orion, "but nobody would draw a picture of how you would get all these A-bombs into place." The Point Loma crew tried equipping the 1:130 model with a two-charge stack, but, recalls Astl, "it didn't work, the first charge went off but the second one jammed." Defusing the live charge convinced Dunne they had to design an ejection mechanism that, if not fail-safe, would at least revert the charges to safe mode if their ejection failed.

For the meter model, a series of high-explosive charges—grapefruit-sized balls of C-4, shaped by hand and cushioned by polystyrene foam inside coffee-can-sized canisters—were ejected through the middle of the pusher plate at quarter-second intervals from a central stack. "It was a very bad temperature environment and a very bad shock environment," says Dunne. Each canister had to withstand the shock of the pre-

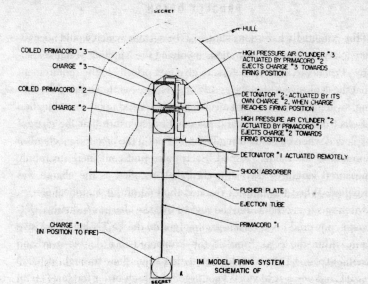

COILED PRIMACORD #3

CHARGE #3

COILED PRIMACORD #2

CHARGE #2

HULL

HIGH PRESSURE AIR CYLINDER #3
ACTUATED BY PRIMACORD #2
EJECTS CHARGE #3 TOWARDS
FIRING POSITION

DETONATOR #2 - ACTUATED BY ITS
OWN CHARGE #2, WHEN CHARGE
REACHES FIRING POSITION

HIGH PRESSURE AIR CYLINDER #2
ACTUATED BY PRIMACORD #1
EJECTS CHARGE #2 TOWARDS
FIRING POSITION

DETONATOR #1 ACTUATED REMOTELY

SHOCK ABSORBER

PUSHER PLATE

EJECTION TUBE

PRIMACORD #1

CHARGE #1
(IN POSITION TO FIRE)

IM MODEL FIRING SYSTEM
SCHEMATIC OF

SECRET

One-meter-diameter flying model: firing-system schematic. Note ballistic envelope labeled "hull."

vious explosion and then escape safely through the remnants of that explosion to detonate at a predetermined distance below the ship. "There were two possible routes to propelling the charge," says Dunne. "The first, to go with black powder, but the gas in the delivery tube would be heating up from previous explosions. The other approach was to use a gas—we used nitrogen—which cools as it expands, so the shock wave meets a cool gas that attenuates the shock pressure going up that tube." Each individual canister had its own miniature pusher plate, attached by shock-absorbing foam, to cushion the blast. This was blown into shrapnel by the exploding charge, making it hazardous to be out in the open anywhere near the flying model, although, if all went well, "penetrating fragments were localized to an angle of about 10° from vertical in a downward direction as anticipated from canister design."

The five separate charges, each powerful enough to bring down an airliner, had to be individually triggered to detonate in sequence, a problem similar to setting up a string of mousetraps to catch five mice in a row, without ever catching two mice at once. "It was decided, because of the potentially hazardous nature of the system, which would necessitate a large number of operations involving the handling of high explosive, Primacord and detonators, to give first priority to the requirement that the explosive system be as safe as possible," wrote Dunne. The timing, switching, and safe/arm mechanism depended upon a combination of electronics, mechanics, and pneumatics to ensure that the charges exploded when ejected during flight, but not if the ejection mechanism jammed or the model crashed. Each pulse unit contained a carefully measured length of detonator cord that uncoiled as the charge was expelled. When the canister reached the end of this umbilical cord, a switch was triggered within the ship so that the charge's individual detonator, powered by its own capacitor, ignited the PETN high-explosive core within the cord. "You tie the Primacord in a double overhand knot," explains Dunne. "The detonation wave goes through at 6,000 m/sec, and when it hits that knot it goes off high-order for sure." If all

Richard Goddard, Walt England, and W. B. McKinney preparing the 1-meter model for flight.

went well, the detonation of the final charge triggered a shotgun shell that ejected a 14-foot-diameter parachute stored in the nose of the ship.

Despite all these triggers, detonators, and lengths of high-explosive Primacord the whole contraption had to be safe enough for the technicians to work on before it was armed for flight, and safe enough to approach afterward, when, as often happened, it crash-landed with live charges still in the stack. "In case the model in flight fails when all charges have not been detonated," Dunne reported, "it is necessary to know that no charge remains on any of the storage capacitors. A bleeder resistor across the firing capacitor allows the charge to leak off slowly, so that after 15 minutes it is nearly certain that there is not enough electrical energy left to fire a detonator." In the fourteen pages of *Safety Procedures at Point Loma Experimental Site* two sentences are underlined for emphasis: "Under no circumstances, shall personnel approach the area before the 'all clear' signal" and "Never cut Primacord with diagonals or steel scissors."

The one-meter models had fiberglass ballistic envelopes—identified as "hull" in the engineering drawings—giving them an uncanny resemblance to the lunar spaceship of Jules Verne. Unfortunately they had trouble getting off the ground. "We'd have a big roar of high explosive, but the damn thing would not move, it would just sit there bathed in this low-density gas," says Dunne. Freeman Dyson came down to Point Loma to observe the launches on weekends. "I think we should suspend these tests until we can get at least 1 g acceleration," he remarked on August 11, 1959. "I took Freeman's advice and changed all my assumptions," says Dunne. "The way to get this thing moving is we'll take a tub and put some gunpowder—it took quite a bit, about a pound—in a silk toroid. It was a loud thump and the thing just lifted up beautifully. I could sense the entrainment of cold air under the pusher plate."

Dunne's notes from that summer of 1959 chronicle the difficulties that led, eventually, to a series of successful flights. June 3: "Excessive damage to shock absorber through ejector tube perforations. Height-of-rise approximately 5 ft." August 5: "Ballistic envelope rupture apparently caused by excessive venting of gases from explosive into envelope through perforations in upper end of ejector tube. Faulty envelope layer bonding also added to failure. Charge canister No. 2 failed and jammed in ejector tube, failing to detonate, safe/arm mechanism operated success-fully. Ejector tube and safe/arm system damaged by fall of model." August 27: "Charge 3 ejected but failed to detonate because disarm mechanism actuated prematurely." August 31: "All charges ejected and fired successfully. Shock absorber and liner again heavily damaged." September 10: "Camera record lost and camera damaged by high accel-eration forces. Ring plate badly damaged. Nylon shock absorber liner moderately damaged. All photo records except Fastax partially lost because shrapnel cut control line at 1.5 sec." September 20: "Accelera-tion lost because of No. 2 misfire. Model lost altitude and parachute failed to open soon enough to break fall. Model heavily damaged. Damage to safe/arm mechanism by fall caused it to remain in armed position." October 17: "Canisters 1 through 5 ejected successfully. All detonated except 5. Since parachute squib was in parallel with No. 5 detonator, parachute was not deployed. Model heavily damaged by fall. Safe/arm mechanism damaged and jammed in armed position. Demo-lition charge used to part Primacord remotely to avoid hazardous dis-arming operation." November 14: "Flight successful in all respects. Height of rise about 185 feet. Parachute deployed at peak of trajectory. Model landed undamaged."

On November 16 Brian sent Freeman, who had already returned to Princeton, a more detailed report: "Wish you could have been with us to enjoy the Point Loma festivities last Saturday. The Hot Rod flew and flew and FLEW! We don't know how high yet. Ted, who was up on the side of the mountain, guessed about 100 diameters, by eyeball triangu-lation. Six charges went off with unprecedented roar and precision. We think we have it all recorded. By now you realize that V_0 is fairly healthy (about 20 diameters per second by means of a one-pound toroid of an ancient Chinese compound). The chute popped exactly on the summit and it floated down unscathed right in front of the blockhouse. As you can imagine, this event let loose quite a bit of enthusiasm, and we are planning a champagne party for Wednesday down at the Battery. We are planning to put the model on exhibit in your room."

Jerry Astl caught the historic flight on film—at 4,000 frames per sec-ond, using a Fastax camera, an extreme version of the spring-powered Robot gun camera he had salvaged during the war. When General

Atomic started doing high-explosive tests, Astl had borrowed a Fastax camera from Convair. "The Fastax I borrowed," he explains, "was still the old Fastax, you put in 400 feet of film, you pressed the button, and a few seconds later 400 feet of film is gone. It didn't have stop and go." General Atomic later purchased their own Fastax that could expose as many as 8,000 frames per second, and Astl almost never missed a shot. "When I was making movies of these flights, it was usually action," he says. "Everybody was in the bunker, the only idiot who was out most likely was me, because I had to run the cameras." Astl also edited the footage, added titles and graphics, and produced a brief six-minute film that helped to keep the project alive at the end of 1959. "After we finished the testing of the flying models, we finished the film and the fellows took it for presentation to ARPA," he recalls. "Before anybody saw the film there was all kinds of debate and Ted said after the film was finished you had never heard such beautiful quiet. They were caught speechless. Bombs explode everything, and here the bombs propelled something and it came down in one piece."

"This seems a little excessive," says retired General Ed Giller, reviewing Astl's film forty years later, in 1999. "It's amazing that it survives that much high explosive, and it keeps going. I wouldn't believe that it would do that." That was the meter model's last flight. The neighbors at Point Loma were starting to complain about the noise and the Orion gang had to move farther out of town. Carroll Walsh found a new site, six miles inland from General Atomic on a decommissioned Marine Corps staging area known as Camp Elliott, in Sycamore Canyon. Formerly a dairy farm belonging to Mr. Green, the new test site, on 1,012 acres, had two small houses, a barn, a wild jackass, and large numbers of rattlesnakes, which "were systematically picked up by a couple of people working on the test program, with forked sticks, and then put into a chickenwire pen, and I remember seeing maybe twenty in there," says Ted.

Green Farm had no neighbors, so the Orion crew could make noise without complaint. Brian Dunne and later Howard Kratz set up a facility for firing explosive-driven plasma jets at sample pusher-plate targets, but there were no more explosive-driven flights. "I had Mike Ames hide the meter model in the cow barn out at Green Farm, up on

"Hot Rod" 1-meter model, with ballistic envelope removed, clears the top of the 75-foot Atlas test tower, November 1959.

the second floor, boarded up," says Dunne. "Experimentalists are prone to cannibalism, and I knew that someday someone would need a piece of aluminum plate or something and they'd just go in and start cutting it up. It was stashed from 1959 to 1979." When Project Orion was partially declassified, Dunne and General Atomic's public relations officer Earl Zimmerman sent the Hot Rod to the Smithsonian. The museum tried to interest Gulf Oil, General Atomic's new owner, in underwriting an exhibit, but, says Dunne, "Gulf didn't want to be in any way associated with anything having to do with bombs."

The success of a 300-pound model driven by high explosives offered no conclusive evidence of the feasibility of a 4,000-ton ship driven by nuclear bombs. But the flights helped to convince Air Force (and later NASA) officials that the project deserved attention, and they inspired the Orion team in 1959. "The purpose of the flying models was to demonstrate that a vehicle possessing in rudimentary form the same engineering components as a full-scale ship, including pusher plate and shock absorbers and ejector system, could be made to function correctly," Freeman later wrote. "The model flights were the most beautiful part of the whole project. We had a launch site on a hillside covered with flowering shrubs and cactus, overlooking the Pacific Ocean. We usually went out early on Saturday mornings to set up the model and were ready for the countdown about lunchtime. I often wondered what the Saturday afternoon sailors on the ocean thought of us, when some weird-looking object rose briefly from the test stand and blew itself into a thousand pieces. I still keep in my desk drawer a bag of aluminum splinters which I collected after one of our test flights, to prove to myself that all these happy memories are not just dreams."

16

Engineers' Dreams

"There was no school we could go to learn how to build these kind of ships. So we just started doing it," remembers Brian Dunne. Before political obstacles intervened, Orion's design was bounded by the laws of physics on the one hand and the laws of economics on the other. Orion's engineers worked in between.

Within a few weeks of *Sputnik*, Ted Taylor and Marshall Rosenbluth had settled on a ship with a takeoff weight of 4,000 tons. This remained the standard-size Orion until smaller, chemically boosted versions were added to the design repertoire in 1961. "Why was it 4,000 tons instead of 5,000 tons?" asks Ted. "I don't know. It just came out that way. What drove that was, arbitrarily, a thousand-ton payload, I think that's what did it. Just to throw it off scale from what people had been used to."

There were two good reasons, besides the impressive payload, for Orion to be so large. First: shielding from radiation. You want to have as much neutron and gamma-ray absorbing material as possible between you and the bombs. "The shielding problems get very rapidly worse when you make the thing smaller," Freeman Dyson explains. "The effectiveness of a shield goes exponentially with the thickness. If you have a couple of feet of shielding you are in good shape, but if you only have one foot it's terrible, it makes a huge difference." In a large Orion ship, the structural mass, spare bombs, propellant, and housekeeping supplies provide adequate shielding for the crew, whereas for smaller vehicles adding the requisite additional shielding carries a heavy payload cost.

Second: it is both difficult and wasteful to make low-yield atomic bombs. The smaller the amount of fissile material, the harder it is to compress it to a critical density and, when it does go critical, keep the resulting explosion from fizzling out. "Below a certain explosive yield of the order of a kiloton, nuclear weapons are grossly inefficient and extravagant," explained Freeman, remaining intentionally vague. Despite Ted's genius for squeezing more bomb out of less uranium or plutonium, there is a point of diminishing returns past which the amount of fissionable material does not scale down. The cost of the implosion and detonating system remains the same or may even go up. You can produce a lower yield, but doing so wastes fuel and results in a dirtier bomb. "As for the bombs, they hope that with lots of high explosive they avoid use of plutonium and use all Oralloy, to avoid plutonium contamination problems," reported Don Mixson after a visit to General Atomic with Lew Allen at the end of the first month of the ARPA contract, in July 1958. Oralloy (Oak Ridge Alloy) is highly enriched uranium (93 percent U-235).

If kiloton-yield bombs are exploded far enough away to be survivable but close enough to deliver significant energy within the angle subtended by the ship, a massive pusher plate is required to capture the impulse without accelerating to a velocity exceeding what the shock absorbers can withstand. It was the need for 1,000 tons of pusher plate, as much as the desire for a 1,000-ton payload, that set the 4,000-ton benchmark for Orion's initial design. "They have about a thousand tons for the ship and a thousand tons for the pusher," reported Mixson. This left 1,000 tons for payload and 1,000 tons for bombs.

The 1959-model 4,000-ton Orion with a 135-foot-diameter pusher plate was designed to cruise on 5-kiloton bombs—low-octane regular given the state of the art in late 1958 and early 1959. Details of the various 4,000-ton vehicles remain classified, but it is possible to reconstruct the general parameters of their design. "At the time when I was on the project, when we were taking off from the ground, then it was just a big dome with a flat bottom and that was it," says Freeman. "It looked more or less like cutting off the front end of a submarine." A later version was 200 feet high and the propulsion system empty weight was 1,700 tons. The standoff distance was about 110 feet, which translates into an angle, subtended by the 135-foot pusher plate, of about 60 degrees. The bombs, initially estimated to weigh 3,000 pounds each, had already been scaled down to 1,870 pounds.

To design an Orion vehicle, you either tailor the bombs to suit the ship or you tailor the ship to suit the bombs. Which comes first, the chicken or the egg? When nuclear fuel is as scarce as it was in 1958, you start with the egg. Ted Taylor knew how to design the minimal bomb. You then configure the propellant to focus as much of the bomb's energy as possible, and tailor the ship to capture as much energy as possible from the propellant cloud. Bomb physics can tell you how tightly the jet of propellant can be focused, which roughly determines the diameter of the pusher plate at a given distance from the bomb. Weapons-effects physics allows you to estimate, given the temperature and density distribution of the propellant cloud, how much distance you need to keep between the pusher and the bomb, and how much impulse is given to the plate as a result.

Disregarding ablation, this leaves three critical engineering problems concerning the ship: 1) How strong, how heavy, and what shape do you have to make the pusher plate to withstand the repeated kicks? 2) How do you absorb the resulting shock, and ensure a stable two-mass or three-mass system, so that the final acceleration is tolerable to the crew? 3) How do you store, select, eject, position, and detonate the bombs?

It was incongruous to have high-priced nuclear physicists spending their time calculating bending stresses in steel plates, and it was dangerous to have them designing ejection mechanisms for nuclear bombs. Mechanical and aeronautical engineers were enlisted to help. By the end of 1959, says Ted, "the Air Force was getting nervous about a project in which everybody that was running everything were physicists, and not engineers." John M. Wild, cofounder of the Graduate School of Aeronautical Engineering at Cornell, and chief aerodynamics engineer at Northrop during the development of the P-61, B-35, and B-49, was

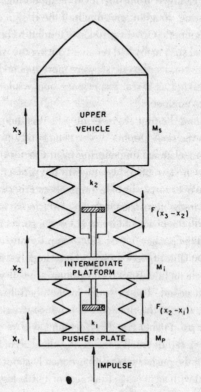

Orion vehicle as a three-mass, two-spring system. Relative mass, pulse frequency, and damping have to be carefully tuned.

UPPER VEHICLE M_s

x_3

k_2

$F_{(x_3 - x_2)}$

INTERMEDIATE PLATFORM M_i

x_2

$F_{(x_2 - x_1)}$

k_1

PUSHER PLATE M_p

x_1

IMPULSE

brought in from the Air Research and Development Command's Mach 20 wind tunnel facility at Tullahoma, Tennessee, to direct the project at General Atomic. Despite the increasing number of engineers Orion remained dominated by physicists—partly because of Ted Taylor and Freddy de Hoffmann, and partly because the project was never granted the nuclear tests that might have given real engineering, as opposed to theorizing, the go-ahead.

The design of Orion could be divided into two distinct regimes: what happens below the pusher plate and what happens above. Below the pusher plate is physics. Above the pusher plate is engineering. But when Orion's physicists reached the surface of the pusher plate, where things changed from physics to engineering, they did not stop. They kept going, roughing out much of the design of the ship in advance of the engineers. Orion's physicists tended to be young, both because of the head start many had received during the war and at Los Alamos and because younger physicists were more inclined to join as implausible an undertaking as Ted's. Experience and wisdom were favored when it came to engineers.

Among the first engineering jobs was the pusher plate—Feynman's "pie in the sky." Dennis W. ver Planck, fifty-two years old and a professor of mechanical engineering from Carnegie Institute of Technology, was the first engineer assigned to the project full-time. "In those days anyone over forty was old," remembers Freeman. "Ver Planck had experience in the aerospace industry and tried to impose some bureaucratic order on the chaos of Orion. He was a good engineer." He began studies of a flat pusher in July 1958. "As presently conceived the pusher will be a flat disk of steel 4 inches thick and 120 feet in diameter," Mixson reported in July 1958. "The pressure pulse will be applied for about ⅓ millisecond. The pressure in the central region will be about 20% greater than at the rim and will produce stresses in the neighborhood of 50,000 psi. Pusher rim displacements will be on the order of a few feet which is rather small considering the size of the pusher." The dimensions of the pusher were proportionately about those of an eighteen-inch cymbal with an average thickness of a little less than one-sixteenth of an inch. Considerable effort went into trying to predict how this 1,000-ton cymbal would resonate when hit. "They have been looking at the low frequency vibrational modes," noted Mixson. "Frequencies are around 1 second. Energy going into these is small."

The physicists working on the ablation problem knew that after the cloud of plasma hits the pusher, the lateral pressure gradient across the surface of a flat plate would produce a flow of hot material toward the edge. To minimize lateral flow, and reduce the effects of turbulent ablation, the pusher should be curved—like a shallow hubcap or a saucepan lid. If you put a greasy plate and a greasy bowl under a hot shower, the plate gets cleaner first. A concave pusher, however, would have to withstand severe hoop stresses, complicating its design. The inflatable primary shock absorbers had to support the pusher evenly against this concentric stress.

When the Orion crew increased from half a dozen to two dozen in 1959, engineer Carlo Riparbelli, forty-nine years old, was assigned the job of analyzing and optimizing the mechanical behavior of a 1,000-ton plate being given a 5-kiloton, twice-per-second kick. Riparbelli, whose mother was an obstetrician and whose father worked for the Italian royal house, grew up in Rome where, as he says, "I had a very easy youth." Graduating with degrees in civil engineering in 1933 and aeronautical engineering in 1934 he went to work for the Caproni Aircraft Company, and became a second lieutenant in the Italian Air Force Engineers after serving in Libya during the early part of World War II. Later in the war he was appointed chief designer for Caproni, now supervised

~~SECRET~~

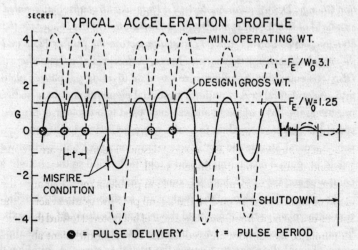

Crew compartment acceleration: pulse interval is 0.86 seconds. Normal acceleration is below 2 g, but rises to as much as 4 g for an empty ship, and goes negative in the event of a dud. Half-momentum charges are required to restart.

by the Germans, whom he remembers as "very efficient—not that turmoil that was the Italian organization." After the war he came to Cornell as an associate professor, moving west during a sabbatical to work for Convair. When he heard about Project Orion he interviewed with Ted, taking a job at General Atomic and giving up his position at Cornell. "We were all excited by this thing," he remembers. "I was also a little afraid to be in the middle of people so completely different. Because I am an engineer." His first appearance before the Orion physicists was a presentation on pusher-plate design. "I gave a talk, and Freeman Dyson liked it, and he encouraged me, and he said, you come and talk to me any time you like. So, I was less afraid after that." Carlo, who died in 1999, kept an espresso machine in his office available to the entire Orion crew. He remembers Project Orion as an orchestra, with all the players performing brilliantly, for the first two years, under the hand of their conductor, Ted.

Riparbelli produced dozens of reports concerning pusher-plate design, among them: *Propagation of a Strain-Wave in a Bar across a Section Change; Deformation Analysis of a Plate-like Structure Represented as a Grid of Beams; Mass and Stiffness Distribution of the Pusher for the 800-Ton Vehicle; Strain Wave Propagation across the Pusher Plate and the Shock Absorber Attachments; Large Deflections of a Lens-shaped Disc.* His engineering studies were based on dividing the pusher plate into an equilateral grid of uniform structural elements and mass nodes, presaging the finite-element analysis now used in computer-optimized structural design. According to Carlo, when he first arrived from Convair, "General Atomic did not have a computer. And I noticed that we would have used one, certainly, and I told Taylor, and so they bought a computer and they put Charles Loomis in charge."

The key to the design of the pusher was to shape the mass distribution of the plate so that it matched the momentum directed at it by the bomb. This was the only way to keep the plate from accelerating unevenly and disintegrating under the resulting stress. A misaligned charge could be catastrophic. "We wound up with something like three times the thickness in the middle as at the edge," says Ted. "That raised the question: suppose the explosion was tilted, and it hit the thin part of the pusher plate with the wrong stuff?" Another question was what happened at the edge. "We used to argue quite a lot about that, whether you wanted to have a flange at the edge to confine the flow, or not," says Freeman. "One day we thought it would be good to have a flange and the next day we thought it would be better not. The advantage of a flange is that you keep the pressure up toward the edge, you get more momentum from the same amount of gas. The disadvantage is that it is hard to calculate the erosion of the edge; if the edge erodes irregularly it may be a disaster, so it's a risky thing to do. Whatever you do in the way of an edge is where you are likely to have trouble. So probably in the end we wouldn't have one. But that was the kind of thing we could argue about all day."

Once the pusher plate is accelerated—at thousands of g's—what happens next? Anything rigidly attached to the other side is liable to be smashed as if hit by a sledgehammer driven by an atomic bomb. In some of the tests of pusher-plate sections subjected to high-explosive charges, heavy steel eyebolts attached to the back side of the plates were catastrophically deformed simply by being unable to keep up with the acceleration of the plate. This is where the gas-bag shock-absorbing doughnuts came in, as a primary cushion between the pusher plate and the intermediate platform to which the secondary, piston-type shock absorbers could be rigidly attached.

The initial idea was to rely on gas bags alone, but it soon became apparent that even if the gas bags could take the shock, there was no reasonable way to restrain the pusher from rebounding off into space (or back toward the Nevada desert) in the event that the next bomb in the sequence was a dud. "The latest method devised for the shock absorbing system is to use a large number of low-pressure gas bags placed between the pusher and the floor of the spaceship," Captain Mixson reported at the end of August 1958. "This is apparently a very good and simple system except when a bomb misfires." Mixson then described an improbable solution that "as presently envisioned consists of a rather complicated arrangement of steel cables, pistons, and magnetic clutches. The total weight of this arrangement including misfire stopper and gas bags is estimated at about 500 tons." Orion went back to the drawing board, where the dual-stage shock-absorber configuration quickly evolved.

"We always made the analogy of a car in which the first stage of the shock absorbers were the tires and the second stage were shock absorbers tied to a rigid chassis," says Ted. "So going along a very bumpy road a lot of what happened was evened out by the tires and big jolts that involved a big displacement were taken up by the shocks." For the 4,000-ton design, with a velocity increment of 10 m/sec (20 mph) per shot, this is an automobile that is hitting 15-foot speed bumps at half-second intervals—800 times in a row. As a 1963 reference to a 34-meter (111-foot) diameter version of the 4,000-ton design explains: "The first-stage shock absorber system, a series of concentric gas-filled tori, serves to reduce the initial pusher acceleration to approximately 100 g's. An intermediate platform couples the first-stage shock absorbers to the second-stage, piston-cylinder shock absorbers, which in turn reduce the accelerations felt by the upper structure of the engine to a few g's or less."

Orion then becomes a two-spring, three-mass dynamic system, exhibiting complex behavior depending on the mass distribution, the pulse period, and how much damping is introduced into the system and where. Carlo Riparbelli produced one of the classic Orion reports, *Parameter Study—Cylinder with Piston*, which analyses the simplest-case, one-spring, two-mass Orion ship and assigns some parametric numbers to the results. "The mechanical system considered here consists of a cylinder and a piston, free in space," Riparbelli explains. "The given initial velocity of the piston relative to the cylinder can be visualized as caused by a sudden impulse imposed on the piston's lower (external) face. The piston is decelerated by the gas pressure while the cylinder is accelerated. The study of the relative motion is the subject of the present report." A short Fortran program is included as an appendix. To imagine an Orion ship in operation requires visualizing not only a series of explosions, but the rhythmic, undulating movement of the ship as it bounds through space.

Orion's dynamic behavior received repeated study for seven years, most intensely by Constant David, a French engineer who joined the project in late 1958. "When a shock is transmitted to a flexible structural system, a pressure wave is generated and travels back and forth throughout that system until it is eventually damped out," he explains in

Minimum Energy Loss in a Two-mass Spring System. "It is sometimes of interest to evaluate the amount of energy dumped into the system during the damping process, especially if the shock is repeated at short intervals . . . when a momentum increment is imparted to such a system by hitting one of the two masses for a very short time, so that the impulse is all delivered before any appreciable displacement of the hit mass takes place." The harmonics of later designs were tuned so that the secondary shock absorbers oscillated one-half cycle between explosions, while the primary shock absorbers oscillated 4½ cycles. Timing was critical. "An explosion timing tolerance of 10 m/sec is allowable (compared to 4 m/sec for a previous study). This is of significant importance," Constant David concluded in December 1964. When Project Orion was shut down in 1965, he was still conducting tests of scaled-down gas-bag shock-absorber assemblies in a bunker at General Atomic's Green Farm high-explosive test facility, and was still simulating the resonant behavior of full-sized Orion vehicles using the enormous analog computer banks at Convair.

There were four main questions concerning shock absorbers: how to achieve a long enough stroke; whether to make them dissipative or non-dissipative; how to tune the resonance; and what to do about duds. As late as December 1964 the Fortran IBM-7044 codes for modeling shock-absorber behavior were still evolving in two separate versions: SAND (Shock Absorber Non-Dissipative) and SAD (Shock Absorber Dissipative). "We were never really settled on whether to drive the shock-absorber system at resonance or not," says Ted. "You could pick up a lot in performance if you did it in resonance in the sense that the pusher plate would be moving down, bouncing off the ship through the shock absorbers, moving down at high speed, and that's when we'd fire. Question: suppose an explosion doesn't work—then it would keep going and so we had to arrange things so that under those conditions the pusher would nondestructively overshoot by a factor of two in distance and then go back and damp out or lock and say, 'OK, we missed one.' I think most people favored locking. It would come down, go back up, and say, 'OK, start me again.' So we had to have a supply of half-momentum charges that would not stop the pusher when it was moving down but start it moving up."

What about a misfire during the initial Earth-to-orbit launch? "It was the rule that we imposed on ourselves that it must not be fatal," explains Freeman. "It was unacceptable that a single dud bomb would put you out of business. And that was one of the major problems. The shock absorber had to be designed so that if a bomb failed to go off you had some way of stopping the plate from running away into space. There had to be some way of catching the pusher plate and bringing it back, which meant the shock absorber became much more difficult to design."

"My technical questions about whether Orion would work the way we said it would were almost entirely tied up, not with what we called the big problem of ablation—I think that can be solved—but with complicated machinery," says Ted. "Things like unspecified types of car trouble, if the car is too complicated."

"We really were a bit insane," admits Freeman, "thinking that all these things would work."

17

Coca-Cola

Jules Verne's lunar adventures, cushioned inside an explosive-driven projectile for their voyage in *From the Earth to the Moon,* had to withstand a single escape-velocity kick. Verne chose dissipative hydraulic shock absorbers, arranged in multiple layers much as the Orioneers envisioned stacking their non-dissipative pneumatic tubes. "This body of water was divided by horizontal partitions, which the shock of the departure would have to break in succession," he explained in 1865. "Then each sheet of the water, from the lowest to the highest, running off into escape tubes toward the top of the projectile, constituted a kind of spring. Undoubtedly the travelers would still have to encounter a violent recoil after the complete escapement of the water; but the first shock would be almost entirely destroyed by this powerful spring."

"The real difficulty with shock absorbers is to get anything with a long enough stroke," Freeman Dyson elaborates. "The peak acceleration that you have to withstand if you are on top of a shock absorber is proportional to V^2 divided by the stroke of the shock absorber, where V is the change in velocity at each explosion. If you want to get a decent kick from each explosion like 10 meters per second, and you want your peak acceleration to be not more than 2 g, the stroke of your shock absorber should be about 5 meters. That's awfully big. It's very hard to get a shock absorber with that kind of stroke, things have to be really whizzing back and forth. It has to be massive and it has to work 500 times with not enough time to cool off in between." The impulsive velocity given to the pusher plate is inversely proportional to its fraction of the total mass, so that if the velocity increment given to the 4,000-ton ship is 20 mph with each explosion, the impulse given to the 1,000-ton pusher is 80 mph at every kick. This difference in velocity, absorbed over 5 meters, is equivalent to driving down the freeway at 60 mph and having one car-length to come to a stop.

The governing principle of shock-absorber design—that acceleration is proportional to velocity squared divided by stroke—suggests three possible approaches: increase the stroke; fire less-powerful bombs at more frequent intervals; or accept a higher acceleration of the ship. In later versions of Orion, acceleration would reach a maximum of 4 g's only when an empty ship was firing its last few bombs in maneuvering into its return-to-Earth orbit after an interplanetary cruise. On a long voyage, weeks or months of zero-g coasting would be punctuated by a few minutes of intense acceleration or deceleration at the beginning and end of each segment of the trip. Most of the time would be spent with the ship spinning slowly, inducing mild artificial gravity so the crew could eat, drink, exercise, and stay in shape. Once in a while things would have to be put away to prepare for the bouncing acceleration of powered flight. Even the initial boost from the ground to 300-mile orbit would last only about six minutes, after which passengers could unbuckle their seat belts and move around the cabin as they wished. In 1958, the thinking was that brief periods of even higher acceleration might be tolerable, perhaps by providing Jules Verne–style acceleration couches for the crew.

"In order to get around some of the shock absorber problems they are considering a 10-g pulse lasting for a smaller fraction of the time," Mixson reported on August 1, 1958. On August 13, Colonel Leonard A. Eddy, one of the Project Orion officers at AFSWC, wrote to the Air Force Aero-Medical Laboratory for information on "Multi-Gravity Tolerance of the Human Body." Explaining that "studies under way on a pulse-type propulsion system indicate that personnel may be subjected to as much as 10 g's for one-tenth of a second at one-quarter-second intervals over a period of about 10 minutes," Eddy requested "any available information on periodic g loading on the human body and on the use of acceleration couches and water immersion to mitigate the effects of g loading and allow personnel to remain alert and able to perform necessary duties."

A load of 10 g is hard even on an exceptional test pilot, and plans for 10-g acceleration were soon abandoned. "The upper limit A = 8 g is imposed because the ship is supposed to carry people and scientific instruments," Freeman explained. The remaining variable is how frequently to eject and detonate the bombs. "We would go back and forth between the charge propellant systems and the frequency," recalls Ted. "Fire twice as many of them with half the velocity change per charge for the same total change, which of course affected the overall acceleration." More bombs meant a smoother ride, like upgrading from a four-cylinder Ford to a Chevrolet V-8. "They are now thinking strongly of reducing the interval between bombs to ¼ second and doubling the total," noted Mixson at the end of July 1958. "This would substantially ease the shock absorber problems as well as easing the loading on the pusher plate since the bomb output would be reduced by a factor of 2." The problem was bomb ejection and economics: firing twice as often is more than twice as difficult, and bombs with half the yield cost more than half as much. "The time available for delivering the charges to the firing position is increased from ¼ sec to ½ sec," it was reported in April 1959, going back the other way. "With the bomb yield unchanged, the average acceleration of the ship is decreased from 4 g to 2 g whereas the peak accelerations remain of the order of 6 g."

These early 4,000-ton ground-launch versions of Orion specified the ejection of about 800 bombs—ranging in yield from .15 kilotons at sea level to 5 kilotons in space—to reach a 300-mile orbit around Earth. Smaller explosions are required at lower altitudes, because the air between the bomb and the pusher plate absorbs energy from the explosion, delivering a more powerful kick. The disadvantage, besides noise, fallout, immersion of the vehicle in the fireball, and a tendency for the surrounding atmosphere to side-scatter radiation at the crew, was that

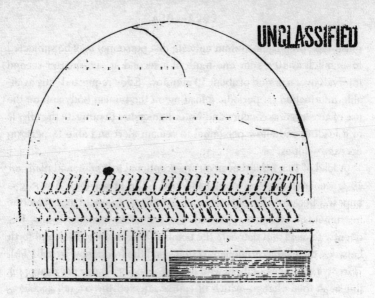

UNCLASSIFIED

*Cutaway view of 4,000-ton, 135-foot-diameter Orion Mark 2 vehicle,
showing shock absorbers and storage of 1,400 bombs.*

as you blast your way up through the lower atmosphere you had to
incrementally increase the yield. "And that was a problem," explains
Freeman, "because you would have to fine-tune the first hundred
bombs."

How do you store and eject all these bombs? "Each of them weighs
half a ton and you have only half a second to get them down a hundred
feet, so it's a major piece of engineering," says Freeman. "Roughly, there
were two ways of doing that: either you shot them out of a gun straight
down the middle, which meant you had to have an opening in the middle of the pusher plate, which was very troublesome, or else you had to
go around the edge, which meant using a rocket with steering so it
could zoom around and arrive in the right place. This rocket going
around the edge was spectacular, you had to light the damn thing and
within a quarter of a second or so it had to zoom out to the edge of the
ship and then turn through 90 degrees and zoom back. That always
seemed to me to be a very risky idea. I always said if you are serious you
have to shoot straight down the middle. And then the trap door was a
formidable problem. It has to open and close in a fraction of a second,

under very rugged conditions with things going bang all the time. If the shutter jams shut then you're finished."

Launching from the periphery of the pusher is not quite as crazy as it sounds. Besides all the problems caused by having a hole in the center of the pusher plate, if you have only a single launcher its firing cycle has to be completed two to four times per second, and any serious mechanical problem is likely to be fatal to the entire ship. With multiple peripheral launchers, each individual subsystem has to fire only once every few seconds, and a failure is more likely to be survivable, the way a car can be kept running on seven cylinders when one ignition wire goes bad.

"For the delivery system they hope to avoid the hole in the pusher by using a gun or bazooka," reported Mixson at the end of July 1958. Mixson's notes describe "a gun a meter in diameter, walls about 1.5 centimeters, 10 meters long, weighing 2.5 tons to project a 1.5-ton projectile at 200 g's. Obviously this can't be reloaded every quarter of a second so you need maybe 10 of them. Can be a bazooka but the gun is easier, you need about a hundred kilograms of propellant per shot. This will probably wind up as a battery of Gatling gun–type gadgets." One early series of sketches show the gun barrels supported on angled pylons around the circumference of the ship. When the shock absorbers are fully compressed, the muzzles extend just beyond the edge of the pusher, allowing unimpeded ejection of a bomb, and then the muzzles are safely protected by the pusher when the shock absorbers have reextended just before the bomb goes off. The pulse units are shunted into the launching tubes from loading bays around the edge of the ship. The scheme looks simple except in the event of a misfire, when an eccentric rocket is required to deliver a half-momentum charge around the edge of the pusher to get the pulse cycle going again.

This plan was soon followed by one that delivered the charges to the edge of the pusher plate on a series of curved rails—a roller coaster that suddenly runs out of track. "Excellent progress has been made in the formulation of a bomb delivery system," Mixson reported at the end of August 1958. "The firing of about 2,600 bombs at the rate of 4 per second is a tremendous problem. This system consists essentially of a series of pairs of rails located around the periphery of the pusher and behind it. The bombs are launched from behind the pusher and, upon sliding down the last portion of the rails are ignited and given (by curved rails) just enough pitch motion that in flight they follow a curved path around the edge of the pusher to the point of desired detonation. This system lends itself nicely to storage of the bombs and the speed of launch desired for this application. How to detonate the bombs at the correct time and place is another question that has not been seriously considered yet." The problem was similar to having to pitch curve balls for an entire season, without ever missing a throw. The plan was for intersecting radio or radar beams to detonate the bombs when they reached the correct position, but in 1958 few of the effects of radiation on electronics were understood. "The first plans were to have these pylons, and toss the bombs over the side," says Jerry Astl. "They would have been all over the space!"

One of Freeman's contributions was to investigate how critical it was whether the bombs ended up in exactly the right place or not. "Dyson has looked at stability," noted Mixson, "and found that for a wide class of delivery systems the ship is stable for random errors in positioning the bomb." This was encouraging. "If you have a bomb that is slightly off-center and it starts to tip the thing over, then the next bomb may or may not make it worse, depending on how you throw it out," Freeman explains. "So what I did was to design the throwing system so that it would automatically correct itself, so if it was slightly off-center the next bomb would bring it back again, so it would become a more or less stable system. That worked quite nicely; it depends on the time of flight, and it turned out that the numbers came out right. It depends on the moment of inertia of the whole ship and the speed at which it is rotating and the interval between the bombs. You have to just do the algebra and either it is stable or it is unstable."

The details of the delivery system were left to the engineers. "Contrary to our original expectations, the ejector system stretched the state of the engineer's art more severely than did the shock absorbers," says Freeman. Orion's specialist in bomb delivery was Michael Treshow, a Danish mechanical engineer who had been trained in shipbuilding in Copenhagen before visiting the United States in 1920 and becoming a permanent resident in 1929. During the construction of the Boulder (now Hoover) Dam between 1930 and 1936 he designed and supervised the installation of the equipment that pumped concrete—more than 8 million tons of it—from where it was mixed to the dam site. "Something over a mile as I recall," says his son, Ken.

Treshow switched to nuclear reactor design and engineering after World War II. He received Q clearance in 1950, while working as a senior engineer at Argonne National Laboratory in Illinois, and held some twenty patents in several fields. "I am recognized as having an unusual talent for invention and development of new ideas and products," he wrote to Ed Creutz in November 1956, seeking a position at General Atomic, "3½ years from now at age 65 I will be compelled to retire from Argonne due to forced retirement rules. I feel this would be too early for me." Treshow was hired by General Atomic in February 1958, at age sixty-four, taking a position as a senior design specialist, with Ed Creutz making special arrangements to bend the company's

OPERATING SEQUENCE

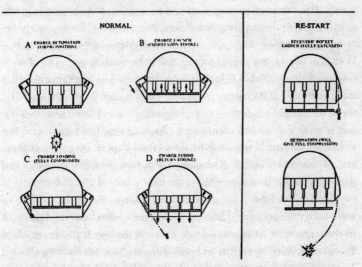

Proposed operating sequence, date unknown, showing normal-mode charge delivery through peripheral launching guns, and delivery by eccentric rocket to restart the engine after a scheduled shutdown or in the event of a dud.

retirement policies so that he could keep working as long as he wished. He soon joined the Orion team, drawing upon his training as a marine engineer and naval architect to produce detailed plans for the various components and permutations of the Orion ship. "He drew beautiful pictures with loving care and was very meticulous," says Freeman. "He was an old-fashioned draftsman, and loved to make everything exact."

You can throw a curve ball in air but not in space, thus small rockets were required to guide the bombs into position beneath the ship. Treshow's *Trajectories of a Rocket with Eccentric Thrust* explains the problem and reveals certain dimensions that were highly classified in 1958. "The takeoff rails will essentially guide the natural movement for the first short distance. Air friction is disregarded. . . . The launching point is considered 21.6 meters from the centerline. Its height is 5.5 meters above the pusher surface and the target E is 33.5 meters below the pusher. The launchers are placed around the edge of the pusher. The rocket is guided during the initial burning and released when the right position has been reached. At this point the jet will be at full power. The mechanical launching system consists mainly of two guide arms. . . . After discharging the rocket, the arms will immediately be moved back where they are essentially sheltered from the blast. . . . Details of this system are, of course, still to be worked out." The Mark 1 version of the 4,000-ton vehicle, which Treshow was working on at that time, carried 2,200 charges, weighing 850 kg (1,870 pounds) each, or about the weight of a Volkswagen, in canisters about the size of two 50-gallon oil drums joined end-to-end. One end was the rocket, and the other end was the bomb, and the device had to perform a perfect somersault during its flight: "The charge will turn an angle of about 180 degrees to a position where the propellant is aimed straight upward at the time of the blast." The pulse interval was one-quarter second, so with thirty-two peripheral launchers each individual launcher had eight seconds between firings to reload. There were four separate levels of storage and delivery conveyors, with 550 charges on each floor.

In the Mark 2 design, developed in early 1959, the storage and delivery system was reduced to two levels, with 700 charges on each floor. "This allows 1,400 charges in live storage," Treshow explained. "An additional 600 charges are expected to be stock-piled outside the conveyors for use in case of interplanetary travel." There were twenty-eight indi-vidual conveyors, terminating in two groups of fourteen launchers dis-tributed around the circumference of the vehicle. The pulse interval was one-half second, giving each launcher a little more than twelve seconds to reload. "In order to save space, no passageways are provided between adjacent conveyors," says Treshow. "Checking the charges before takeoff can be carried out by persons sliding in on roller pads above and below the charges. Such roller pads can move on light rails at right angles to the conveyor rails." Someone like Carroll Walsh would have been squeezed in among those 2,000 bombs for one last inspection before launch.

Michael Treshow devoted his attention to everything from shock absorbers to parametric design studies that laid out the broad range of possible vehicles, from 200 to 10,000 tons. His drawings, few of which have been declassified, are remembered as exquisitely detailed. "The ship was about 120 feet high so it was big, like a ten-story building," says Freeman, describing the earliest version. "It was just a big flat dome, it wasn't particularly aerodynamic. It was so heavy it did not matter. The bottom 20 feet or so were mostly shock absorbers and then above that you had machinery borrowed from the Coca-Cola Company for the handling of the bombs, like a Coke machine where you put in a quarter and get out a Coke bottle. The bombs are arranged in racks and are shunted along; as each one was used the next one would move in. They came in a regular sequence and then they would get snapped into the catapult that launched them down the middle. So that occupied the next 30 feet or so. And then above that you had the dining room and sleeping quarters for the crew."

A successful Orion launch would depend upon being able to select exactly the right flavor of bomb at exactly the right time. Although the link to Coca-Cola may have become exaggerated, bottle-handling equipment was definitely involved. "Oh yes, the Coca-Cola people did come," confirms Freeman. "We had interesting conversations with a lot of people, and many of them had to be in an unclassified context," says Ted. "One major source of information was the Coca-Cola Company, where we got detailed descriptions of how they set up mass production systems for Coke bottles and all kinds of mechanical stuff." Jerry Astl remembers reviewing the ejection system with Michael Treshow. "I saw

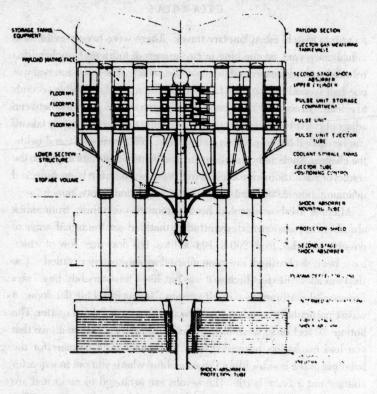

Propulsion-module cross section, ca. 1962, showing four levels of pulse-unit storage, plasma deflector cone, meteoroid protection shields, coolant storage, and two-stage shock absorbers.

the drawings and we discussed it. I agreed with him one hundred percent. He didn't design that, he said, why should I bother? Vending machines already have something like that, and it works and is well proven. All we need is to make a few changes to make it sturdier, and what he had was pretty damn good-looking.

"When it comes to the charges you will need several, maybe, ten different levels of yield," explains Astl. "You will have to load them into a revolving Gatling gun so you can grab the proper yield because you don't know when you need that special yield. To have instant access to it you simply have a rotating drum and when it comes around you yank it out into the chamber. You have an advantage—you are not going at any fantastic speed. At the beginning, Ted was hoping that maybe we can fire four times per second. That's a little scary. When you get it down to say one per second it might be realistic."

In the later 4,000-ton versions of Orion, the shock absorber stroke was extended to 33 feet (10 m) and the pulse frequency to 1.1 seconds. Average acceleration during propulsion periods was 1.25 g, tolerable to all but the most delicate of crew. In attempting to sell Orion, for post-Apollo missions (including a 400-passenger lunar ferry), to NASA, the General Atomic project team pointed out that "both the pulse frequency and the acceleration profile are reasonably well simulated by a child's backyard swing operating through an arc some 65° each way from vertical."

All the later Orion designs ejected the bombs through the center of the pusher plate, and relied on massive cylinder-and-piston shock absorbers that were non-dissipative but actively cooled. The vaporized shock absorber coolant (water or ammonia) was recycled as propellant to eject the charges, and there were direct linkages between the shock absorbers and the pumps that sprayed anti-ablation oil at the pusher, at the top of each cycle, through a series of nozzles fitted to the central launching tube. There would be four externally visible events in each pulse cycle: the ejection of the charge, signified by a puff of steam; a brief spray of anti-ablation oil to coat the pusher and the "plasma deflector" that protected the muzzle of the ejection tube; the explosion of the bomb; and the flash of plasma against the plate.

On the bridge of an Orion ship on active maneuvers, the primary control would be the regulator for pulse-detonation timing—equivalent to the spark advance lever by which the driver could manually advance or retard the ignition timing on a Model T. Down below, past the layers of charge storage magazines, the engine room would be filled with steam lines, coolant reservoirs, and tanks of anti-ablation oil, and permeated by huge pistons reciprocating back and forth between the compressed gas within the shock absorbers and the impact of the bomb-driven plasma out in space. The crew would be watching oil levels, steam pressure gauges, and critical voltages, but as the bombs descended with a hiss of vapor once per second, they would have little indication that they were aboard a spaceship from the age of nuclear energy rather than a storm-tossed vessel from the age of steam. Jules Verne, born in 1828, or Michael Treshow, born in 1894, would have been equally at home aboard Orion. Below decks, the engine room would appear as familiar to a steam engineer from the nineteenth century as to a rocket technician from the twenty-first.

18

Enceladus

On August 15, 1958, Freeman and Ted flew from San Diego to Pasadena to visit the U.S. Army's Jet Propulsion Laboratory at Caltech. JPL, where the Explorer satellites were being built, was preparing to launch the 143-pound *Explorer 6*. "The reception there was rather cool," reported Freeman. "The lady at the front office decided Taylor and I were a pair of crackpots and tried to get rid of us. After half an hour of arguing we got inside and then it all went very well."

"I can just imagine the two of them showing up at a place like JPL, which was trying hard to get these little bitty satellites up and saying, 'We're here to talk about a 1,000-ton satellite powered by nuclear bombs,'" says Lew Allen, who was supervising ARPA's contract with General Atomic and later became director, under NASA administration, of JPL. Adding to the disconnect in scale between Orion and JPL, Freeman and Ted were not in Pasadena to talk about launching a satellite. They were there to discuss auxiliary vehicles that might be carried aboard Orion on its interplanetary tour. "We were beginning to look at what sort of rockets to put in the payload of the 4,000-ton vehicle for landing on Ganymede," says Ted.

"We really thought the thing was going to fly," Ted continues. "And once it flew it was no big deal to decide to go to Saturn or Jupiter, or somewhere else. And plunk down on satellites or not, because it was high thrust. We did look at backing into various-size objects including, at some point, landing on asteroids by having the last explosion be just as you were settling down on the surface." Landing the mother ship on larger objects such as Mars or Ganymede, against gravity that was even one-third or one-sixth of Earth's, was risky, both because of the danger of crashing the ship and because the landing site would be contaminated by the last few bombs. "We were environmentally conscious of some of the questions raised by landing on Io or Ganymede or whatever—bang, bang, bang, and then how about all this radioactivity? First sign that here come the humans is a whole bunch of Cesium 137 and whatnot! Neutrons first, then gamma rays. We spent a fair bit of time thinking about that."

When Project Orion's contract was signed, the largest payload lifted into orbit—*Sputnik III*, launched by the Soviet Union on May 15, 1958—weighed 2,926 pounds. The 4,000-ton, 2 g–acceleration Orion vehicle proposed in 1958 was intended to deliver 1,600 tons to a 300-mile orbit, 1,200 tons to a soft lunar landing, 800 tons to a soft lunar landing or a Mars orbit and return to a 300-mile orbit around Earth, or 200 tons to a Venus orbit followed by a Mars orbit with a 300-mile Earth orbit return. An "Advanced Interplanetary Ship," powered by 15-kiloton bombs, with up to 4 g acceleration and a takeoff weight of 10,000 tons, was envisioned as 185 feet in diameter and 280 feet in height. Its payload to a 300-mile orbit was 6,100 tons; to a soft lunar landing, 5,700 tons; to a Venus orbit followed by a Mars orbit and back to a 300-mile Earth orbit, 4,500 tons; to a landing on an inner satellite of Saturn and return to a 300-mile Earth orbit—a three-year round-trip—1,300 tons.

By the time of the visit to JPL, Freeman had a specific destination in mind. Enceladus, 312 miles in diameter, is the next-to-innermost moon of Saturn, discovered by William Herschel in 1789. Its gravity is ⅟₂₀₀ that of Earth—enough to enable a secure landing, but with an escape velocity of less than 400 mph, making it easy to depart. Enceladus is about as dense as a packed snowball, and a long way from La Jolla— about 800 million miles, some nine times the distance from Earth to the

Sun. If Earth were a billiard ball, our moon would be a marble 6 feet away; Mars a golf ball at ¼ mile; Jupiter an overinflated beach ball at 2 miles; Saturn an underinflated beach ball at 4 miles; and Enceladus a peppercorn about 3 feet from the beach ball's surface, 2 feet beyond its hula hoop–size rings. To an observer on Enceladus, orbiting Saturn every thirty-two hours, Saturn would appear about 3,000 times the size that Earth's moon appears to us. Saturn and its rings would fill the Enceladean sky, changing phase from hour to hour, illuminated by the pale light of a distant sun.

During July 1958, Project Orion quadrupled in size, yet the entire project group was still small enough to meet informally in Ted's office whenever a new problem or a possible solution came up. "We are about 12 altogether at this point," wrote Freeman on July 31, 1958. "It is very different from a month ago when we were three." The million dollars from ARPA and the increasing involvement of the Air Force had suddenly lent credibility to Ted's ideas. "Within this first month they have spent about $40,000 and think their work output has been pretty good for this," Mixson reported after his visit on July 29. To Freeman, the spaceship was "slowly taking shape and becoming more definite, like a figure being chiseled out of a piece of marble." The first TRIGA reactor—as imaginary as Orion only two summers ago—had gone into operation on May 6. Orion was moving ahead almost as fast. In between calculating opacities and designing pusher plates, shock absorbers, and bomb-delivery systems, the Orion crew spent more and more time thinking about where to take the ship. "We were all champing at the bit to get on with it and get out there," says Ted. "What Orion could do was much more interesting to me than how it worked, nearly the reverse situation from my work on the bombs."

"The official mission at the beginning was just Mars," Freeman explains. There was no formal mission statement as to what would be done on Mars, or why. To Air Force generals or congressmen, there was always the argument that if we did not send Orion to Mars the Russians might get there first. To the engineers, the 20 km/sec velocity required for a round-trip to Mars offered a benchmark around which to design a first-generation ship. To the mission planners, Mars offered a test of life-support systems and a goal for a shakedown cruise. Freeman spoke up for science in general and biology in particular. "I think the study of whatever forms of life exist on Mars is likely to lead to enormous and unpredictable steps in understanding the mechanics of life in general," he wrote.

Burt Freeman calculated expedition timetables, though warning, in *Minimum Energy Round Trips to Mars and Venus,* that these "approximate departure dates are by no means to be taken as exact programs for any actual flight." Departing Earth during a favorable outbound period, and then waiting on Mars for a favorable return, the numbers worked out as follows: Earth to Mars, 258 days; then a 454-day wait; Mars to Earth, 258 days; for a total of 970 days or 32 months. Possible departure dates were: October 1960, November 1962, January 1965, and February 1965. The consensus was to aim for 1965. These were minimum-energy voyages; the trip could be made in less time or at different times at the expense of additional bombs. Venus could be included by abbreviating the stay on Mars. "We would have liked to fly by Venus and have a close look at it," says Freeman Dyson. "Certainly we didn't know the atmosphere was as dense and hot as we know it is now, but I think we already knew that the surface was not a possible place to visit. Also we knew that Venus has no moons, and that already made it less interesting than Mars."

In a brief appendix, *Landings on Mars' Satellites,* Burt Freeman noted that "the two satellites of Mars offer interesting vantage points and might be used as bases. Phobos would be particularly useful due to its unusually low altitude." Phobos is only 16 miles long, about the size of Manhattan, and fewer than 4,000 miles up. "Escape speed might be ~10 cm/sec, large enough that a person couldn't jump off." If that person threw a baseball, however, it would exceed Phobos's escape velocity and never come back.

Burt Freeman was excited by the physics of Orion, but was not obsessed with personally going to Mars. "The obtaining of opacities was really our main business—this was just a little side excursion," he says. His calculations showed the advantages of Orion's high thrust. "Takeoff from Earth and departure for Mars would require 15.2 km/sec if takeoff and acceleration into the transfer ellipse are two separate maneuvers, while only 11.6 km/sec is needed if the thrust is all applied during takeoff." Transit time is reduced by accelerating quickly and maintaining full cruising speed until reaching the destination, rather than accelerating slowly and having to begin deceleration long in advance.

Had Orion departed as scheduled, a landing on our own moon would have been included—at least to plant the United States flag. Mars, however, had water to support an extended stay and supply propellant for the voyage back. "We assumed that you could pick up propellant on Mars, water probably," says Freeman Dyson. "What we would have done would have been to go to the North or South Pole where there is plenty of water. It wasn't clear whether you would really want to, but landing on Mars would be much easier than landing on Earth. We wanted to make it a four- or five-year stay so that you would really explore the whole planet. I remember saying that we should be like Darwin's *Beagle,* which took five years."

Landing Orion on Mars, using bombs for the descent, might have been perceived as bombing a national park. More likely the ship would have remained in orbit, or used Phobos as a base, while the Martian surface was explored using chemically powered landing craft. A later mission study proposed sending multiple 4,000-ton Orion ships to Mars, landing one of them permanently on the surface to serve as a base. "This excursion would put twenty personnel on the Martian surface for a period of approximately one year. Ecology systems and supplies for two years would be provided," it was explained. "The ORION engine would be used to decelerate the vehicle down to a few thousand feet off the ground and several hundred feet per second velocity and then would be jettisoned. The separated payload compartment would then be landed by means of chemical rockets." An illustration accompanying the proposal shows "the payload compartment sitting on its shock-absorbing landing gear while in the distance some of the crew are inspecting the remains of the ORION engine." This would reduce or at least appear to reduce contamination of Mars. "For the early part of setting up the base, perhaps as many as fifty persons would be on the surface, all but twenty of them returning to the orbiting ORION vehicles by means of the landers/returners. After a stay of forty days or so, the orbiting ORIONs would return to earth leaving the twenty personnel to their tasks until the next favorable date for a trip to Mars."

It was frustrating, for the first six months of 1958, to be making plans to explore the solar system that could not be openly discussed. The ARPA contract was signed on June 30, and a brief press release, lifting the veil of secrecy, was issued in Washington on July 2. Freeman responded by drafting *A Space-Traveler's Manifesto,* dated July 5, 1958:

> Either through inadvertence, or by a deliberate act of wisdom, the American government has announced to the public that we are working on the design of a space-ship to be driven by atomic bombs.
>
> It is my belief that this scheme alone, of the many space-ship schemes which are under consideration, can lead to a ship adequate to the real magnitude of the task of exploring the Solar System. We are fortunate in that the government has advised us to go straight ahead for the long-range scientific objectives of interplanetary travel, and to disregard possible military uses of our propulsion system.
>
> From my childhood it has been my conviction that men would reach the planets in my lifetime, and that I should help in the enterprise. If I try to rationalize this conviction I suppose it rests on two beliefs, one scientific and one political.
>
> 1) There are more things in heaven and earth than are dreamed of in our present-day science. And we shall only find out what they are if we go out and look for them.
>
> 2) It is in the long run essential to the growth of any new and high civilization that small groups of men can escape from their neighbors and from their governments, to go and live as they please in the wilderness. A truly isolated, small, and creative society will never again be possible on this planet.
>
> I think the much abused argument, "if we don't do it the Russians will get there first," has, in this case, some force. But I would wish to pursue the work with equal intensity if no Russian program of space-exploration existed. My purpose, and my belief, is that the bombs that killed and maimed at Hiroshima and Nagasaki shall one day open the skies to man.

GENERAL ATOMIC
DIVISION OF GENERAL DYNAMICS CORPORATION

SUBJECT
W.O.
BY
SHEET
DATE July 5 1958 LOCATION

A Space- Traveler's Manifesto.
Freeman J. Dyson.*

Either through inadvertence, or by a deliberate act of wisdom, the ~~government~~ American government has announced to the public that we are working on the design of a space-ship to be driven by atomic bombs.

A propulsion system of this type was proposed several years ago by Stanislaus Ulam at ~~the~~ Los Alamos. The idea was ~~energetically~~ revived, improved, and energetically developed by Ted Taylor, ~~who is now of General Atomic~~ who is now the leader of our study project at General Atomic. Since ~~~~ the government announcement has been made, I feel free ~~to~~ to make public a personal statement of the hopes and ~~purposes~~ aims which impel me to take part in this work.

---

* On leave of absence ~~from~~ the Institute for Advanced Study, Princeton, N.J. Now at General Atomic Division of ~~General~~ Dynamics Corporation, San Diego, California.

On June 28 the last General Atomic employees left the Barnard Street School and moved to the new laboratory site. It was an easy walk to the bluffs at Torrey Pines, where on most afternoons a strong breeze blew in from the cool Pacific as the inland mesas baked in the Southern California sun. A narrow strip of eroded upland, just north of La Jolla Farms, was home to the Torrey Pines Glider Club, an informal group of enthusiasts who shared the ownership, upkeep, and operation of a two-seater, wood-framed, fabric-covered sailplane and a war-surplus gas-powered winch. On weekends, if the wind was blowing and enough volunteers showed up, the glider was assembled at one end of an undulating, unpaved landing strip whose other end disappeared off the edge of a cliff. A signal was given to the winch operator, and then with a full-throttle roar and a smoking clutch the quarter-mile cable went taut. The glider, its handlers running beside it as it picked up speed, was launched upward at a steep angle, dropping the towline shortly before it passed over the winch at the edge of the cliff. If skills and conditions were favorable, you could glide for miles, coasting along the updrafts up to Del Mar or beyond; if you or the wind failed, you landed on the beach and the glider was disassembled and carried in pieces up one of the steep canyons that permeated the sandstone cliffs.

Early in the summer of 1958, Freeman struck up a conversation with some of the ground crew and decided to join the club. The weekends that one year later he would spend helping to fly the explosive-driven models of Orion at Point Loma he now spent gliding at Torrey Pines. "I was out in the sun and wind for eleven hours, from 8:30 till 7:30," he reported on July 13, two weeks after the ARPA announcement was made. "I came out to put the glider together in the morning and stayed to take it apart in the evening. Most of the day I spent just doing odd jobs, pulling the towing wire, wheeling the glider around, and so forth. What I like about gliding is that most of the time when you are not flying there are lots of jobs to do and it is a friendly group of people. Of course the best part of the day was the two flights. One lasted 15 minutes and the other ten. We fly up on a wire which is pulled by a winch, then let go of the wire and sail around in the wind where it rises over the cliffs. Today it was a good strong wind and we could stay up as long as we liked, with the ocean far below on one side, the yellow cliffs on the other."

On August 2, after making three flights, Freeman reported that "the controls are very peculiar. One expects it to steer like a car but it doesn't. You move the control and nothing happens for about two seconds. Then it starts to turn much too fast and you have to turn it back hard the other way. I am still scared of it and that makes it exciting." The lag in response time was similar to that of the control system that Freeman had recently analyzed for a two-bombs-per-second Orion: you steered the ship by shifting the position of the bombs, but had to allow a few pulse cycles for the course changes to take effect. Freeman also learned to operate the winch. "It is a fearsome machine, you have to jam down the accelerator until it screams at a certain pitch (there is no speed-ometer) and then let it go gradually up. I always was much more scared of the winch than of the glider. But today I gave about ten winch-tows and the pilots said they were satisfactory. So I am now 'checked out on the winch.'"

The cooperative, adventurous spirit of the glider club was exactly what Freeman believed was required for the colonization of space. By summoning the courage to be winched off a cliff at 60 mph, his chances were improved of being aboard Orion when the signal was given to launch. "I had five flights and I feel better at it every time," he reported on August 16. "I am not scared as I was at first and that helps. Especially I enjoy the landings and I am beginning to be able to hit the intended spot."

That same weekend, Freeman finished a twelve-page report, *Trips to Satellites of the Outer Planets,* concerning the feasibility of going to the moons of Jupiter or Saturn and back. Freeman's view of Orion's "veloc-ity decrement to land on satellite" looks like this:

$$I_s = \sqrt{U_s^2 + \left[V_s - 2V_s^2 / \sqrt{U_p^2 + 2V_s^2}\right]^2}$$

"The satellites of the outer planets are the only places where we know for certain that hydrogen exists in abundance and is accessible to a spaceship," wrote Freeman in the introduction to his report. "In addi-tion, the satellites would be able to supply unlimited quantities of the other light elements, carbon, nitrogen and oxygen, which are necessary to maintain life and also useful as propellants. The high escape velocities of the outer planets, while an obstacle to landing on the surfaces of these planets, are a great help to landing on their satellites."

"The general nature of the maneuvers is as follows," Freeman explained. "The ship takes off from earth in a direction parallel to earth's orbital velocity, at a time when this will put the ship into a hyperbolic orbit intercepting the planet P. The ship approaches the planet as close as possible to its surface, and there makes a velocity-change bringing it into an elliptical orbit about the planet. The elliptical orbit is chosen so that the ship arrives at the satellite orbit tangentially. A final velocity-change at the satellite surface is required for landing on the satellite."

The compelling reason to land on a satellite would be to pick up propellant. Two obvious other sources were out: the gas-giant planets are too big to land on; comets are moving too fast and too hard to find. The moons of Jupiter and Saturn looked to be the best places to stop. "They definitely do have the right stuff, and we know where they are," says Freeman. "The problem with the satellites of Jupiter is just that the gravitational field of Jupiter is so strong. So it's hard to get a velocity match, once you dive in toward Jupiter you are going so fast it is difficult to match with a satellite. So the satellites of Saturn are easier, because Saturn is not as big.

"We knew very little about the satellites in those days. Enceladus looked particularly good. It was known to have a density of .618, so it clearly had to be made of ice plus hydrocarbons, really light things, which were what you need both for biology and for propellant, so you could imagine growing your vegetables there. Five-one-thousandths g on Enceladus is a very gentle gravity—just enough so that you won't jump off."

After calculating the details for several representative trips Freeman noted, "The meaning of these numbers may be roughly summarized as follows. Round-trip voyages to satellites of Jupiter in 2 years require total velocity increments of the order of 60 km/sec. Round-trips to satellites of Saturn in 3 years require total increments of 80 km/sec. For the Orion system, working at an effective exhaust velocity of 50 km/sec, these trips need mass ratios of 3.3 and 5.0 respectively. The design of the ship would have to be quite different from that of the original model which is supposed to reach 20 km/sec. with a mass-ratio of 1.5. But there seems to be no compelling reason why ships with mass-ratios of 3.3 or 5.0 should not be built." Each velocity change adds a certain cost in bombs, and each bomb adds a certain cost in takeoff mass. The mass ratio is the ratio of the mass you start out with to the mass you have left when you get back. The mass ratio for an Apollo return trip to the Moon is about 600 to 1.

Freeman saw two ways to improve the situation for Orion: first, use atmospheric braking to reduce the number of bombs. A lot of fuel is consumed in slowing down when you get to Saturn, and then slowing down again when you return to orbit Earth. "It is quite likely that velocity decrements can be made by sweeping through the outer layers of planetary atmospheres without expenditure of propellant," he noted. "If this is possible, the effective velocity increment needed for a round-trip is very substantially reduced." The return of Orion after a voyage to the outer planets would be almost as spectacular as its launch had been three years before: approaching Earth at 30 km/sec (60,000 mph) the ship would present its pusher plate toward Earth and fire off a rapid series of bombs, changing course into an elliptical orbit that would graze the upper atmosphere in a series of fiery bursts of atmospheric drag.

The second part of the strategy is to gather propellant for the return trip at the destination, thereby reducing the average takeoff weight of the bombs. "We assume that we can use as propellant either ice, ammonia, or hydrocarbons," wrote Freeman, explaining why Enceladus was such a good place to stop. "We suppose that each propulsion unit contains one-third of its mass in the form of the bomb and other fabricated parts, and two-thirds of its mass in the form of propellant. This means that, when propellant refueling is possible, only one-third of the mass required for the homeward trip need be carried out from Earth." When you put these numbers together the end results were astonishing: "With the use of atmospheric drag a round-trip to satellites of either Jupiter or Saturn could be made with a total velocity increment of the order of 40 km/sec. With refueling and braking, all the satellites become accessible with a round-trip mass-ratio less than 2."

This meant that the first-generation, 20 km/sec ship designed for a shakedown cruise to Mars could easily become a 40 km/sec ship that would depart for the outer planets in a few more years. Orion's motto,

"Saturn by 1970," was coined. "The Orion system, peculiarly well suited to take maximum advantage of the laws of celestial mechanics, makes possible round-trips to satellites of Jupiter in 2 years, or to satellites of Saturn in 3 years, with takeoff and landing on the ground at both ends," Freeman noted in concluding his report. "Using the outer planets as hitching-posts, we can make round-trips to their satellites with overall velocity increments which are spectacularly small. The probability that we can refuel with propellant on the satellites makes such trips hardly more formidable than voyages to Mars."

"The mission was the grand tour of the solar system," remembers Harris Mayer. "But we also thought of it as a real commercial enterprise, because of the payloads you could carry. And you could bring back things from space to the earth. At that time, 1958, we were not worried about taking off from the ground. We knew how to make nuclear explosions in the atmosphere, and the characteristics are different than in space and we could take advantage of it. So it wasn't until much later that you had to get this thing up into space some other way."

"Oh, yes, he wanted to go," says Mayer concerning Freeman's plans. "I was chicken. Look, I knew enough about the space business, that this was dangerous. You had to be crazy to go. The astronauts today are very, very adventurous and brave people. But Enceladus was the one he wanted to go to then. What was remarkable is that he would come and talk to me and it was as if everything were all done."

Forty years later, Freeman and I review a two-page handwritten General Atomic calculation sheet, "Outer Planet Satellites," dating from 1958 or 1959. It lists, for nine different satellites, ten different parameters such as orbital velocity, escape velocity, density, and gravity that determine the suitability of the satellites as places to land. Freeman smiles as he carefully studies the numbers.

"Enceladus still looks good," he says.

19

Deep Space Force

"From 1951 through to the atmospheric test-ban treaty, I participated in over one hundred atmospheric tests," says Don Prickett, now eighty-two and in excellent health. "We had a test series in Nevada every spring and a couple out in the Pacific every year. A test series out in Nevada might be eighteen, twenty shots. Anywhere from one kiloton to twenty, forty, fifty, something like that. I had my maximum dosage every shot, every test series. Once you hit that maximum, you didn't go near it again. I had two rads every series. Today you say two rads and people faint."

Don Prickett lives with his wife, Mary, in a log house that he and his father, a hard-rock miner and prospector, built by hand at an elevation of 7,500 feet in the San Juan Mountains near Durango, Colorado, above the trout-bearing waters of Vallecito Creek. His diet includes sourdough pancakes descended from a culture he started as a physics student in 1946. An active partner in several gold-mining ventures, he still does a little prospecting himself. "Don has always had various schemes for getting gold," says Lew Allen, his former boss at AFSWC, "hampered by two things: the price of gold has been lower for the last twenty or thirty years, and it's incredible how effective the early gold miners were."

Trained as a physicist and a prospector, Prickett worked with nuclear weapons for half a century, from uranium ore to weapons effects. "My father got quite involved in uranium prospecting," he explains. "He had a little diamond drill and he would trailer it around and poke some 100-, 200-foot holes. It was strictly radiation count with a Geiger counter, you had to get a sample of it and just see how hot it was. We found some stuff that was good, northeast of Albuquerque, but never quite good enough. All the good stuff was taken by the time we got out there looking around. At that time the AEC would jump on anything that looked good. You could count on them to help you sell it or they would buy it or tie it up."

Nuclear physics came naturally to Prickett. Not content with being a theoretician, or even an experimentalist, he wanted to tackle the full-scale development of atomic energy, firsthand. "When I was at Ohio State my biggest ambition was to get to be the test pilot on the nuclear-propelled aircraft," he says. During the 1950s, before returning to Albuquerque to succeed Ed Giller as director of research at AFSWC, Prickett worked on nuclear R&D out of the Pentagon. "Anything nuclear came across my desk," he explains. "If it didn't fit under blast, radiation, or thermal, if it was effects on aircraft or effects on ships, or anything else, those were all my projects. I was the program director of them. I was there at the big one on Bikini." This was Castle Bravo, the first test of a solid-fuel, room-temperature, "deliverable" hydrogen bomb. Exploded on February 28, 1954, it yielded 15 megatons, almost three times what had been expected, producing a fireball more than three miles across.

"I had seen up until that time maybe fifty shots at least, atmospheric shots out at the test site, so I wasn't really startled," says Prickett, describing how, with Navy Captain George Malumphy, he maneuvered a remote-controlled merchant ship into the path of the bomb's fallout to test an automatic washdown system being developed for decontamination of surface craft. "I knew it was going to be big, but Malumphy and I were at least thirty miles from ground zero. And só when the order came on for countdown we put on our dark goggles. And sure enough it went off and it was a full two minutes anyway before we took off our goggles and then it was so awesome that all Malumphy could say was, 'My God, my God, my God!'"

The AEC set off the bombs, while the Department of Defense did their best to gain as much weapons-effects information as possible from every shot. Most of his projects, says Prickett, "were AEC development tests in which we hung on to get anything we could." Prickett's group chose another shot in the Castle series to test the structural response of a B-47 bomber to blast, by flying the aircraft dangerously close to where the bomb was scheduled to go off. "The AEC was just nervous as hell about us playing around out there on these shots with aircraft anywhere near them," he recalls. "They couldn't stand the publicity of having an accident so they were very, very conservative. We had done all the previous theoretical work and static testing on the B-47 at Wright Patterson and wanted to put it into position to get about eighty percent of design limit load for the blast effect. And so the project was approved even though the AEC was very unhappy about it. When it came time to position the aircraft, the AEC was in control of the safety end of it, and the trigger on the shot. We had a racetrack pattern set up with a radar control and checkpoints, so you know exactly where you're going to be within a second or so. When we came down to the final approval on it, before shot time, the AEC balked and said, 'You're too close. We don't believe your calculations, you're going to have to back off.' We said that will give us only fifty percent of the load, that ruins the project. And they said we don't care, that's all you are going to get. We didn't say anything, we said OK, and went back to talk to the test pilot who was flying the airplane. He knew how much work had gone into this. And he said, 'I'll take care of it. Don't worry. I'll take care of it.' After he hit his last checkpoint, he poured the coal on and got up into position where we wanted to be. And we got what we were after. But the AEC never knew about that."

In the spring of 1958, General Atomic's proposal for a bomb-propelled spaceship was hand-carried to the Pentagon by Ted. This was the only place, besides the AEC, where a project involving thousands of nuclear bombs could be discussed. "I received the initial proposal when I had the nuclear desk in R&D in the Pentagon," says Prickett. "I met Ted when that proposal came in. It was not very detailed, conceptual, as I remember, but enough to get our attention." The concept did not appear crazy to Don Prickett. In the overall spectrum of nuclear weapons effects, lifting 4,000 tons of Orion into orbit above a series of kiloton-yield explosions might not be too great a stretch. "It's one of those potentials that never got to its potential," he says. "We were all excited. We thought we had something that would eventually be something, but it wasn't politically correct. Everybody knew that it was reaching out, but that's the only way you can make big steps."

The Pentagon's problem was how to justify sponsorship of Orion in the absence of a specific military requirement for sending thousand-ton payloads into space. In anticipation of NASA, the distinctions between military and civilian space programs were being drawn. "It was a very long battle inside the White House as to whether the space program, post-*Sputnik*, was to be a civilian program or a military program," says Bruno Augenstein. "The majority vote went with NASA at that time, but it was a very complicated era. You had General LeMay calling for the Air Force to run the total national space program. At one time the Air Force proposed to form an interplanetary expedition force. That's how adventurous they were. Those were exciting times!" Assigning manned space exploration, on the scale of Orion, directly to the Air Force was politically untenable in 1958. The United States Army, with friends in high places, feared only one thing more than finding Soviet cosmonauts on the Moon: finding that the United States Air Force had arrived there first. The Army had relinquished nuclear weapons to the AEC in 1946; getting them to give up Wernher von Braun and his manned space program to NASA was still two years away in 1958.

ARPA's sponsorship of Orion assigned interim management to the Air Force, while reserving a seat at the head of the table for NASA, expected to step in and take the lead once its mandate from Congress was defined. When NASA support for Orion failed to materialize, the Air Force assumed responsibility by default. As ARPA's role in space was brought to a conclusion, toward the end of the Eisenhower administration, by Herbert York, military missions went to the Air Force and peaceful missions to NASA. Orion was caught in between—because of the bombs. "The situation of ARPA was reminiscent of the partition of Poland between Prussia and Russia in the eighteenth century," Freeman later explained. "Taylor's efforts to interest NASA in Orion during this period met with no success." As Ted describes the predicament: "The

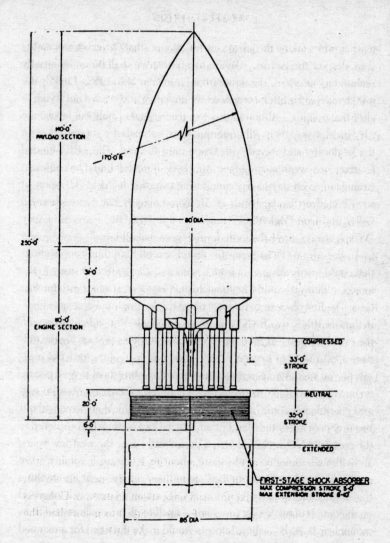

Four-thousand-ton Orion vehicle, military payload version, ca. 1962.

Air Force people knew about nuclear weapon design in a lot of detail. NASA didn't understand the workings of Orion at all."

Just as Ted had reassured his mother before going to work at Los Alamos that he would not be building weapons, Freeman reassured his mother, when taking the job at General Atomic, that Orion was not a warship, despite the bombs. "We are happy that we shall be under strictly nonmilitary auspices," he wrote from La Jolla in May 1958. "Luckily the military are so far quite convinced we are crazy, and we are not trying to alter this opinion." Although this was true at higher political levels, the Air Force physicists in Albuquerque were enthusiastic supporters from the beginning and stayed with Orion until the end. The ARPA-funded contract was written up by the Air Force Research and Development Command, with day-to-day monitoring assigned to AFSWC, where it soon ended up in the hands of Air Force officers like Lew Allen, Ed Giller, and Don Prickett. "We nicknamed it 'Putt Putt,'" says Ed Giller. "Which always made the more formal types make a face."

Under AFSWC's auspices, the search was on for military applications that could justify advancing from a million-dollar feasibility study to the tens of millions it would take to begin development, starting with nuclear tests. The first place to go for long-range thinking on Air Force questions, in the late 1950s, was RAND, "a refuge for people who didn't get on with the establishment," as Freeman says. "The prospects of studying the military applications of a space vehicle with a payload of the order of magnitude you suggested certainly stimulated the interests of several people on our research staff," answered RAND in response to a request to suggest possible missions, "since the payload of the vehicle involved is about two orders of magnitude larger than any we have seriously considered in the past." RAND reviewed Orion periodically over the next few years, and although generally enthusiastic about its technical feasibility, were never able to identify any immediate military requirement for anything that large. Unfortunately for Orion, RAND's analysts were well informed on the details of two secret programs—satellite reconnaissance and thermonuclear ICBMs—whose success would make the need for a manned surveillance or retaliatory platform obsolete.

"We have to face some kind of a moral or ethical problem, in deciding whether to lean for support mainly on the Air Force or on NASA," Freeman wrote in May 1959, as the first year's funding from ARPA came to an end. "The Air Force is naturally interested in our ship mainly as a military weapon, while NASA is supposed to be interested in scientific exploration. So ideally we ought to be working for NASA and avoiding the Air Force. However, in practice the issue is not so simple. Firstly, there is no doubt that as soon as our ship flies at all, both the Air Force and NASA will insist on having one; so it does not really make that much difference who pays for the initial development. Secondly, the Air Force is much less bureaucratic, and generally easier to work with. So we decided at least for the time being to stick with the Air Force. I think this was a wise decision. To imagine that a space-ship of this kind could be built without any military consequences would be only self-deception. Of course we are all sorry the military aspects have to come into the picture. But that is the way things are."

Unlike the Apollo ships that carried astronauts to the Moon, Orion was an all-purpose, reusable craft. The same underlying vehicle could serve as merchant ship, research vessel, reconnaissance platform, orbital command center, or battleship, as circumstances changed. Possible military applications began with Freeman's original suggestion that "to have an observation post on the moon with a fair-sized telescope would be a rather important military advantage for the side which gets there first," and grew more ambitious, and at times implausible, from there. "Space platforms should be examined also, as well as the movement of asteroids and the like," suggested Lew Allen in October 1958.

"After NASA was formed, the Air Force had to justify supporting Orion on the grounds that it had military significance," says Ted. "So I spent a lot of time thinking about that and really got carried away, on crazy doomsday machines—things like exploding bombs deep under the Moon's surface and blowing lunar rocks at the Soviet Union. There were versions of Orion in which the entire retaliatory ICBM force was in one vehicle, which was very hard, and any time anyone tried to fire at it it would turn around and present its rear end at the bombs coming at it. We were doing something for the project that we didn't want to do but had to to keep it alive, we thought."

"In the early days of the project," remembers Pierre Noyes, "Freeman and Ted talked about whether it would have been wiser to sell NASA on the project and have it under civilian auspices from the start. It was clear that the main payoff would be in space exploration rather than military applications. But they were eager to get ahead with it and accepted Air Force sponsorship, which was available right away. In my

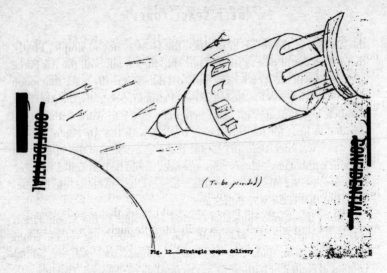

CONFIDENTIAL CONFIDENTIAL

(To be provided)

Fig. 12—Strategic weapon delivery

Multiple independently targeted warheads are launched by a 4,000-ton Orion vehicle that has de-orbited from its station in deep space and entered a hyperbolic Earth-encounter trajectory to perform a retaliatory strike.

view, their Faustian bargain had unfortunate consequences. Some horrendous projects came up as possible military missions. I even did a minor calculation about whether one of them would destroy the ozone layer. But, to my knowledge, neither Freeman nor Ted turned their minds to a serious search for a military mission. Had they done so, and knowing their talents, I suspect that they might have saved the project at the cost of an even more Faustian bargain."

A May 1959 Air Force briefing revealed some "possible military uses of the Orion Vehicle," including reconnaissance and early-warning, electronic countermeasures ("possible to get a terrific number of jammers over a given area"), anti-ICBM ("possibility of putting many early intercept missiles in orbit awaiting use"), and "ICBM, orbital, or deep space weapons—orders of magnitude increase in warhead weights—clustered warheads—launch platforms, etc." Finally, there was "the Horrible weapon—1,650-ton continent-buster hanging over the enemy's head as a deterrent." It was this possibility that came to the attention of Noyes.

In the 1950s, it was easy to build arbitrarily large, powerful hydrogen bombs, but difficult to build small ones. Exceptionally large bombs, however, inflicted diminishing returns, since immediate damage by blast and radiation is governed not only by the size of the bomb but by the distance to the horizon of the curving Earth. When the Soviets exploded a 58-megaton bomb in 1961 it raised concerns that a bomb this large "just blows a hole out of the atmosphere and you lose most of the explosive force," says Noyes. "But with a platform that could lift enormous weight, like Orion, you could go up high enough, and have a big enough explosion, to irradiate an enormous area. Because this would be above the ozone layer, you would think that the ultraviolet wouldn't get through. Well, you actually burn through the ozone layer, with the scale they were talking about. So then the question is, what happens to the ozone layer? That was why for a long time I wasn't worried about the ozone layer, because it was easy to show that it gets reestablished within a minute. Take it out, and it reforms again. It's very stable, if all you have are the constituents that are there naturally. What changes the picture completely are the chain reactions that the various industrial products make. But that's a more recent realization. That horrendous gadget would get through it, but if it was a cloudy day, it wouldn't be very good. It wasn't much of a weapon as far as I could see."

"There was a lot of controversy about that," remembers Ted, "not just whether the doomsday bomb payload for Orion was a good idea to think about, but technically, whether energy emitted by explosions in space would convert to high temperature by impact with the upper parts of the atmosphere and then reemit that energy at frequencies with a long range that would then hit the surface. There were people who argued that this was not possible. But there clearly are ways of designing the bomb in such a way that a substantial fraction of the energy that intercepts the earth strikes the surface as light and heat. The simple summary was that something on the scale of the payload that we visualized for the 4,000-ton vehicle could destroy half the earth. That was not viewed with enthusiasm by anybody that I can remember, but it was an interesting outer limit. It would play hell with the upper atmosphere. At that time—and I think now—people really had no good basis for figuring out what it would do."

Such thoughts were difficult to repress. "It was part of the addiction," says Ted. In his personal journal he noted: "Spent most of the day discussing effects of very high altitude, big explosions. George Stuart's IBM 704 code for calculating the thermal energy delivered to the ground is generally agreed to have the correct physics in it." And three days later: "Had vile thoughts in the evening about how to use antimatter for wiping out populations. Perhaps someone should write a book called *101 Ways to Eliminate the Human Race* and call it quits."

The problem was how to distinguish the defensive from the offensive when deploying weapons in space. "Only delicate timing would determine whether satellite neutralizations were offensive or defensive," explained a secret telex on "Global Integration of Space Surveillance, Tracking, and Related Facilities," marked "For Eyes of the USAF Only," from the commander in chief of the Strategic Air Command in Omaha, Nebraska, on May 31, 1959. Beyond the Moon, science would take the lead, but this did not preclude a role for the Air Force in deep space. "There presently exist no military requirements beyond cislunar space," a classified Air Force summary admitted in May 1959. "However, one must note that one reason there are no military requirements for a deep space vehicle is simply that no one has ever before seriously considered sending a large, manned, useful payload to this area for military purposes."

This was not necessarily at odds with the nonmilitary goals of Freeman and Ted. "Because the Air Force was paying for it, we assumed we would have some military people on board," says Freeman. "But it would be as they do in the Antarctic when the Navy runs the Antarctic logistics for the science that's done there. It doesn't mean that the Navy does the science but they have a lot of Navy people around. So we expected it would be like that; Ted would have been the chief scientist, with some Air Force officers responsible for the operation of the ship."

One of these officers would have been Captain Donald M. Mixson. "Mixson was an enthusiast. He'd have been the first man on board," says Don Prickett. Mixson and Prickett saw Orion as a way to sustain the type of creative, fast-moving effort that the proliferation of peacetime bureaucracy was bringing to an end. "Mixson and Prickett were fed up with the Air Force system and Orion was a way to put a burr under the Air Force saddle blanket," explains Brian Dunne. Mixson shuttled back and forth between Albuquerque, Washington, and La Jolla, giving endless briefings in support of Orion, and becoming the leading advocate for an Orion Deep Space Force.

Mixson, who wanted to help the physicists do physics and the engineers do engineering, instead spent much of his time fighting the bureaucracies that kept getting in the way. A typical difficulty, at the beginning of the ARPA contract, was how to get Orion documents that had been created while the project was under the auspices of the AEC transferred to Department of Defense custody, without physically sending the documents back to AEC headquarters, and then to Department of Defense headquarters, leaving the Orion scientists without access to their own work. "This was supposed to be impossible to accomplish this way until I agreed to personally sign for the documents," Mixson reported. "Solving this ridiculously simple problem took the best part of the 30th. Now I own the documents and have them out to GA on hand receipt. It is a continual source of amazement to me that technical types can move mountains but administrative people stumble over mole hills."

Captain Mixson was devoted to weaving and painting in his spare time. "We had drinks or dinner at his house in Albuquerque quite often," says Ted, "and as soon as he got home, he would start weaving because most of the time he was angry at what had happened during the day, and he'd found that the way to relax was to weave as fast and furiously as he could." Mixson bent some regulations but adhered rigidly to others. Carroll Walsh once found a plastic bottle shaped like the still-secret 4,000-ton design. "I thought, holy smoke, there's the Orion! So I just sat it on my desk and never made any comments about it or anything like that," says Walsh. "And one time Mixson came here and saw that thing and had a fit! 'Oh! You, with a Q clearance! Wow! How *could* you do that?' And he took it home with him! He probably still has it, the hound dog!"

Mixson intermediated between the physicists in La Jolla who saw Orion as a way to visit Mars and the generals in Washington who saw Orion as a way to counter the Soviets on Earth. "Mixson was the point man on application, with Strategic Air Command and Air Research and Development Command," explains Don Prickett. "He was a tireless worker and stayed very close to SAC in terms of future system concepts." One of them was the deployment of an Orion fleet. *Military*

Implications of the Orion Vehicle appeared in July 1959 and was, according to a declassified Air Force summary, "largely the work of Mixson, aided by Dr. Taylor, Dr. Dyson, Dr. D. J. Peery, Major Lew Allen, Captain Jasper Welch, and First Lieutenant William Whittaker. The study examined the possibilities of establishing military aerospace forces with ORION ships and these were conceived as: (1) a low altitude force (2-hour, 1,000-mile orbits), (2) a moderate altitude force (24-hour orbits), and (3) a deep space force (the moon and beyond). The report recommended that the Air Force establish a requirement for the ORION vehicle in order to prevent the 'disastrous consequences' of an enemy first."

Mixson gave four separate briefings on military applications of Orion, over just three days in July 1959: "7 July: Briefing to ARDC staff personnel—about 20 people and a private meeting with General Davis. 8 July: Briefing to USAF Air Staff—about 50 people. 9 July: Briefing to Gen. Demler and his immediate staff. Briefing to AFCIN, about 25 people from Directorate of Targets, etc. They will poke around in USSR for indications that USSR is working on this." No evidence of a Soviet Orion program turned up, but this did not dampen the enthusiasm of the Strategic Air Command. General Thomas S. Power, who had succeeded Curtis LeMay as SAC's commander in chief, initiated USAF QOR's (Qualitative Operational Requirements) for a "Strategic Aerospace Vehicle," a "Strategic Earth Orbital Base," and a "Strategic Space Command Post" with Orion in mind. Don Prickett flew out to General Atomic with Mixson for a briefing with General Power. "It was a wide-open discussion on potential and what we were going to do with it when we got it," says Prickett. "And Power of course didn't have any problem knowing what to do with it."

By 1960, the world's nuclear stockpile was estimated by John F. Kennedy at 30 million kilotons, whose primary mission was to deter a first-strike attack. Orion offered an alternative to keeping all this firepower—some ten thousand times the total expended in World War II—on hair-trigger alert. Mixson's original study has yet to be declassified, but a later, anonymous General Atomic report on potential military applications of Orion appears to incorporate his description of the Orion Deep Space Force:

Once a space ship is deployed in orbit it would remain there for the duration of its effective lifetime, say 15 to 20 years. Crews would be trained on the ground and deployed alternately, similar to the Blue and Gold team concept used for the Polaris submarines. A crew of 20 to 30 would be accommodated in each ship. An Earth-like shirt sleeve environment with artificial gravity systems together with ample sleeping accommodations and exercise and recreation equipment would be provided in the space ship. Minor fabrication as well as limited module repair facilities would be provided on board.

On the order of 20 space ships would be deployed on a long-term basis. By deploying them in individual orbits in deep space, maximum security and warning can be obtained. At these altitudes, an enemy attack would require a day or more from launch to engagement. Assuming an enemy would find it necessary to attempt destruction of this force simultaneously with an attack on planetary targets, initiation of an attack against the deep space force would provide the United States with a relatively long early warning of an impending attack against its planetary forces. Furthermore, with the relatively long transit time for attacking systems, the space ships could take evasive action, employ decoys, or launch anti-missile weapons, providing a high degree of invulnerability of the retaliatory force.

Each space ship would constitute a self-sufficient deep space base, provided with the means of defending itself, carrying out an assigned strike or strikes, assessing damage to the targets, and retargeting and restriking as appropriate. The space ship can deorbit and depart on a hyperbolic earth encounter trajectory. At the appropriate time the weapons can be ejected from the space ship with only minimum total impulse required to provide individual guidance. After ejection and separation of weapons, the space ship can maneuver to clear the earth and return for damage assessment and possible restrikes, or continue its flight back to its station in deep space.

By placing the system on maneuvers, it would be possible to clearly indicate the United States' capability of retaliation without

Committing the force to offensive action. In fact, because of its remote station, the force would require on the order of 10 hours to carry out a strike, thereby providing a valid argument that such a force is useful as a retaliatory force only. This also provides insurance against an accidental attack which could not be recalled.

"Such a capability, if fully exploited, might remove a substantial portion of the sphere of direct military activity away from inhabited areas of the opposing countries in much the same manner that seapower has," another General Atomic study concluded, echoing the argument that had struck such a responsive chord at SAC. Mixson, according to Freeman Dyson, "had read Admiral Alfred T. Mahan's classic work, *The Influence of Sea Power upon the French Revolution and Empire,* and his imagination had been fired by Mahan's famous description of the British navy in the years of the Napoleonic Wars: 'Those far distant, storm-beaten ships, upon which the Grand Army never looked, stood between it and the dominion of the world.'" Lew Allen, later chief of staff of the Air Force, remembers Mixson's Deep Space Force as "a very imaginative battle group in the sky idea, with these things running around," and admits that "somewhere in there I began to think we were losing touch with reality." Was it crazy to imagine stationing nuclear weapons 250,000 miles deep in space? Or is it crazier to keep them within minutes of their targets here on Earth?

"Orion would be more peaceful and probably less prone to going off half-cocked," says David Weiss, the aeronautical engineer and former test pilot who shared Mixson's enthusiasm for Deep Space Force. "We were looking at a multinational crew, the same sort of thing that's going on in NATO, and we would have had safeguards—a two- or three-key system in order to launch anything." The deterrent system we ended up with, instead, depended either on B-52 crews kept under constant alert, or on young men stationed underground in silos, or underwater in submarines, waiting, in the dark, for a coded signal telling them to launch. "At SAC, this was always the weak point," continues Weiss. "You were sitting there listening to your single side-band and it would come through either on a cell-call frequency, which is assigned to you, or on a

206

barrage broadcast, and it would tell you to open up your target packets."
There were about twenty minutes available to verify the extent of
an enemy attack—or false alarm—before launching an irrevocable
response. The threat was tangible. "I went to Vandenberg Air Force
Base with Brian Dunne," remembers Jerry Astl, "and they invited me to
go into the launching silo, with a Titan intercontinental missile sitting
there with three nuclear warheads on it, waiting for a launch code. We
went into the silo and could actually pet that damn sucker."

Instead of living underground like prairie dogs in North Dakota, or
incommunicado in submarines, the Blue and Gold Orion crews would
have spent their tours of duty on six-month rotation in orbits near the
Moon—listening to eight-track tapes, picking up television broadcasts,
and marking time by the sunrise progressing across the face of a distant
Earth. With one eye on deep space and the other eye on Chicago and
Semipalatinsk, the Orion fleet would have been ready not only to retal-
iate against the Soviet Union but to defend our planet, U.S. and U.S.S.R.
alike, against impact by interplanetary debris.

Once Orion ships were in deep space orbit, the outer planets would
be within easy reach. The temptation would have been impossible to
resist. "When you would go out privately with people in the Air Force,
here in La Jolla, and talk about what's Orion for, it was to explore space,
no question about that," says Ted. The '60s might not have become "the
sixties" had events unfolded as envisioned by Mixson and Prickett. The
'50s might have just kept on going, thanks to Deep Space Force.

20

Jackass Flats

"General Atomic has chosen to cling firmly to the concept of a manned ship," Lew Allen noted in October 1958. The thinking at the time was to launch from an armored barge out at sea, after some initial tests in an isolated area of the Nevada Test Site known as Jackass Flats. "The general idea was to have people on board all the time," Freeman remembers. "I think forty was the standard number. It was like a submarine, with three men for each job. There certainly would be tests involving a few bombs, maybe going up a couple of miles, but if you wanted a full-scale flight then you might as well go the whole way."

"We assumed it would be somewhere near La Jolla in the Pacific," Freeman answers, when asked about the location of the launch. "The bombs in the beginning were fairly low yield. The barge would have to be built like a battleship, but you want it to stay afloat." The ascent into orbit would be under automatic control, with no intermediate course to choose from, during those initial six to eight minutes, between straight up or aborting the flight. "The latest steering scheme for the full-scale vehicle," Second Lieutenant Ron Prater reported in April 1959, "is to place a chemical rocket at the very nose of the ship, mounted so that it will rotate to point in any direction perpendicular to the main axis of the ship."

Once Orion was out in space, its navigators would plot the ship's current position and calculate future maneuvers and course corrections in advance. "That's what you needed these forty guys for," explains Freeman. "They would have been using a sextant and working out the navigation on graph paper." Among the surviving Orion documents are hundreds of pages plotting optimum trajectories for high-thrust Earth orbit maneuvers, Mars visits, Jupiter and Saturn encounters, satellite rendezvous missions, and lunar colony support—all worked up by hand on light-green Keuffel & Esser graph paper. Orion would be steered by the stars.

In September 1959 it was decided to bring someone on board to start thinking about test flights, and that person was aeronautical engineer David Weiss. "They were looking for someone with a background in flight testing," he remembers. "And I was a little misled in that I believed Freddy de Hoffmann had a very short time scale. They were talking about flying it in two or three years. I've been into flight-test projects where, on an experimental airplane, we knew even three or four years ahead of time what it was going to look like, enough for them to start building simulators for us to fly. So, that's what I had looked forward to. Hopefully I would have flown the damned thing."

Weiss is a third-generation military pilot, born in 1929. "I lied about my age for the Air Force," he explains, "and wound up getting some B-29 experience in World War II." His uncle flew B-17s. His father, later a pilot for Luddington Airlines, trained in the U.S. Army Air Service under Billy Mitchell, who led an armada of nearly 1,500 airplanes in World War I. After the war Mitchell argued so vehemently for an independent Air Force that he was court-martialed for insubordination in 1925. David Weiss's grandfather had worked for the other side in 1918, flying giant *Riesenflugzeuge*, or R-planes, four-engine metal bombers that could carry up to 4,000 pounds of bombs. "They bombed Paris from just over 20,000 feet," says Weiss. "The Allies couldn't reach them in the fighters. They had electrically heated flying suits, and they had oxygen, but not enough, so that on the way in to the target, the bombardier had the oxygen and on the way back, the pilot had the oxygen because he had to land the airplane. They were bombing the Paris rail yard and doing it in a very civilized manner by calling the French over the telephone and telling them at what time they would arrive."

Weiss believed in Orion not only as a retaliatory deterrent, but as a boost-phase anti-ballistic missile shield. "You could park several of these ships in orbit," he says, "and from there, the propulsion and dynamics looked excellent, in terms of knocking things down. The atmosphere was working with you rather than against you, because you could see stuff coming up. You'd do it with depleted uranium rods, to just simply shred them, or use high explosives, and whatever didn't collide with an ascending ICBM would then hit the atmosphere and burn up. It really was a much better way to do ABM, there's no question about that."

After graduate school, Weiss took a job test-flying Convair B-36 bombers, the six-engine, propeller-driven monsters that served, briefly, as the means of delivering first-generation, 42,000-pound hydrogen bombs. Later retrofitted with an additional four jet engines, the B-36 had a wingspan 20 feet greater than a Boeing 747 and could cruise at 50,000 feet. "Some of the heavy takeoffs we did were at an unheard-of over 500,000 pounds—that's 250 tons, and starting to approach Orion size," he explains. "We did fifty-hour flights, which would take us 10,000 miles easily, and would have reached any target of interest at that time. Going out of a place like Thule that's a round-trip to almost anywhere— assuming Thule was there when you got back." Weiss then taught air-craft and missile design at the University of Michigan, and in 1959 he followed his colleague David Peery to General Atomic. "Peery couldn't really describe Orion, but he said, 'It'll do for us in the space age what the B-36 is doing right now.' And that's what clinched it in terms of com-ing to San Diego," says Weiss.

Project Orion's plans, at the end of 1958, were to start off by launch-ing a 50-foot-high, dome-shaped, 50- to 100-ton unmanned "recover-able test vehicle," with a 40-foot-diameter pusher plate, propelled to an altitude of 125,000 feet by 100 to 200 explosions ranging from .003 to .5 kiloton in yield. An "orbital test vehicle" was to weigh 880 tons and would be 80 feet in diameter and 120 feet in height, propelled into a 300-mile orbit by 800 bombs of .03 to 3-kiloton yield. This trial-sized

Orion was still estimated to be capable of carrying 80 tons to Mars orbit with a 300-mile Earth-orbit return. By the end of the first year it was evident that the leap to 50- and 880-ton test vehicles was too ambitious and "a step by step progression to the full scale 4,000-ton vehicle" was in the works. The first step, as proposed to ARPA in the spring of 1959, would be "a small scale model with a pusher about 10 feet in diameter and the whole model weighing about 5 tons. The model would be taken up to high altitude by airplane or balloons in order to reduce drag effects where it would be released. Propulsion would be by a few high explosive shots culminating, perhaps, in 3 or 4 very small atomic shots." Plans called for launching this model by June 1960. The next step would be an unmanned 40-foot-diameter model weighing 400 tons, "which will carry a useful payload of 60 tons into orbit using 500 one-hundred-ton atomic shots." This was scheduled for completion early in 1962.

The first million dollars from ARPA was set to run out on May 30, 1959. "Ted Taylor and I will now spend a week doing battle for our project," Freeman wrote while flying from San Diego to Washington on April 26, 1959. "We shall see various potentates in the Air Force and the Government. They may (a) cut off the funds when our contract expires next month, (b) continue as we are with a gentle expansion, or (c) decree a major and rapid expansion. We shall argue for (c) and hope to get (b)."

They got (b). At the final briefing on April 30, 1959, AFSWC and General Atomic jointly requested an additional $5,600,000 to continue the project for another year. According to Mixson, this "reflected the high level of confidence and enthusiasm in the workability of the propulsion concept and a feeling of urgency that grew out of the dawning knowledge that this project was of great and immediate—if not decisive—importance to the nation's defense effort. The feeling was bolstered by the release to the press of the capabilities of the propulsion scheme, which suggested that if other nations were not already interested in this concept they soon would be." ARPA granted an additional $400,000 to sustain the project through September 14, 1959. During this period there was intense debate in Washington over how ARPA's space activities would be divided up, and to what extent Orion would play a role in space exploration and defense.

"The people in Washington sent down a committee of inquisitors to find out if our claims for this space-ship are technically sound," Freeman reported from La Jolla on July 4, 1959. "We spent a lot of time answering their questions and arguing with them. They seemed quite favorably impressed. But Washington will not make up its mind what to do about us until August." The political arguments remained unresolved. Committing the Air Force to a large manned space project would alienate both NASA, who had already been promised the Moon, and congressional critics looking for evidence of Pentagon excess. Yet there were equal political liabilities to committing NASA, should they accept custody of Orion, to a project involving so many bombs. There were good reasons for just letting the whole thing drop. Since Orion had friends in high places the project was kept on life support.

At the end of July, Lew Allen flew to Washington to argue in favor of Orion before the propulsion panel of the Air Force Scientific Advisory Board. "ARPA has about decided to proceed at $120k/month," he reported. One of the objections under consideration by the advisory board was that since Eisenhower had committed the United States, unilaterally, to a moratorium on all nuclear tests as of October 31, 1958, there was no point proceeding with Orion as long as the moratorium was in effect. "I believe this is a little shortsighted," countered Allen. "If we believed we would never use bombs there would be no point in proceeding with Putt-Putt at all. I'm sure that on some basis we will do limited, maybe peaceful, testing. We should proceed as if this were the case."

"Our space-ship project is going through a rough time," Freeman reported on August 14. "We have still not had our budget approved for next year, and there is a possibility we may get the axe." A compromise was reached that saved the project, but not by much. ARPA would support Orion at its current level, under the auspices of AFSWC, for another year, but during that time would transfer the project either to NASA or to the Air Force. Neither organization was enthusiastic about sponsoring the project on its own. "It was felt at command headquarters that the Air Force would not be unduly concerned if the project management passed from ARPA to NASA," notes the Air Force account compiled in 1964. For the Air Force to advance Orion beyond a feasibil-

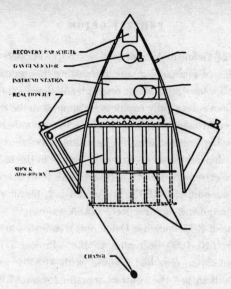

RECOVERY PARACHUTE
GAS GENERATOR
INSTRUMENTATION
REACTION JET

SHOCK
ABSORBERS

CHARGE

Twenty-ton test vehicle: 21 feet in diameter; 35 feet in height; number of charges, yield, and date unknown.

ity study, they would either have to come up with an unequivocal military requirement, enlist the cooperation of NASA, or both.

In late August 1959, ARPA granted another $1,000,000 to extend the original contract for a further twelve months. On September 23, 1959, Herbert York, now Eisenhower's Director of Defense Research and Engineering, a new top-level position with direct financial authority over some 80,000 individual projects, announced "a plan for the progressive and orderly transfer of space projects from the Advanced Research Projects Agency to the military departments." In a telegram to de Hoffmann and Ted Taylor, Art Rolander (former counsel to the AEC, who had acted against Oppenheimer during his security hearings in 1954, and was now General Atomic's vice president and Washington office manager) added that "this means that the Air Force now has the responsibility for 'Space.' Will explain Orion implications upon my return." Orion would go to the Air Force unless NASA could be persuaded to take the reins.

On January 29, 1960, York wrote to NASA headquarters seeking their assistance in disengaging Orion, in whole or in part, from the

Department of Defense. The answer was no. "Although the ORION propulsion device embraces a very interesting theoretical concept, it appears to suffer from such major research and development problems that it would not successfully compete for support in the context of our entire space experimentation program," NASA responded on February 10. "Among other uncertainties, the question of political approval for ever using such a device seems to weigh heavily in the balance against it. It would be extremely difficult to divert funds from nearer term projects for the support of ORION. We would not, therefore, favor any arrangement requiring such support." NASA was out.

ARPA Project 4977, known as Orion, was transferred to the Air Force effective March 10, 1960, becoming Air Force Project 3775. The good news was that Orion now had a home, with AFSWC as a directing agency rather than just the contract monitor for an ARPA feasibility study that was already in its second year. The bad news was that Orion was now removed from the mainstream of the national space exploration effort, with decreasing chances, despite continued technical recommendations at high levels, of ever getting the political go-ahead. "Orion had to either be adopted as the principal means of getting to the moon or else it wouldn't fly," Freeman explains. "It was either us or Wernher von Braun's big rockets. Once the decision was made to go ahead with the Apollo system and Saturn 5, then it meant we were out." The decision to favor Apollo over Orion was made long before Kennedy made his public announcement, on May 25, 1961, that the United States was going to land men on the Moon by the end of 1969.

The Air Force faced an increasingly difficult struggle to justify a role for the military in deep space. "When ARPA decided to turn it over to the Air Force then it became, effectively, a military project," says Freeman. "Although the Air Force was reasonable about it. They understood that it was really a fraud and they were supporting it for reasons they couldn't openly acknowledge. By law, the Air Force was not supposed to support anything except for military requirements and I couldn't see any military requirements for this that made any sense. Once it belonged to the Air Force you could never do what I wanted it to do. As soon as it grew big it would attract political attention and then it would be resisted because no one really wanted the Air Force to have a big new weapons system like that. That was the point at which I gave up my hopes that it would really take us to Saturn. When I left at the end of that year, the project was still going strong. But I think politically it had already failed by that time."

Back in La Jolla, progress was being made against the major technical problems: ablation, shock absorbers, pusher-plate engineering, and pulse-unit design. Thanks to formal and informal collaboration between General Atomic physicists and their colleagues at the AEC's weapons laboratories, smaller and more directional nuclear explosives were in the works. Numerical models continued to evolve, and, when the test moratorium was lifted, these codes were verified by the explosion of actual bombs. "We should think of Orion as paving its own way through the nuclear explosion test ban, rather than simply waiting for it to disappear," suggested Ted.

As bombs became smaller and their output better collimated, it became possible to contemplate smaller vehicles, so that even as expectations of full-scale funding diminished, hopes for a proof-of-principle test flight remained. "Confidence in the propulsion concept has risen so high that the initiation of a program leading to the construction and flight of a research vehicle is now warranted," AFSWC announced on April 1, 1960, proposing "a nuclear test vehicle capable of orbiting a 200-ton payload in the 1965–66 time period." The financial plan, expected to be endorsed by the Scientific Advisory Board, called for $4,800,000 for fiscal year '61 and $55,000,000 for fiscal year '62 and envisioned "placing the Research Test Vehicle in orbit by fiscal year '65." Mixson supplied the requisite military justification: "The successful completion of this project will satisfy some or all of the requirements of General Operational Requirement 173, An Advanced Strategic Space Weapon System; General Operational Requirement 156, Ballistic Missile Defense System; and such other GORs as pertain to the utilization of space systems for combat, reconnaissance, surveillance, communication, and navigation."

"The Air Force, from the chief of staff on down, were all charged up and ready to go at the end of the first year," remembers Ted. In the fall of 1960, Ted's optimism rose further with the hope that a new administration in Washington might take a more active approach to space.

"Marshall Rosenbluth reported that Kantrowitz, now on a committee advising Kennedy, reports the committee wants to establish a 1-A priority for Orion," Ted noted in his journal on November 7, 1960. "I fervently hope Kennedy wins tomorrow!" Kennedy did win, and in January 1961, Jerome Wiesner, chairman of the incoming president's Ad Hoc Committee on Space, issued a report. "We must encourage entirely new ideas which might lead to real breakthroughs," he advised. "One such idea is the Orion proposal to utilize a large number of small nuclear bombs." But by this time the foundations of the Apollo program were already in place. Mars and Saturn would have to wait.

The president-elect also commissioned a more detailed space policy study, reporting to General Bernard Schriever, commander of the Air Force Ballistic Missile Division, and organized by Air Force assistant secretary Trevor Gardner, who asked Ted to lead the group. The study, "which apparently has been specifically requested by Kennedy," was to occupy a full two months, Ted noted on November 15. "So, I'm caught between the devil and the deep blue sea—the worst time in the Orion project's history for me to be taking off for a couple of months on the one hand, and the possibly crucial importance of being in on the workings of this committee on the other."

Ted accepted the assignment, and succeeded in guiding the uniformly distinguished but otherwise disparate members of the Gardner Committee to a consensus calling for the Air Force to move boldly into space. "Economical space travel on an enormous scale seems to me to be a certainty before the end of the century," he noted privately. "What we're doing now with chemical rockets seems quantitatively analogous to flying cargo across the country in a Boeing 707, and throwing away the airplane at the end of the trip! I expect to see the day when a round-trip to the moon will cost less than an airplane trip around the world costs now."

The meetings began in Los Alamos on December 4, in temporary quarters provided by Norris Bradbury in a facility that had been built to house the new IBM supercomputer, due to arrive in March. After a week of preliminary discussions Ted reported that the group had set three major goals: "1) Establishment of a manned orbited space laboratory, probably via orbital rendezvous & assembly, using chemical rock-

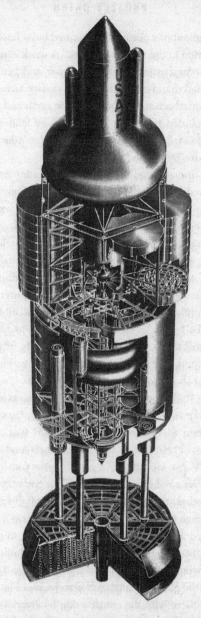

*U.S. Air Force military payload version of a 10-meter-diameter Orion
vehicle: pulse units are stored in individual helical magazines.*

ets; 2) Establishment of a permanent manned lunar base; 3) Carry out a manned expedition to the surface of Mars." A week later he was able to add that "Bruno Augenstein, Keith Brueckner, and I came up with the notion of a manned round-trip to the moon's surface, using Atlas-Centaur, and rendezvousing both in orbit around the earth and in orbit around the moon. Concluded that three men could be landed and return to earth orbit in a 5,000 lb. final wt. vehicle, using ten Atlas Centaurs in all. Could this be done by the end of 1964??"

After "much discussion of military vs. nonmilitary aspects of space," the group reached a "general conclusion that a dividing line really does not exist." By the end of January, when the group was writing up its final report, Ted noted that "we are certainly all agreed now that the Air Force should go all out for man in space." In conjunction with the Los Alamos working group, Gardner invited a supplemental advisory group (of "face cards," as he called them) to meet in Washington, where Ted presented a summary of the envisioned space program for review. "Charles Lindbergh was on that committee, he had all the clearances," remembers Ted. "I took an instant strong liking to him—the famous boyish grin is still there, though he is in his early fifties. He seemed intensely interested, particularly in the possibilities for manned space travel. We talked about how Orion worked and how it was an important part of the space study committee findings that Orion should go, for half an hour or an hour in several walks around the Pentagon, mostly on the third floor." When the committee's final report was issued and presented in a series of briefings in Washington at the end of March, it was well received. "We've kicked a field goal," Trevor Gardner told Ted.

"The consensus among the members of the committee was to go for this several-hundred-million-dollar proof test of Orion," Ted recalls. "That didn't change the course of anything, but it was a real high point, because it looked as though the project was going to go. We had this prestigious Air Force committee recommending building Orion and opening up the whole solar system. We would manage it from San Diego and at that time the plan was to take off from Jackass Flats. The assembly would be down there with the construction by a variety of contractors. That was the peak of my expectations of actually participating."

A list of 105 individuals, with security clearances, who attended a Project Orion briefing at the Air Force Ballistic Missile Division in Los Angeles reveals the contractors who were standing by. There were four representatives from Boeing, five from Convair, six from Firestone, four from Hughes, four from McDonnell, three from Lockheed, three from Martin, five from Northrop, twelve from North American Aviation, and six from Norair. Things would have been hopping at Jackass Flats. "We were trying to shift the scale of effort and build things, in particular what we called the twenty-ton flying model, an actual model of the whole thing, and fly that up through the atmosphere, with very small nuclear explosions, after ground testing with high explosive," explains Ted. "The idea was that we could mock up the mechanical effects by detonating sheet high explosive of the right type and density and thickness to get any kind of a pulse that we wanted, with the shock-absorber system upside down on the ground.

"We had designs with maybe a hundred explosions, basically a scaled-up version of the Putt-Putt. We'd then use shaped high explosive charges, so the pulses would be stretched out. We would know that it could take the initial shocks, but then would it take the momentum transfer? All the way to the top, repeatedly, and would it fly? The delivery systems for the explosives and so on, of that twenty-ton model, became a sharp focus, the next thing we'd do. We were planning to do that the next year, but that got to be pretty big money, probably ten million dollars a year."

"The whole time between 1960 and 1964, this thing was coming along well," remembers Don Prickett. "The theoretical work was paying off and you got to the point where you had a little test program that sort of gets you interested. But the scale-up, the money it took to go beyond that, was an order of magnitude more. We could have done some more engineering and theoretical work at a slower pace. But we all felt it was time to make a step forward in the engineering end, and that was to go to bigger models. That's a lot more money, and you need another test base somewhere. Jackass Flats gave us security and avoided the press."

Jackass Flats, designated Area 25 of the Nevada Test Site, lies seventy-five miles northwest of Las Vegas, over the Funeral Mountains and across the Amargosa Desert from Death Valley, between Yucca Mountain and Yucca Flat. "They did a lot of strange things in Nevada," says Bud Pyatt. Some of the strangest things were done at Jackass Flats. It was the site for a series of open-core reactors (named Kiwi, after the flightless bird) that were tested for application to nuclear-powered rockets, with one million gallons of liquid hydrogen propellant stored on site. Larger Orion tests would probably have had to move to the South Pacific, but Jackass Flats, only 300 miles from La Jolla, was the perfect place to start things off. "I get very excited right now just thinking about that thing being out there and flying it," says Ted. "Not because it was nuclear, but because we would then want to go nuclear in flight-testing the real thing, that is, the 4,000-ton vehicle scaled down to a couple of hundred tons."

By late 1961 bomb design had improved to where the propellant could be collimated within a cone of 22.5 degrees, allowing a standoff distance of 75 feet for a 200-ton ship with a pusher-plate diameter of 30 feet. Some 800 pulse units weighing 220 pounds each would deliver a 44 ft/sec kick every three-quarters of a second, for an acceleration of about 2 g. This test vehicle would have been unmanned, so Dave Weiss would still have had to wait for a chance at a first flight. He did, however, plot Orion's course. In addition to engineering studies such as *ORION Charge-Propellant Fire Control*, he produced a series of mission studies such as *Maneuvering Technique for Changing the Plane of Circular Orbits with Minimum Fuel Expenditure; Computation Techniques for Fast Transit Earth-Mars Trips; A General Discussion of Earth-Mars Interplanetary Round-Trips; Arrested Rendezvous, a New Concept;* and *Comments on Use of Lunar or Planetary Material for ORION Propellant.* "NASA was very jealous about the idea of these round-trips to Mars," he says.

Weiss also did the predesign and weapons configuration on a large scale model of Orion, constructed at the request of SAC, that was presented by General Thomas Power to President Kennedy at Vandenberg Air Force Base in early 1962. This model—"Corvette sized," according to Weiss—was built by a subcontractor in San Diego at a cost of $75,000 and appeared only briefly at General Atomic before being packed up for shipment to Vandenberg late one Friday night. "We suddenly got word that the government wanted this thing up in Vandenberg," remembers

Ted. Some remember the model as "bristling with bombs," others that it was equipped with 5-inch guns. The cutaway exposed the command centers and quarters for the crew—"Big enough so that at least one person, I think maybe a couple, were inside the model when Kennedy was there," says Ted. "It was an interesting model," says Weiss. "We had warheads of various caliber. I pretty well standardized on something around twenty-five megatons; we had a bunch of them, enough to make it suicidal for anybody to even contemplate going after either the Orion or simply doing a first strike on the United States. We also had Casabas shown on the model—something Kennedy had never heard of.

"We designed a reentry vehicle to go along with the thing, and these are the vehicles that we had in the scale model," Weiss explains, referring to a number of auxiliary space-shuttle-like landing craft. "And Kennedy was impressed with them; they'd hold about as many people as he'd ever put on a PT boat." Here at least was something on a scale that Kennedy could relate to; by most accounts the scale of Battleship Orion left him questioning the sanity of the project and certainly did not win his support. "We were looking at the scale model—and this was when Kennedy was there—just simply discussing how powerful it could be," remembers Weiss. "And I said, 'Well, it would take out every Russian city over the population of 200,000 if we wanted to build the next larger model. We'd have enough weapons to do that.'" According to Ted, "Kennedy was shown a model of Orion that had 500 Minuteman-style warheads on it, and the means for propelling them out with directional explosives. He was absolutely appalled that that was going on, had no use for it. So not everybody greeted the project with enthusiasm. They did when it was presented as a way of exploring space and mostly were very disapproving when it was presented as a space battleship or anything like that."

The model disappeared from sight. Doug Fouquet, who had served as General Curtis LeMay's public information officer at the Strategic Air Command from 1953 to 1955 before becoming public relations director at General Atomic, says that "it had a lot of compartments, it was like the *Enterprise* on *Star Trek*." He remembers it being flown up to SAC headquarters "in the hold of a C-97" and that de Hoffmann requested him to accompany it but he turned the assignment down. Weiss, who last saw it "up in Vannieland" thinks "it's probably sealed up in a box in one of these salt mines that they keep stuff in. God only knows where, it could even be at SAC." He remembers that in 1967, just before he left General Atomic, "some people came and talked to some of the Orion people; they talked to me, and they knew about the model. And I asked one of them, 'Do you know where it is?' He answered, 'If I knew, I couldn't even tell you.'"

The delivery of that model to SAC headquarters may have been Orion's final flight. "Although I'd love the first flight bonus, the whole thing was a moot point," Weiss now admits about the dreams of forty years ago to be aboard Orion when it launched. "Unlike an airplane, the Orion vehicle would have the glide ratio of a rock and must either reach orbit or be 'splashed' or 'smashed' as safely as possible. Unless a pilot could uniquely operate or save the vehicle better than any on-board triple-redundant flight management system, he has no business being aboard. The worst experimental accidents seem to often be accompanied by having more than the minimum human crew complement aboard. The time to introduce observers and/or flight crew is after Orion is in orbit and after the space worthiness of the vehicle has been determined and deemed adequate for its next mission by inspection and repair. Needless to say, many in the military do not agree with an unmanned launch; and particularly that the first people to board it in orbit should be engineers!"

21

Fallout

"How bad was it to take off, say, from the Nevada Test Site?" asks Ted. "We actually took a couple trips out there, to Jackass Flats. We didn't have to go there, I suppose. But it was exhilarating to imagine watching this thing take off, starting with very low yields because of the air, then gradually building up from like twenty tons per explosion up to a kiloton when there was no atmosphere, and more. To get out of the atmosphere it was a small number, like a hundred. A hundred nuclear explosions is not a small number, but these were very small. We kept pointing out that flying Orion through the atmosphere from the ground involved much less yield of stuff in the atmosphere than we'd already done with nuclear tests, setting off huge fission energy–release two-stage bombs."

By 1958, worldwide atmospheric testing was approaching 100 megatons per year. Tests were being conducted on the ground, in the air, underwater, and, at Bikini and Eniwetok, aboard barges, since if tests on low coral islands were continued there might not be enough of them left to constitute an atoll when testing stopped. Bombs were being placed at the tops of towers, dropped from aircraft, shot from guns, lofted by balloons, and launched into space by rockets. "In those days they were really fooling around," says Freeman. "It was just like a fireworks show, you could shoot up almost anything you wanted!" The Eisenhower-Khrushchev moratorium, announced on August 22, 1958, lasted from October 31, 1958 to September 1, 1961. There was a flurry of activity at Livermore and Los Alamos, and a flurry of radioactivity in Nevada, just before the testing stopped. "I came back at one A.M. this morning from a week at Livermore where they make bombs," Freeman reported from La Jolla on October 31, 1958. "The days I was there were the last days before the test ban went into effect, and they were throwing together everything they possibly could to give it a try before the guillotine came down. There are so many wild ideas and enthusiastic people at this place, I almost felt sorry to come back here at the end of the week."

Two weeks earlier, on October 13, 1958, a memorandum of understanding had been signed between the Air Force Special Weapons Center, represented by its contractor General Atomic, and the Atomic Energy Commission, represented by the University of California Radiation Laboratory, formalizing the state of cooperation between La Jolla and Livermore "in laying plans for small subsurface, surface, or high altitude tests, and particularly, for the work on 'clean,' small atomic devices." It was no accident that this agreement was signed just as testing was coming to a halt. Orion supporters were lobbying the State Department for an exemption for underground tests of up to 1 kiloton and extra-atmospheric tests of up to 50 kilotons—an exemption that would have allowed both Orion and some of the wild ideas under development at Livermore to go ahead.

After the moratorium went into effect—with no exemptions—the weaponeers kept designing bombs. And the Orioneers kept making plans for a nuclear test to determine whether the ablation problem was as tractable as they thought. They had hoped to send a small bomb and a small pusher plate up into space (but not into orbit) by rocket, detonate the bomb, and recover the plate by parachute; now, instead, they made plans for a contained, low-yield explosion, either in an evacuated underground cavity or in a specially constructed vacuum tank. Would a sample pusher plate, and the associated numerical models, hold up?

"This was the reality check," says Freeman. "If anybody was serious about this, then you would have to do this underground test.

"The idea was we would be allowed one test shot and if that turned out well we might get a go-ahead. It was designed to be more or less contained so that you could get in there and study the debris afterward. The main point was to reduce the pressure very fast. You have an excavated cavity in the ground, with your pusher plate on one side and the bomb on the other with a vacuum in between. So you'd throw the debris at the plate, but the problem is you would get a very high pressure in the cavity and that would destroy everything. But if you could get the pressure after the explosion and the first rebound from the surface down in a few milliseconds, then the cavern could survive. So I designed a scheme where you had a huge number of balls of charcoal suspended in the chamber. They occupied a fairly small part of the volume so they wouldn't interfere much with the blast wave but as a result of the blast wave they would disintegrate and spread soot all over the chamber, which would absorb the radiation very fast.

"It was clearly not good for high-yield tests, but up to something like one hundred tons it could have worked," says Freeman, who remembers driving to Albuquerque with Ted to talk to the Air Force and AEC about conducting the test in an aboveground vacuum tank. "It was within the range we were interested in. You had a pressure of something like one thousand atmospheres, which could have blown the thing completely apart, if it wasn't immediately reduced. You filled up the whole space with charcoal dust and that soaked up the energy in about a millisecond. It would have been a nice toy to play with. The weight of the carbon was several hundred tons." According to Freeman the idea was never used, but Bud Pyatt, who remained active in the United States testing program, says, "No, it was. It was a very hush-hush test, in Nevada. It was called 'Diamond Dust.'"

After all the megatons that had been detonated in the open, it would seem that a small, contained Orion test could be conducted without raising environmental or political obstacles, and that it should be easy to distinguish between a constructive project like Orion and the business of developing more destructive bombs. There were, however, at least three military implications inherent to the proposed Orion tests.

First, the question of decoupling: whether small nuclear explosions can be decoupled from their characteristic seismic signal, making them difficult to detect. The prospects for a permanent test ban, then under intense debate, depended largely on whether such a ban could be enforced. Hans Bethe argued that it could, Edward Teller that it could not. "The public is on the side of Bethe, the facts on the side of Teller," Freeman wrote. "I have been very much in the middle of this fight." Avoiding the technicalities, he announced to the readers of *Foreign Affairs* that it would be possible "to build a building, looking externally like a normal industrial structure, within which kiloton explosions can be contained. One may envisage a weapon testing facility bearing on the outside the inscription 'Kazakhstan Consolidated Steel Mills' and carrying on a legitimate business of steel fabrication as a side line." The requisite hundreds of tons of charcoal could be delivered without raising any alarms.

Second, testing the effects of nuclear explosions on protected and unprotected surfaces in a vacuum would have implications for the design of anti-missile and anti-satellite weapons, and for understanding how to defend against such attacks. Third, the underlying concept of directed-energy explosions, a key element of any Orion test, had inescapable military consequences in that directed-energy devices are the *only* kind of nuclear weapons useful in close combat, since they can be directed *away* from one's own forces. These were significant questions in 1959. ARPA's initial survey of anti-missile technology concluded that "the advantages of the directed nuclear explosion are: (1) the greater lethal range, and (2) the capability of directing the explosion products so as to give some protection to friendly elements which may be nearby and which would not survive an isotropic explosion of the same yield." No matter how peaceful its intentions, Orion was inextricably linked to the development of weapons. Bomb tests could be decoupled, but Orion could not.

In July 1959, Freeman, Ted, and Brian Dunne made a visit to Jackass Flats, where, as Freeman explains, "we hoped to carry out our first crucial demonstration of feasibility with a real bomb." Although they were in Nevada to make plans for a single explosion, underground, it was impossible to stand there in the empty desert without imagining Orion's full-scale launch. "Only once in my life have I experienced absolute silence," says Freeman. "That was Jackass Flats under the midday sun. It is a soul-shattering silence. You hold your breath and hear absolutely nothing. There in the white, flat silence I began for the first time to feel a slight sense of shame for what we were proposing to do. Did we really intend to invade this silence with our trucks and bulldozers, and after a few years leave it a radioactive junkyard? The first shadow of a doubt about the rightness of Orion came into my mind."

The shadow of atmospheric fallout had loomed over Orion from the start. "World-wide contamination and contamination of launch site" was subheading #10 under "Task 5, Overall design integration" in the original ARPA contract. Although two months later it was noted that "no thought has been given to shielding, launching, or contamination yet," as soon as the basic characteristics of the ship and its propulsion charges were approximated, estimates of the fallout from typical missions were made. These studies were deeply classified, since any specific discussion of fallout reveals technical details about the design of the bombs. For the sponsors of Orion, there was the added problem of revealing the huge *number* of bombs that would be involved.

Fallout had become a hot political topic in 1954, when the Castle Bravo shot at Bikini yielded more than 15 megatons instead of the predicted 6, severely irradiating a Japanese fishing boat, the *Lucky Dragon*, and contaminating the inhabitants of Rongelap and Utirik. Soviet tests had rained fission products on Japan, and strontium 90, with a half-life of twenty-eight years, was turning up in mother's milk and children's bones. Leaders, including Adlai Stevenson, Albert Schweitzer, Linus Pauling, the World Council of Churches, and even the pope, were calling for an end to atmospheric tests. "My mother liked Orion," says Ted. "But she didn't like the bombs."

Three broadly distinguishable forms of fallout would be produced by an Orion launch. First, radioactive material would be kicked up directly by any initial blasts near the ground. "In order to avoid contaminating surface areas and the atmosphere," it was suggested, in 1959, to use "high explosive shots to 400 or 500 feet after which small nuclear shots would be used for the rest of the atmosphere and aerospace." Second, fission products would be released directly into the atmosphere by the

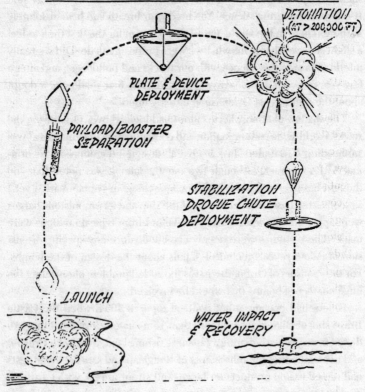

SPACE TEST SEQUENCE

DETONATION
(AT > 200,000 FT)

PLATE & DEVICE
DEPLOYMENT

PAYLOAD/BOOSTER
SEPARATION

STABILIZATION
DROGUE CHUTE
DEPLOYMENT

LAUNCH

WATER IMPACT
& RECOVERY

Proposal, ca. 1960, to launch a sectional pusher plate by rocket to an altitude of 200,000 feet, detonate a small nuclear charge, and recover the plate.

100 to 200 explosions it would take to get above the stratosphere, if not completely into space. Finally, there were the fission products produced once Orion was above the stratosphere, and, several hundred more explosions later, in orbit around Earth or making its departure for somewhere else.

Boosting Orion vehicles above the atmosphere with chemical rockets reduces the immediate fallout, and it was suggested that with later, hybrid versions of Orion the fallout problem had been solved. Space is a high-radiation environment, and there is no reason to fear that fission products that *stay* in space would do anyone any harm. Unfortunately for Orion, a significant fraction of fission products released anywhere in Earth's *magnetosphere*—not just within Earth's *atmosphere*—will slowly spiral in along magnetic field lines and eventually reach the ground.

This was demonstrated by a joint Los Alamos–Department of Defense test named Teak, yielding 3.8 megatons at an altitude of 250,000 feet above the South Pacific on August 1, 1958. "Teak, which we looked at very carefully, had tungsten in it, for reasons that you don't need to know," Freeman explains. "This tungsten was highly radioactive and essentially one hundred percent of it came down all over the earth over the course of many years. Very little gets away, because as long as anything is ionized it will be trapped in the magnetic field and only the neutral atoms escape. Most of the time the sunlight ionizes it and eventually it slides down the field lines into the atmosphere and comes down to the ground. The only way you could avoid this would be to launch over the North Pole where the field lines go straight out, and use very unsymmetrical bombs so you can be sure the debris is going outwards and not inwards. In that way you might be able to cut the contamination down to ten percent, but it was completely out of the question to get acceptably free from fallout this way. As far as the public is concerned ten percent is just as bad as a hundred percent."

The question for Orion, in 1959, was really two questions: how much fallout would be produced, and what would be its effects? "I remember working on the fallout problem as my main responsibility for some months," says Freeman, whose work is evidenced by at least one known (but still classified) report, *Radioactive Fallout from Bomb-Propelled Spaceships*, dated June 2, 1959. "We did very careful calculations, long before we had such good evidence as we have today. It's quite easy to do rough arithmetic. What you really need to know is in the case of very low doses how many rads you have to absorb on the average to kill one person. That's the important number.

"The official number at that time was 100,000. That was the official United Nations number, derived from the Hiroshima and Nagasaki statistics. It is now known that that was wrong, and in fact the correct number is more like 10,000. So it's a factor of ten worse than the U.N. said. But we knew that already, because some doctors in Glasgow had measured the effects on babies who had been exposed to X rays in the womb and they got much smaller numbers. In 1958 that evidence already existed, although the U.N. hadn't taken that into account. So we were more conservative than the U.N. and used the number 10,000, which is now more or less accepted as being right.

"At least half of the flight, assuming that we went to Mars or someplace, would be within the earth's magnetic field, so half of it would come down, and the total amount of fission products we produced were about a megaton, so we would be putting about half a megaton of fallout into the atmosphere. At that time both the United States and Russia were testing huge bombs in the atmosphere, something like a hundred megatons a year. We estimated we would be adding one percent to the existing bomb tests. Then the question is how many people were the existing bomb tests killing. That was hotly debated at that time.

"If you spread this radioactivity over the earth more or less uniformly and use this number of 10,000 person-rads per death it worked out something like a thousand people got killed every year by the existing bomb tests. This meant about ten people would be killed per mission from Orion. That was a number that I took very seriously. You were condemning something like ten people to death if you didn't do something to reduce the fallout. That to me was the real show-stopper.

"That's why I went to Livermore, because I thought we could make clean bombs. Unless the bombs were cleaned up drastically the thing really made no sense. But what I discovered when I went to Livermore was that this was more difficult than I had thought. What Livermore could do was something like a factor of ten. This was called the neutron bomb, producing neutrons without fission, and neutrons you could easily absorb. That would have meant killing one person per mission—on the edge of being acceptable considering that all these big projects kill people one way or another. From today's point of view, it's unacceptable. But in those times it wasn't so clear. I had thought we could make really clean bombs, down by at least another factor of ten. Fortunately, as it turned out later, none of the ideas that Livermore was considering worked. All the practical designs for Orion were based on ordinary fission bombs. And for me that was a fatal flaw."

Freeman left the project at the end of September 1959. The free-wheeling days of physicists doing engineering and engineers doing physics were over. "It was starting to become bureaucratic," he remembers. "There were about fifty people and that's too many to have this kind of unstructured activity." The days of designing bombs on the back of an envelope, then testing them six months later in the Nevada desert or out in the Pacific were also over, not just because of the moratorium, but because of the tremendous increases in costs and institutional bureaucracy standing in the way. For the next six years, Project Orion kept chasing after that first, critical nuclear test—which kept receding from its grasp. On several occasions the project either secured the funding for a test but not the permission, or the permission for a test but not the funding. They never secured both at the same time.

Ted and his colleagues at General Atomic remained close to their counterparts at Livermore and Los Alamos, but the prospect of an actual test program raised potential conflicts with the AEC weapons labs. "The concept for charge propulsion originated in the AEC Laboratories," it was noted during an Air Force briefing on the state of the project in February 1961. "The Scientific Group at General Atomic is composed primarily of former AEC Laboratory personnel who took to General Atomic the concept and much of the technology necessary to conduct the research program. The principal investigator, Dr. Taylor, has translated the basic idea into what appears to be a workable design, aided on an informal personal contact basis by AEC scientists at the Laboratories." Now that Orion appeared to be moving ahead toward spending real money and exploding real bombs, there was some grumbling at the AEC. "At least unofficially now they have the attitude that the charge propellant work being done at General Atomic is an infringement upon AEC responsibilities and seem to resent the General Atomic work in this area. This work is being conducted by some of the best AEC scientists hired by General Atomic." In July 1961 Don Prickett met with General Alvin R. Luedecke, general manager of the Atomic Energy Commission, attempting to smooth out some of the Orion-related issues between AFSWC and the AEC. According to Prickett, "He was more concerned, however, that General Atomic be kept out of the bomb design field."

Although the moratorium was still in effect, plans for testing were going ahead. "It wasn't clear during the moratorium whether we'd ever do testing again," says Harris Mayer, "but it's not that testing in itself is wrong, bad, or anything like that. There's nothing in nature that prevents you from doing very responsible tests. It's we who make the rules about this, not nature." The moratorium ended suddenly with some particularly irresponsible tests. "The Soviets burst forth with an astonishing forty-five shots in sixty-five days beginning on September 1, 1961," says John S. Foster, director of Livermore at the time. "Of these, fourteen were above a megaton, and one yielded sixty-three megatons." For Livermore and Los Alamos, it was now full speed ahead. There was a big push to test anything available, especially in the Pacific, and it looked as if Orion might be able to tag along. "We went back out to the Pacific for a sequence of tests, in '61," remember Bud Pyatt. "And we had the drawings, the equipment, everything was ready, to take a model out and do a test on Orion out there. We were all getting geared up and ready to go. I even had my bathing suit packed." At the last minute, permission for the Orion test was withdrawn.

From one fiscal year and one test series to another, the Orion test proposals kept hitting political obstacles or falling through bureaucratic cracks. In 1962 it was decided to move the proposed Orion tests from the Nevada Test Site to White Sands Missile Range, at Holloman Air Force Base in New Mexico, emphasizing that Orion was a propulsion system, not a weapon system, in the hope that the approaching test-ban treaty would contain provisions for nonweapons projects to still go ahead. "Dr. Kavanu and Dr. McMillan seem to favor Holloman to lend credibility to our argument that these are propulsion tests and not weapons tests," Don Prickett reported after a trip to Washington to meet with State Department and Defense Department officials in August 1962. "Mr. Foster, Admiral Parker, and their staff seemed very receptive to our rationale as to why any weapon test moratorium agreement should, if possible, permit continuation of our testing on the ORION Project. Foster's staff stated that Foster would be talking to the

President on the subject. So there is hope we may at long last get the top-level policy decision with respect to ORION and its relations to future moratorium agreements. If the United States disarmament paper reflects the stated feelings of the Disarmament Staff with respect to Project ORION we will have clearly established at the highest level of the Government that the project is propulsion and not nuclear weapons."

Hopes of exempting Orion from the test ban were short-lived. "I didn't want to have a test ban as long as there was a realistic hope of going off to Mars, but by that time it was clear it wasn't worth fighting for Orion if it cost us the test ban," says Freeman. "At the end I switched from being against the test ban to being for it." Freeman spent the summer of 1963 working for the Arms Control and Disarmament Agency in Washington while the final negotiations in Moscow were under way. "We were in the old State Department building on C Street, where you still had the feeling that it belonged to a generation of gentlemen diplomats. We had big windows looking straight out on the street, so anybody who just happened to look in the window could have seen all kinds of top-secret documents lying on our desks." Freeman worked under Frank Long, chief of the Science and Technology Bureau, who went to Moscow with Averell Harriman to negotiate the treaty. Kennedy was determined to reach an agreement, but left it to Long and Harriman to decide where to draw the line.

"Although most of the questions weren't scientific, it was the scientists who did most of the work, and ran the show to a surprising extent," Freeman explains. "The main subject we were talking about that summer was Plowshare, the other peaceful use of nuclear weapons. Sometimes the United States wanted to do it and the Russians didn't. And sometimes the Russians wanted to do it and we didn't. But that particular summer the United States wanted to do it, and the Russians did not. It was the stumbling block that was making it difficult to negotiate the treaty. The Russians insisted that peaceful explosions had to be included in the ban. The United States insisted that they shouldn't. And at that point, just by accident everybody else was away at the weekend and I happened to be there. And the question came back from Harriman through Long to Washington: 'Can the United States accept giving up on peaceful explosions?' I was alone in the office. I thought very hard: 'This is the

PRELIMINARY GROUND HAZARD ASSESSMENT
—OPERATIONAL FAILURE MODES—

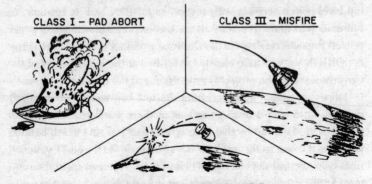

CLASS I – PAD ABORT

CLASS III – MISFIRE

CLASS II – FAILURE TO ORBIT

Possible launch hazards, ranging from Class III (a single dud charge reenters the atmosphere and falls to Earth intact) to a worst-case Class I (the entire ship, loaded with one thousand pulse units, falls into a launch-pad fire, 20,000 kg of high explosive detonates, and a certain amount of plutonium is dispersed).

death of Orion, and is it right or is it wrong?' And I said, 'Yes, sure we can.' The treaty went through, very fast, within a matter of days."

"Technically, one could rather easily have made a test ban that would still allow Orion to develop as a nonsecret project with international support and that's what we would have liked," says Freeman. "But politically it was just obviously absurd at that time." Ted, in contrast, did not concede that bomb-propelled spaceships were out. He argued that "the treaty is a web into which ORION has, circumstantially, become enmeshed, but which does not necessarily provide a permanent obstruction to its development," making the point that if the treaty was successful, it would lead to a climate of international cooperation in which a joint space project could go ahead, and if the treaty failed, then the arms race would be back with a vengeance and Orion should be pursued unilaterally by the United States. "Indeed, the international situation could well deteriorate to one wherein a degree of urgency in ORION development would be necessary," he wrote.

It was public antagonism to fallout, not the particular wording of the test-ban treaty, that brought Orion to a halt. All big projects kill people, but some deaths are more acceptable than others. In a large construction project, or a conventional space program, a few people will die by accident, but when they do, it is publicly evident who paid the price. Fallout diffuses too anonymously between cause and effect. Even if the risk is well below one death per mission, there will always be a thousand people to whom that slight increment in the statistics appears to be too great a price. The statistical background noise, instead of concealing the effects of a project like Orion, exaggerates them, since the tendency is to assume cause wherever there is even the remote possibility of effect. It makes little difference to what extent the fear is quantifiable or not. "Our Orion press release has been stalled by the Military Liaison Committee," complained Ted during one of the periods when funding had been secured and it looked as if things were moving ahead. "Specifically, General Loper objects to publicly describing something which generates fallout." The fallout problem meant that Orion could never compete openly for political support.

The last major gasp in the life of Project Orion was a 1963–1964 design, mission, and cost study performed by General Atomic for NASA, consolidating much of the earlier work on the 4,000-ton vehicles, and extrapolating downward to smaller, chemically boosted designs. Fallout receives two pages in the four-volume 725-page final report. Nine pages are devoted to crew compartment noise.

"Fission-product trappage in the atmosphere, from current pulse-unit designs, would result in radioactive fallout," the authors admit. "It is concluded that orbital start-up is an effective countermeasure to fallout for most missions. Each mission will have to be analyzed in more detail, however, in order to assign a quantitative figure to the penalty incurred." For a typical Earth-Mars mission, there is a rough estimate of fission products produced: "Pulse units for the 10-m vehicles generate a yield of approximately 1 kiloton per pulse. Earth-departure maneuvers for typical Mars missions (several hundred to over 1,000 pulses) result in total yields of some 0.5 to 1.2 megatons, producing a quantity of fission products that must be reckoned with." By limiting Orion engines to orbital start-up and recommending that "low-level nuclear-pulse operation should be restricted to regions of magnetic latitude 40° north or south," it was claimed that "trappage by the earth's magnetic fields of the fission products that do not intercept the earth's atmosphere can be reduced to the point of being almost negligible."

Freeman disagrees. "There's no way you could avoid the fallout coming down," he says. "I always felt it was more or less deliberate deception to pretend that chemical boosting could be a clean way of launching. The only advantage would have been to avoid the more immediate problems of the neighbors complaining about the noise." He criticizes the GA-NASA final report as "full of evasions and euphemisms—the kind of document that justifies the distrust of ordinary citizens against nuclear enterprises of all kinds. It never even mentions the question that any honest assessment must face: how many people would die of cancer from the Orion fallout? When I was working for the project, I spent much of my time calculating numbers of deaths. That was for me the most important question to be answered, and I tried hard to answer it honestly. No trace of my work appears in this document. Unfortunately, I do not know whether my estimates of numbers of deaths were even included in an official report. Most likely, the managers of the project made sure that my numbers never appeared in documents that outside critics might read, for the same reason that discussion of crew survival rates never appeared in any documents that we wrote at RAF Bomber Command during World War II."

Freeman's hopes for Orion had rested on the fact that "there seems to be no law of nature forbidding the construction of fission-free bombs." In 1964, when the GA-NASA study was published, its authors still clung to the belief that "improvements in the design of the nuclear devices (by reducing the fraction of total yield due to fission) might achieve reduction factors of 10^2 to 10^3." This belief in small, fission-free bombs has largely evaporated. It is now as remote as the 27-cents-a-gallon gasoline you could buy in La Jolla in 1959.

One exception is Ted. He remains convinced that small, clean bombs could propel Orion—but he still fears, more than ever, that such devices would be irresistible as weapons, until we outgrow the habit of war. "There are lots of different routes to that final result of a very, very clean bomb, but not pure fusion," he says. "The cleaner the better, down to a point where it really doesn't matter anymore. One can argue all day about what that limit is without shedding any light until one starts talking about very specific designs, and then it does matter a whole lot. Could you make one-kiloton explosions in which the fission yield was zero, which is bad news on the proliferation front, but could turn Orion into something quite clean? How clean a bomb can you make? The answer is it can be as clean as something not radioactive at all. Would that change everything? I don't know."

Freeman thinks Ted is wrong—and Ted hopes Freeman is right.

2 2

Huntsville

"Project Orion is now generating so much interest throughout the government that you can expect a continuous stream of visitors," Don Mixson warned Ted Taylor on June 19, 1959. "It is not the intent of the Air Force Special Weapons Center that such interest be discouraged. However, unless some control is exercised over visits, I believe your work will be seriously impaired." Visitors wishing to meet with Ted at General Atomic would have to obtain approval through Albuquerque first. Mixson made one exception: "the possible visit of Dr. von Braun."

German-born rocket pioneer Wernher Magnus Maximilian von Braun joined the three-year-old *Verein fur Raumschiffahrt* (VfR, Society for Spaceship Travel) as a student in 1930 at age eighteen. Founded on July 5, 1927, at the Goldnen Zepter (Golden Scepter) tavern in Breslau (now Wroclaw, Poland), the group's premise was that "out of small projects, large spacecraft can be developed which themselves can be ultimately developed by their pilots and sent to the stars." On July 23, 1930, the small band of amateurs, including von Braun, static-tested their first liquid-fueled rocket engine; it ran for 90 seconds, consuming 6 kg of liquid oxygen, 1 kg of gasoline, and producing 7 kg of thrust.

Von Braun's days as an amateur ended in the fall of 1932, when the German army became interested in his work. Under military sponsorship, he led the development of the V-2 rocket, some 5,000 of which were produced. Fueled with liquid oxygen and alcohol, the V-2 was 46 feet long, weighed 27,000 pounds, and developed 56,000 pounds of thrust. Nearly 4,000 of these missiles, delivering one-ton warheads, were fired during World War II, but, limited to conventional high explosives and inertial guidance, they did little damage in proportion to their cost. Toward the end of the war von Braun abandoned his headquarters at Peenemünde on the Baltic coast, retreating to the Bavarian mountains where he secreted the most important documents and dispersed his research group. He then surrendered to the Americans, assisting them in recovering fourteen tons of technical papers, 100 disassembled V-2 rockets, and 125 colleagues, who followed him to the United States. The rockets went to the Army's White Sands Proving Grounds in New Mexico and the scientists went to Fort Bliss in El Paso, Texas, where U.S. Army Ordnance provided the resources to resume designing rockets where the work in Germany had left off. The captured V-2s were launched between 1946 and 1951, their warheads replaced with a succession of instrument packages and second-stage space probes that gave the American space program a pre-*Sputnik* boost.

In June 1950 the U.S. Army Ordnance Missile Command, under the directorship of von Braun, moved from Texas to the vacant Redstone Arsenal and munitions factory in Huntsville, Alabama, selected partly for its proximity to the Atlantic Missile Range at Cape Canaveral, Florida, where the next generation of rockets could be launched. Von Braun's group produced a series of direct successors to the V-2, starting with the Redstone medium-range tactical missile and ending with the Apollo-boosting Saturn 5, whose first stage, burning for 2.5 minutes, consumed 28,000 pounds of liquid oxygen and kerosene per second, producing 7.5 million pounds of thrust.

After the U.S. Air Force separated from the Army in 1947, the Army justified staying in the missile business on the ground that missiles were a form of artillery, an argument that could be taken only so far. The problem for von Braun and his Huntsville colleagues, who wanted to build larger and larger rockets, was that Ted Taylor and his Los Alamos colleagues were building smaller and smaller bombs. The military now wanted *smaller* rockets—of little interest to von Braun. Atlas and Titan boosters, now able to deliver warheads more powerful than anyone knew what to do with, would instead be adapted to put Mercury and Gemini space capsules in peaceful orbits around the earth. The original Saturn booster program, initiated by ARPA in late summer of 1958, was transferred to NASA in 1959 from the Department of Defense. On July 1, 1960, von Braun's entire operation in Huntsville, known since 1956 as the Army Ballistic Missile Agency, was transferred to NASA, becoming the George C. Marshall Space Flight Center, or MSFC. The Moon was next.

Von Braun failed to show up in La Jolla, so on September 12, 1960, Ted went to Huntsville instead. "I am very curious to see what the reaction of the classical rocketeers will be," he wrote to Stan Ulam just before his trip. Von Braun was uninterested—at first. "When I began talking about the temperatures that were involved, and the reason for the small amount of ablation of the pusher plate, he literally went to sleep," remembers Ted. "Then I turned on the movie of that flight of the Putt-Putt and he woke up and became a strong supporter from that point on." The sight of the explosive-driven Orion model, blasting off from its launchpad at Point Loma, must have reminded von Braun of his own days spent at the VfR's *Raketenflugplatz* in 1932. The VfR's first few rockets had exploded by accident; the Orion model delivered a series of spectacular explosions by design. The Orioneers were amateurs with an idea that just might work—no crazier than mixing liquid oxygen and gasoline in 1931.

In November 1960 Ted met with von Braun during the Gardner Committee's space study meetings in Washington, but "he seemed less sharp than in Huntsville in September," according to Ted, "and the committee gave him a hard time. I have a feeling the spirit has been knocked out of the man by our government bureaucracy." Both NASA's organizational hierarchy and von Braun's chemical rockets were reaching maximum size. N-level bureaucracies, like N-stage rockets, suffer exponentially as N goes up. Saturn 5, weighing 6,000,000 pounds at launch, was barely able to get three people to the Moon and back. There were two ways to make it go farther: add another, much larger stage at the bottom, or put something different at the top.

To von Braun, Orion offered a way to extend the limits of chemical rockets. To Project Orion, von Braun's boosters offered a way to overcome the political and technical difficulties in launching Orion directly from the ground. Ted credits Frederick Ross with suggesting a boosted launch. "Sparked by Ross's comments," he noted on October 14, 1960, "I looked at what we could do using the Saturn booster, which makes it possible to scale a useful Orion down to a gross weight of 125 tons! This means 50 tons payload in a 300-mile orbit, 30 tons on the moon, over 20 tons back to a low orbit around the earth. Spent most of the evening estimating the neutron and X-ray heating for the 125-ton ship, and the shield weights required for a crew of about 8. The heating requires cooling the pusher, but is not outlandish. Got all excited imagining the following schedule: 2-ton model flying with high explosive in 1962, 20-ton model flight tested above the atmosphere by end of 1964, flight to the moon and back with 8 men in the 125-ton ship by the end of 1966."

A Saturn 5 can lift 100 tons into low Earth orbit, or about 400 tons to the edge of the sensible atmosphere at 300,000 feet. The eight-engine first-stage Nova booster envisioned as a step beyond the Saturn 5 could loft Orion vehicles weighing up to 2,000 tons, or even 4,000 tons using "Super-Nova" or Nova II. The Air Force predicted that a 4,000-ton Orion, lofted by a 3,765-ton chemical booster, could deliver 1,480 tons to a soft landing on the Moon—versus 240 tons for the envisioned 8,000-ton all-chemical Nova II.

"This way of going about Orion may bring the big chemical rocket 'lobby' behind us, and suddenly generate serious enthusiasm for the project almost everywhere," hoped Ted. Gaining the support of von Braun and the chemical rocketeers was not enough. Orion needed the approval of the nuclear propulsion community within NASA—already allied, in support of Rover, with the AEC. Rover, initiated in 1955 in an attempt to develop a nuclear-powered ICBM capable of delivering first-generation thermonuclear warheads, had the jump on Orion on three fronts: it was an established program already supported by the AEC; having lost its military justification it had already cultivated the NASA sponsorship required to stay alive; the technology, having nothing to do with bombs, was unclassified and familiar to conventional rocketeers. The operating principle—liquid hydrogen propellant is passed through

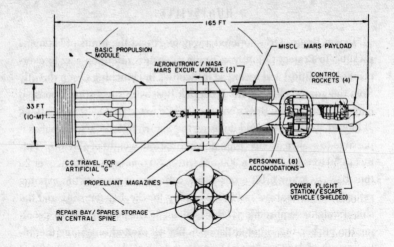

Mars exploration vehicle designed by General Atomic for NASA in 1963–64: the empty propulsion module, weighing 100 tons, would be boosted into orbit by a Saturn 5. Earth-orbit departure weight is 600 tons, with a destination payload of 80 tons—including two Mars Excursion Modules that weigh 32 tons each. Eight personnel and 2,782 kiloton-yield pulse units are carried for the 450-day trip.

the otherwise meltdown-hot core of a nuclear reactor—was easy to comprehend, even if problems such as radiation shielding and extreme temperatures were difficult to solve.

Orion's nemesis within NASA was Harold Finger, who became director of nuclear systems in 1958 and manager of the joint AEC-NASA Space Nuclear Propulsion Office in 1960. Finger believed Rover, not Orion, should be the first step toward post-Apollo visits to Mars and permanent bases on the Moon. "We need to walk before we run. And walking is Rover and Orion is running," he argued, according to Ted. Finger had joined the National Advisory Committee on Aeronautics (NACA) at age twenty in 1944, participating in its metamorphosis into NASA in 1958. His first assignment, at NACA's aircraft engine research lab in Cleveland, Ohio, had been testing captured German and Japanese turbochargers, leading him to jet engines and advanced propulsion concepts, including the prospects for nuclear propulsion in space. In May 1961, two weeks before Kennedy's Moon-landing speech, Finger gave a talk urging the United States to aim directly for Mars, since this would accelerate the development of nuclear propulsion and a visit to the Moon could be made part of the trip. In 1959 he was appointed NASA's representative on the advisory board to ARPA on Project Orion, drafting the statement declining ARPA's offer to transfer Orion to NASA, after which the project went to the Air Force instead.

"We went to General Atomic and had extensive briefings from Ted and others," remembers Finger. "My main position, frankly, was 'Gee, this is an interesting concept, but how do you go about *developing* this concept?' That was my main concern. Look, we're used to developing everything on the ground. How are we going to test it? I said I have no question that you guys know how to build the explosive device. But I do question the ablative capability of the pusher plate; it's got to withstand thousands of impacts. And then you have the shock-absorber system. You have to test it and you have to test it repetitively. How do we really go about developing this to the point that we can put it up on a Saturn 5— at the time we didn't have a Saturn 5—and have a reliable operation? That was my main concern, and to this day it still is."

After NASA declined Orion, the project kept resurfacing every year or two for review. On September 25, 26, and 27, 1961, there was an extensive series of meetings with NASA officials at General Atomic, chaired by Harold Finger, who took the position that the Air Force should continue the project but NASA should hold off on becoming involved. According to the Air Force, NASA's reviewers "agreed that 15 years and 10 billion dollars would represent optimistic estimates for the development effort," and were unwilling to support the project on any more modest middle ground. NASA's position was summed up at the end of 1961: "It is recommended that we do not pick up this project. The feasibility of such a device for use in vehicles is most marginal and it is possible that it never would be made to work. In addition, the project is most expensive and to continue the cost would be at the level of $2 million to $3 million a year." Don Prickett, who represented the Air Force during the discussions with NASA, strongly disagreed. "There are always two philosophies encountered during the research phase of new concepts," he argued. "One which says that if the concept has potential for a significant step forward it is worth a considerable effort to solve the problems even if this effort involves high risks. There is the other philosophy which approves only of research in which there are no real fundamental problems to be solved but rather improvement of established technology. What we need is more people working on novel ideas to solve some of the problems rather than viewing the problems as unsolvable."

General Atomic's estimated costs and development schedule appeared wildly optimistic by the standards of aerospace. "I used the word 'ship' rather than 'craft,' because the protagonists for this system talk in terms of heavy shipbuilding construction and assembly methods," Finger explained in describing Orion to a symposium on Mars exploration in June 1963. His chief concern was that Orion could not be tested on the ground, in the style of von Braun's static-test facility in Huntsville, or the Rover engine-test facility at Jackass Flats. "It is always proposed that the system will be developed in flight. I think this is nonsense. I know of no system which has been developed in flight." He also noted that NASA had yet to define any mission for Orion, beyond exploring Mars. "You have to build it and try it before you really know you could integrate the elements of the system. And then if we did it and got it working, what would we use it for?"

It was nuclear physicist James C. Nance who succeeded in enlisting NASA's support. Born in Arkansas in 1927, Nance came to General Atomic in 1960, after seven years as a project engineer on the Aircraft Nuclear Propulsion program at Convair aircraft in Forth Worth, where, as part of the flight-test crew for the Aircraft Shield Test Reactor, he was the first person to operate a nuclear reactor in the air. After three years as Ted's assistant, he became the manager of Project Orion in the fall of 1963, remaining at its helm until the end. "Ted and I had an informal agreement where he pushed AF/DOD and I pushed NASA, notably von Braun and MSFC," says Nance, who secured a small study contract from the Future Projects Office of the Marshall Space Flight Center in Huntsville, supporting about six people at General Atomic for six months. This contract, beginning in July 1963, was critical in demonstrating that Orion had NASA support—what the Air Force needed in order to continue its sponsorship without an immediate military requirement having been defined. The test ban was looming, and Orion's status as a

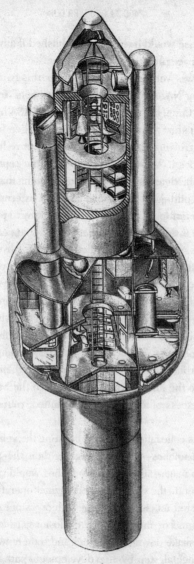

Crew quarters for the 10-meter Mars exploration vehicle, showing (at top) the navigation station, radiation-shielded propulsion control center, and storm cellar, with lateral passageways to the rest of the ship. The furnishings in the main crew quarters (widened section) would be used under artificial gravity during coast periods and appear upside down.

peaceful enterprise would have to be established if any exemption was to be made for space propulsion using bombs.

"Jim Nance was very good at going after things; it was really his doing that we got NASA to put money in," explains Ted. "Von Braun's interest was one thing, but getting money from NASA headquarters was a whole other matter." Nance kept the project alive for a further two years, although growing opposition to the project reduced his role, as Freeman describes it, to being "very good as the captain of a sinking ship." Nance lobbied persistently for Orion, arguing that nuclear energy was essential to post-Apollo missions and that external explosions are intrinsically superior to an internal reactor as a way to propel a ship. "An old analogy here is that of flicking a hot coal off a rug back into the fireplace (impulsive system)," he explained. "If done adroitly, the interaction time is insufficient to burn your finger. But if you pick it up and set it in the fireplace, it is a different story (steady-state system). Note that the same payload is carried through the same velocity increment in both cases." Rover is equivalent to holding the coal in one's hand while walking across the room. Orion is equivalent to skipping the coal across the rug. NASA got the point. "Vehicles utilizing such an engine and operating from earth orbit could typically deliver 45% of their gross weight as useful payload to the lunar surface, over 40% to the Mars surface, and could carry in excess of 25% in a fast, manned, round-trip to Mars," promised Nance.

Nance and his colleagues proposed boosting the vehicle into orbit in three separate launches—first the engine, then the payload section, finally the bomb magazines. Further launches would deliver a crew to assemble and operate the ship. "Manned engines operating from parking orbits can be tested much in the same fashion as ocean-going vessels, i.e., short runs (one or more nuclear explosions) to long complicated maneuvers can 'shake down' the engines and train crews." NASA could follow the incremental, step-by-step development path they were accustomed to, and Huntsville would have an excuse to keep launching Saturn or Nova boosters—constituting the bulk of the program's costs.

The NASA study—which never mentioned "bombs"—was performed in three stages. First, preliminary bounds were placed on vehicle performance and size. Second, engineering studies were conducted, resulting in a detailed conceptual design. Third, mission studies examined possible voyages, including the assignment of estimated operational costs. To supervise the mission studies NASA and General Atomic brought in one of Wernher von Braun's former Peenemünde colleagues, Krafft Ehricke, from the Atlas-Centaur program at Convair Astronautics. "The Atlas was a great success at that time and they wanted somebody with that sort of factual experience," explains Thomas Macken. Ehricke produced a detailed survey of the accessibility of the solar system to Orion, believing the age of space colonization was at hand. Macken remembers "one particular meeting when he talked about mining uranium on the Moon, and then you could take off from there to the end of the universe."

NASA started off thinking of a 1,000-ton ship, driven by 2-kiloton bombs. General Atomic had a five-year head start, with preliminary studies of a series of 4,000-ton, interplanetary-capable designs, as well as 20-ton, 200-ton, and 800-ton orbital test vehicles. Thanks to specialized computer codes, these existing designs could be readily adapted to NASA's requirements. In presenting the alternatives to NASA, General Atomic differentiated the possibilities into three operational modes (disregarding the original mode of taking off directly from the ground).

In Mode I, "the engine/vehicle combination, loaded to full gross weight, is lofted above the sensible atmosphere prior to pulse-engine startup." The Orion engine, with its shock absorbers fully compressed, is attached by explosive bolts allowing it to kick free from the expended booster before ejecting the first of its bombs. The bombs start firing at between 60 and 100 km altitude, which relaxes the demands of a surface launch, but still entails a high initial pulse rate and a risk of catastrophic failure in the event of missing even one or two shots. On the other hand, it relaxes the demand on the boosters, since a one-stage chemical booster is enough. "The chemical rocket systems planned to loft the nuclear pulse propelled vehicle above the atmosphere are called 'lofters,'" the General Atomic scientists explained to their NASA sponsors at an opening briefing in June 1963. "This terminology is intended to remind one of the less stringent operational requirements for such chemical rockets as compared to large space boosters."

In Mode II operation, the basic Orion engine, lofted just above the atmosphere as in Mode I, is then "self-boosted into orbit, but in an off-loaded or perhaps 'empty' condition. The payload and a full supply of propellant is then taken aboard in orbit." This relaxes the demands even further than Mode I, since the Orion engine carries only a brief series of bombs for its initial kick from the upper atmosphere into orbit. General Atomic proposed a 1,400-ton engine, with a 34-meter-diameter pusher plate for operational modes I and II. This required an enormous booster—of great interest to von Braun. "We had some great big boosters to get it out of the atmosphere and then start the nuclear business," says Hans Amtmann. "The moon rocket wasn't big enough."

In Mode III operation, the engine, propellant, and payload, "packaged in modules of approximately equal mass and diameter," and weighing "for example, one million pounds each," are boosted separately into orbit and assembled there. Much lower thrust is required, and pulse frequency is not critical when the Orion engine starts up. Standard launch modules could be assembled in different combinations to suit different mission plans. "For low-mission-velocity tasks, such as earth orbit–lunar orbit–earth orbit transportation, one or two propellant modules could be used with a large number of payload modules. For planetary missions, a large number of propellant modules could be used with one or two of payload." A 500-ton engine, "compatible with Nova-class boosters," was proposed for Mode III.

The study group assumed, as a baseline for comparisons, a payload of 500 tons would be sent to orbit Mars. Missions to land on the Moon or orbit Jupiter were considered in less detail. Halfway through the study, NASA requested that the size of the vehicles be scaled down, with the 500-ton ship becoming the large version, and most of the design effort being focused on a 100-ton engine that could be boosted into orbit by an off-the-shelf Saturn 5.

"NASA mission constraints on the propulsion system were far less demanding," the summary to General Atomic's final report explained. "Most of the significant results of this study concern a 10-m-diameter propulsion module, which is about half the size of the smallest module that has previously received serious design consideration, but which has very impressive (scaled) performance capability in the orbital start-up operational mode. Much of the credit for appreciating such a vehicle's capability goes to NASA for recognizing the logic and value in this size vehicle in spite of its poor propellant economics and comparatively degraded specific impulse." This was a tactful way of saying that what NASA was interested in was a watered-down version of Orion. Mars was in; Enceladus was out.

The 10-meter (33-foot) -diameter Orion vehicle underwent intense design, engineering, and mission studies over the next few months. A variety of configurations, all built around the same basic engine, were explored, assuming representative 450-day missions to Mars, including a 50-day stay. These missions ranged from an eight-man orbital exploration mission carrying only 1,650 pounds of destination payload, requiring an Earth-orbit departure weigh of 600 tons, to a twenty-man mission carrying a 330,000-pound destination payload, with an Earth-orbit departure weight of 1,200 tons. It would require four to nine Saturn launches to build up the basic vehicle in orbit, and for safety it was recommended that a convoy of at least two vehicles make the voyage at the same time. Small "space taxis" would allow transfers between separate ships. The pulse units, of nominal kiloton yield, would weigh 311 pounds and would be ejected at .86-second intervals, with 2,782 pulses required per trip. The vehicle would range between 160 and 204 feet in length depending on how many propellant magazines, with 900 pulse units in each layer, were loaded in revolving chambers around its central spine. The ships were long and slender, completely unlike the original dome-shaped vehicle imagined in 1958 and 1959.

Instead of spinning like a top, to provide artificial gravity around the circumference of the observation deck in the upper dome, the NASA vehicle would be tumbled end over end: "During prolonged coast periods, artificial gravity is attained by slow rotation (approximately 4 rpm) of the entire vehicle. Three spin-ups and spin-downs are provided during a typical exploration mission." The crew quarters and command station have two sets of furniture so that floor and ceiling can be interchanged: right-side up for use during acceleration periods, upside down for use during artificial gravity mode. Detailed drawings were made of every aspect of the ship, and aeronautical engineers like Thomas Macken, who began his career in 1934 working on wooden biplanes for Avery-Rowes in Manchester, now spent his time on details like shock-absorber

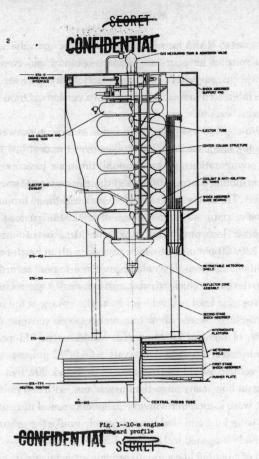

SECRET

CONFIDENTIAL

CONFIDENTIAL SECRET

Fig. 1--10-m engine
inboard profile

Details of 10-meter Orion engine designed under contract to NASA's Marshall Space Flight Center, 1964.

attachments, cooling fluid recirculation, crew-compartment shielding, and determining the extent of meteroid-protection required during an eighteen-month trip to Mars and back.

Smaller Orion vehicles, lacking the inherent radiation shielding of more massive designs, required the crew to take shelter in a shielded compartment during engine operation and in the event of solar storms. Conditions would be cramped. "For short duration missions (nominally about thirty days with an upper limit of ninety days) relatively crowded conditions are assumed satisfactory, including bunk sharing and acceleration couches only in the combined powered flight compartment/storm cellar," noted Walter Mooney in *Orion Personnel Accommodations,* issued in September 1963. "For longer missions (nominally 450 days, but from say 90 days to 1,000 days or beyond) more spacious conditions will be required; for example, it is felt there should be no bunk sharing and, desirably, private sleeping rooms should be provided each individual crewman. Special areas for eating, exercising, and entertainment will be desired for any long space missions." Gone were the luxurious accommodations Ted and Freeman had imagined in 1958. The smaller Orion engine required high-density, tungsten propellant, so the original plans to recycle crew waste into the bomb canisters as propellant no longer held. "For the longer missions complete water recovery including urine distillation may be desirable," it was acknowledged. NASA Orion crews would be flying coach.

The 10-meter vehicle could perform a bare-bones mission to Jupiter, but a 20-meter (65.6 feet) -diameter version, designed to be lofted by Nova-class boosters, was preferred. This would take a twenty-man crew and a 100,000-kg destination payload into orbit around Callisto, the second-largest moon of Jupiter, from where chemical-powered landings on Callisto and unmanned probes to the Jovian surface would be launched. Velocity increments for the mission, with return to Earth orbit, totaled 64,000 m/sec, and the voyage would take 910 days. Earth-orbit departure weight would be 6,000 tons, including 8,291 pulse units, each weighing 993 pounds.

Even this 20-meter ship was much reduced in size and performance from the original Orion designs. "The propulsion modules of this study are rather austere and inefficient in comparison with the apparent potential of nuclear-pulse propulsion," explained the authors of the final NASA report. In making their initial precontract briefing to NASA, the Orion group had explained that "there will also be a small effort applied to updating current data on a massive 'third generation' vehicle concept, and to approximate its feasible size limitations." This was envisioned as a vehicle capable of velocity increments totaling more than 300 km/sec, and "of a size to put it in the planetary colonization transport category." In the final report, only a few pages are devoted to these third-generation ships.

Two "advanced-version hypothetical vehicles" are described. "Vehicle A is assumed to have a specific impulse of 10,000 sec and a thrust of 10 million lbs.; B was assigned a specific impulse of 20,000 sec and a thrust of 40 million lbs. The additional ground rule was the assumption of a near-earth-surface initiation of nuclear-pulse operation." These 4,000- and 16,000-ton ships, capable of mission velocities of up to 500,000 ft/sec, are the last official trace of the ocean-liner-class Orion vehicles that Ted and Freeman were working on in 1959.

In the final report to NASA, potential problems were largely dismissed. A typical Mars mission would consume only 28 percent of the United States' annual production of plutonium, assuming the least-efficient conversion methods, and only .06 percent if breeder reactors went full speed ahead. Launch sites in Alaska and Australia were investigated, but it was concluded that Florida would be satisfactory, for a boost-to-orbit Saturn 5 start. Eye burn was manageable. "Since high-altitude nuclear explosions are visible from a large area of the earth's surface, there is reasonable probability that several individuals would be looking at the detonation points. We determined conservatively that at altitudes above about 90 km, the flux would not be sufficient to cause retinal burn to the unprotected eye." Fallout was believed to be adequately diminished by orbital start-up at higher magnetic latitudes, with a more serious hazard being a launch-pad explosion of a booster carrying a full load of bombs. The worst-case scenario assumed "that approximately 1,000 pulse units would fall in the fire and all the high explosive (20,000 kg) would detonate. Assuming current nuclear-device design practice, there would be *no* nuclear explosion or criticality event." There could be big trouble, however, even if the bombs did not explode. "A more serious problem would be the possible burning or vaporization of plutonium, which could produce a downwind inhalation hazard and ground-contamination hazard. If all of the plutonium available were vaporized in the form of an aerosol, a substantial down-range hazard might exist."

General Atomic estimated that a Mars mission, using Saturn-boosted, 10-meter Orion vehicles, could be conducted for something under $2 billion in development and direct operating costs. "Nuclear pulse clearly appears to be the most promising long-range advanced propulsion system which could be available in the middle eighties or sooner," Krafft Ehricke argued, introducing his 425-page analysis of interplanetary missions and their comparative expense. For typical Mars missions, the Saturn 5 launches were determined to make up over 60 percent of the direct operating costs.

Ted was convinced that the project was back on track for Mars. "ORION has crossed a major milestone, I believe, in getting some formal support from NASA," he wrote to Freeman on July 11, 1963. "This will be the first time since the summer of 1958 that we have had a clear charter for more than a few months." The test ban appeared imminent but not insurmountable, and when NASA's interest in Orion became public, Freeman sent congratulations to Ted. "The great thing that has happened to strengthen your position is the general realization, even among the public, that chemical rockets have nothing to offer beyond the trip to the moon," he wrote. "The effect of the treaty on Orion is likely to be quite healthy in the long run. It means the emphasis is automatically pushed away from military applications and toward long range exploring missions. It is just what we always wanted to do."

23

Death of a Project

NASA's support for Orion was short-lived. Huntsville remained enthusiastic, and Wernher von Braun even issued a white paper, *Nuclear Pulse Propulsion System—Its Potential Value to NASA*, which, although eventually leaked to the Air Force, was "withheld from general circulation for several months." But without support from Washington, Huntsville could do little else. "NASA headquarters is fighting any further support with a vigor which I think is way out of proportion to the low level of support which Huntsville is proposing," Ted reported to Freeman at the end of 1963. "Many people in NASA like to string everything out in a line, which makes it unthinkable to them that serious work should be started on ORION until after a nuclear rocket is carrying useful payloads around. Some officials even suggest that a good time for ORION might be about 1990!"

Ted regarded Project Orion's struggles as an example of Fermi's Law: "If you don't fail a good part of the time you're not doing your job." Orion succeeded in advancing science, but failed to advance against politics, because it pushed too many limits at once. "Orion had a unique ability to antagonize simultaneously the four most powerful sections of the Washington establishment," Freeman explained upon the death of the project in March 1965. "The remarkable thing is that, against such odds, with its future never assured for more than a few months at a time, the project survived as long as it did." Freeman held four groups of people responsible: the Defense Department, the heads of NASA, the promoters of the test-ban treaty, and the scientific community as a whole. Two other groups—the AEC and the general public—stood by at the execution, one of them unwilling and the other unable to help.

The Department of Defense—excepting the physicists at AFSWC, the adventurers at ARPA, and the deep space warriors at SAC—viewed Orion either as subverting bombs and dollars for nonmilitary purposes, or as the ultimate in expensive weapons systems removed from fighting real wars on the ground. NASA—excepting a minority at Huntsville—viewed Orion as a reckless leap beyond Apollo, an unaffordable competitor to Rover, and an unacceptable public relations risk because of the bombs. The test-ban establishment—excepting Hans Bethe—either ignored Orion completely or viewed it as a dangerous extension of the arms race, the promise of peaceful explosions in space a loophole best left closed. The scientific establishment had no reason to defend a project that was too deeply classified to openly advance science in space. The AEC, absent from Freeman's list of critics, supported Orion initially but then grew increasingly ambivalent about a bomb-driven project that did not belong to one of its own labs.

The public learned little about Orion until the project was at an end. "For reasons which I always find elusive, the Defense Department is very touchy about dissemination of Orion information to the public," pondered Ted in 1963. "I frankly think that this is because they are afraid of an upsurge of public support." Lew Allen remembers a flight from California to Washington, when "Ted got up and explained to the entire body of the airplane what this idea was, and asked would they think it was worth the money for them to have a dollar of their taxes a year go to funding this project, to see if they could really make it work to go to the planets. And needless to say, he got an overwhelming vote for it from the entire airplane."

The amount of money spent on Orion—$10.4 million over seven years, supplemented by about $1 million contributed by General Atomic during periods when outside funds were scarce—was trivial in proportion to the debate over its cost. The government's contributions were as follows (not including AFSWC's staff and logistical support): AEC—$5,000; ARPA—$2,325,000; AF/DOD—$8,070,000; NASA—$100,000. Even the much larger sums requested in hopes of advancing to nuclear tests and working models were modest by the standards of NASA, the AEC, or the Department of Defense. "When you look at some of the early budgets that were proposed for Orion, it's almost absurd," says Bruno Augenstein. "A few tens of millions of dollars? When you think of what was being spent on other programs at the time, many of which were not successful, it is fascinating."

At its peak, the project employed fifty people at General Atomic and was spending $150,000 a month. Throughout seven years of work, nothing turned up that conflicted fundamentally with the optimism of 1958. "The end result was a rather firm technical basis for believing that vehicles of this type could be developed, tested, and flown," Freeman claims. "The technical findings of the project have not been seriously challenged by anybody. Its major troubles have been, from the beginning, political. The level of scientific and engineering talent devoted to it was, for a classified project, unusually high." The endless succession of obstacles discouraged the scientists in La Jolla and frustrated the project officers in Albuquerque, who were impatient to move ahead. "Orion, in its current status within the DOD, is plagued primarily with non-technical or pseudo-technical problems (no military mission, large development costs, need for nuclear tests, difficult to flight test, etc., etc., ad infinitum)," complained Ron Prater, who had taken over after Don Mixson had been transferred to the Strategic Air Command. "The real technical problems are currently relatively well in hand."

Upon President Kennedy's inauguration in January 1961 there was a changing of the guard at the Pentagon, with Robert S. McNamara becoming secretary of defense. Much had changed since 1958. The initial shock over *Sputnik* had subsided and the clandestine arms and surveillance race, being fought with unmanned missiles and satellites, had been eclipsed by the public spectacle of manned space flight, which now belonged to NASA, not the Department of Defense. Orion was a relic of the Air Force's once-grand designs. "McNamara was against

PRINCIPAL MILESTONES

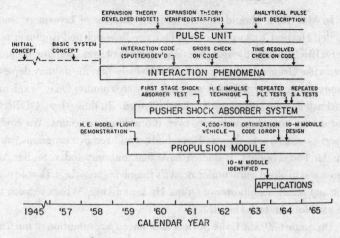

Project Orion milestones, 1957–1965, along five related theoretical and experimental design/development tracks.

these Air Force extravaganzas," explains Freeman. "He wanted the military to concentrate on doing down-to-earth things, fighting real wars rather than playing around with technical toys. He was always an enemy of the Air Force and a friend of the Army, more or less."

When Orion was transferred from ARPA to the Air Force, the contract, administered by the Research Directorate of the Physics Division at AFSWC, officially fell under the Ballistic Missile Division of the Air Research and Development Command. In April 1961 the Air Force was reorganized, with Orion going to the Space Systems Division of the newly created Air Force Systems Command. Orion was neither a satellite nor a missile, and whenever its budget rose above $2 million, the threshold requiring Department of Defense approval, it stood out like a sore thumb. AFSWC did its best to shelter Orion from its critics, but the project found itself in trouble every time it tried to grow. Whenever Orion officials asked for an amount like $30 million, the response was either that this was too much for a feasibility study, or too little for the development of anything in space. "Every time you push a number into the next column, it gets attention," says Ed Giller. "We had to either get on or get off the pot," adds Don Prickett, "and what they said was get off the pot."

In May 1961, Harold Brown, formerly director of Livermore, succeeded Herbert York as director of Defense Research and Engineering,
or DDR&E, where the real decisions about Pentagon spending on programs like Orion were being made. "In the early '60s, the military departments ran in a very different way than they are running today," explains
Augenstein, who served under Harold Brown. "In those days, DDR&E
had a very complete authority over the military programs. We could
insert programs into the Air Force budget and remove programs from
the Air Force budget. It doesn't have that authority today. So the Air
Force was in a real sense under Brown's thumb in those days. Harold was
not, as I recall, a supporter of Orion. He kept asking, 'What's it going to
be used for? And who needs it?'"

On August 30, 1961, the Soviets announced a resumption of nuclear
testing, and on September 1, 1961, they ended the thirty-four-month
moratorium with a 150-kiloton atmospheric test. Additional tests followed on September 4 and 5, prompting Kennedy (whose first reaction
was "unprintable") to announce that the United States would resume
testing as well. There was an intense, behind-the-scenes debate over
whether to set off as many bombs as quickly as possible, demonstrating
that the United States had not been caught off guard, or exercise
restraint. This was Orion's chance.

By the end of September Orion's project officers were ready with
plans for a series of seven nuclear tests, using 20-foot-diameter pusher
plates and low-yield, spherical-assembly bombs. Three tests would be
performed in vacuum tanks and four would be lofted by rocket to an
altitude of 200,000 feet. These plans generated considerable interest
within the AEC and Department of Defense, including preliminary
approval from Harold Brown, but no agreement over who would supply
the funds. By November 1961 Orion officials at AFSWC and General
Atomic had revised their proposals and were seeking $15 million in
emergency funding to conduct five tests that would be lifted by balloons
and two that would be exploded in underground tanks. Permission to
use White Sands Missile Range for the balloon shots had been obtained,
distinguishing the Orion experiments from the ongoing Nevada weapons
tests.

The amount of money was reasonable and the experiments well

thought out. The AEC was discovering that underground tunnels were expensive to dig, difficult to instrument, and prone to "containment" problems. Orion offered a plausible justification for testing at high altitude or in space, and the tests could help answer questions about X-ray ablation and high-altitude electromagnetic effects that were critical to warhead survival and missile defense. The Soviets had exploded fifty more bombs by the second week of November, and the hawks at SAC were pointing to Soviet duplicity about test preparations during the moratorium as justifying deployment of Orion as a show of force. Livermore and Los Alamos were prepared to supply the sub-kiloton devices, to be designated as propulsion tests, not weapons tests, keeping the door open should NASA change its mind. Everything was set to go.

Harold Brown, however, decided it was time to get Orion's nose out of the Defense Department tent. "On 28 December 1961, the Department of Defense disapproved emergency funds for Project ORION, relinquished its support of the project, and authorized the expenditure of up to $98,000 over a period of 60 days to terminate it," AFSWC's historians reported. On January 1, 1962, Space Systems Division advised the Special Weapons Center to proceed accordingly unless otherwise instructed within forty-eight hours. With no further word from the Pentagon, AFSWC had no choice but to start closing things down. The deciding factor was probably not the emergency funding requested for the 1962 test series but the $33,250,000 budget that had already been submitted to the Department of Defense for fiscal year 1963. Hundreds of millions of dollars (including what DDR&E referred to as "astronomical" plutonium costs) might be next.

"Orion was an answer to a completely unstated question, and I think that had a lot to do with its lukewarm reception," says Augenstein. "The McNamara regime was very heavily focused on the notion of finding a justifiable role for these things. A lot of interesting capabilities went by the wayside. Harold Brown had a very strict rule that if there wasn't some stated military justification for a program, he wasn't going to fund it. Orion certainly came within that rubric as far as he was concerned.

"The Orion program, on paper, worked better and better the bigger it got," Augenstein continues. "And that was a novel thought to a lot of people. When something had to be four thousand tons to be superior to any contemporary system, that didn't lead to a lot of jubilation, because you knew you had to take a lot of steps to get there, and those steps are going to be expensive. Orion was a victim of external circumstances that had little to do with the pros and cons of the program itself. There were a lot of powerful forces in Washington at that time: NASA with its manned program, the DOD and USAF with their circumscribed and covert programs, which they didn't want to jeopardize in any sense. There was a manned Apollo program in NASA and the DOD space program was tied up in this very covert National Reconnaissance Office, NRO. The fact that Orion was a manned program, in the Air Force, played a counterproductive role with NASA in the end."

Orion was rescued, at the beginning of 1962, by its allies in Washington, aided by the realization that the work at General Atomic had implications for certain immediate problems of nuclear defense. "Clearly the feasibility of Orion has not been established," Hans Bethe cabled to Joseph Charyk, undersecretary of the Air Force, on January 18, 1962. "However, the project seems far more feasible today than it did when

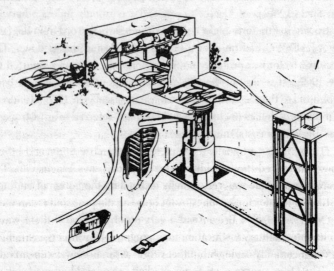

Repetitive high-explosive test facility designed by Hans Amtmann and Ed Day in 1964 to allow pulse-per-second testing of a full-size 10-meter Orion engine on the ground.

work was started. With a concept as radical as this, the development usually goes the other way, namely that the problem looks more difficult after three years of work than at the beginning. It seems to me that the funds requested, some $2 million, are sufficiently small that a way should be found to make them available and to continue the work of this excellent group." The Air Force agreed. "We have taken steps to reprogram funds to keep the technical group at General Atomics active," Charyk answered. "Work will be primarily oriented toward the fundamental problems of ablation and the energy-focusing mechanism. Both of these areas, we believe, may contain fundamental payoffs, not only in the propulsion area but in relation to their possible application in focused energy weapons, nuclear effect on re-entry vehicles, and discrimination in the area of decoys and penetration aids." This last point was critical: when faced with a cluster of incoming objects, how do you distinguish the warheads from the decoys? With radar you cannot tell the difference between a bomb and a balloon, but by flooding incoming targets with a bomb-driven pulse of directed radiation it becomes possible to distinguish—or even incapacitate—them at a distance that remains as deeply classified in 2001 as in 1961.

By August 1962 Orion had received an additional $1,795,000 from the Air Force and was lobbying for further support. Orion officials appeared before the Congressional Joint Committee on Atomic Energy, and a five-year technology development plan contained renewed proposals for nuclear tests. General Power at SAC, not to be outdone, endorsed a ten-year program that would spend $4.5 billion on building a deep-space fleet by 1973. General Atomic started making arrangements with the AEC to perform the initial tests. But in late September AFSWC received word that Harold Brown had decided against the test program "on the grounds that there was no military mission for man in space." On November 2, McNamara officially disapproved the proposed Orion tests.

Orion was being squeezed to death between two opposing extremes: too little interest from NASA and too much interest from the Strategic Air Command. "Those big briefings by SAC with a hundred slides of variations, themes, and more variations on the theme 'whoever develops Orion will rule the world' had a very negative effect on a lot of people," says Ted, "and I think that had a lot to do with it being easy to kill." Ted remembers the 8-foot-high model of an Orion battleship being displayed in a classified area of the Pentagon either shortly before or after being presented to President Kennedy at Vandenberg Air Force Base in early 1962. "Many who saw it in Washington were appalled," he says. "Making that model was a serious mistake." The Department of Defense was willing to sustain Orion as a theoretical study, but without a firm military requirement or the commitment of NASA to a civilian mission they were not going to let it off the ground.

Thomas Power's Qualitative Operational Requirement (QOR) of January 1961, calling for a Strategic Earth Orbital Base "capable of sustaining extremely heavy, composite payloads from low orbits to lunar distances and beyond," whose "integrated facilities and systems for effective mission accomplishment must include all functions that permit survival, surveillance, and weapons delivery . . . unrestricted by propulsion or payload limitations," was not the kind of requirement that DDR&E had in mind. "Men as wise and critical as Harold Brown and McNamara could easily see that the military applications of Orion are either spurious or positively undesirable," Freeman observed. Every few months the project came up for review by one advisory panel or another, and the recommendations were generally the same: the science was sound but its application was undefined.

"There is certainly a chance that a clear-cut need will emerge for a propulsion system with a high specific impulse and large thrust," concluded the Air Force Scientific Advisory Board in 1964. "If that should happen, it would be desirable to have at least one approach sufficiently far advanced in research and development, so that the U.S. could proceed quickly and confidently toward that goal. ORION is one of the very few concepts that hold promise for this purpose. For these reasons the majority of the Panel members feel that the decision should be made to pursue ORION through its next logical step. If a need for ORION should eventuate, the Panel believes that the need is as likely to be in the peaceful exploration of space as in the military use of space. For this reason, the Panel feels that, in the future, sponsorship (funding) of ORION should come jointly from NASA and the Air Force. The Panel recommends that the Air Force try to bring about this change."

A series of meetings were held January 13–16, 1964, in Huntsville, attended by officials from NASA, AFSWC, and General Atomic. NASA officials were told that "Fiscal Year 1965 signified the 'end of the line' for ORION under exploratory development." The Air Force would be proposing an advanced development program for Orion in fiscal year 1966, but, to gain approval from the secretary of defense, "the Space Administration would have to express strong support." The result was the "full support of Dr. von Braun contrary to persistent opposition from Mr. Finger." Huntsville's conclusion, based on the past six months of mission studies, that Orion would outperform Rover/NERVA had little effect either on NASA Deputy Administrator Hugh Dryden, NASA Director James Webb, or the joint AEC-NASA Space Nuclear Propulsion Office (SNPO). NASA's Office of Manned Space Flight (OMSF), led by George E. Mueller, architect of the Apollo program, sided with Huntsville and von Braun. "The in-house battle was bitter and hard-fought between OMSF and Nuclear Rocket interests (and NASA management)," says Nance. "OMSF had convinced themselves that on practically every mission criterion of importance, Orion scored significantly better than any propulsion system under consideration. Mueller and von Braun went down swinging. Dryden and Finger emerged the champions."

The Air Force, giving up on NASA, began preparing to shut things down. "In accordance with guidance from Hq, USAF, the proposed effort has been designed to bring the research program to a logical stopping point at the end of FY 64," AFSWC officials explained in requesting a final $2,820,000 to bring Project Orion to a close. "The end result of this procurement will be a complete series of 'mothball' reports summarizing in detailed handbook form the results of all previous research in nuclear impulse propulsion. Such handbooks will preserve the essential data from this project in a systematic form and will allow the project research to be discontinued and restarted later, if so desired, with a minimum loss of continuity."

Ted and the AFSWC gang kept lobbying the Pentagon, while Nance kept lobbying NASA. "The Air Force and General Atomic were able to pick up strong support within DOD," inside sources reported. "However, the Defense Department still felt it could not afford to continue supporting

PROJECT ORION

this effort without, in effect, putting the military in space. But it did give its blessings to a proposed joint effort with NASA and the AEC."

General Atomic and AFSWC proposed a two-year continuation of proof-of-principle research, including three underground nuclear tests, for a total cost of $12 million split between fiscal years 1966 and 1967. DOD was asked to put up $8 million and the AEC $4 million. DOD responded that it would be willing to supply half of the requested $8 million, provided NASA would supply the other half. The AEC refused to advance any funding, but confirmed that if DOD and NASA agreed to cooperate on Orion, AEC would contribute the bombs. "Los Alamos was willing to talk," says test director William Ogle of their response toward Orion, "but in general took the attitude 'bring money and then we will play.'" Orion's fate was in NASA's hands. "The result of the DOD and AEC positions has been to hang the fate of the program on NASA as the only agency that could justify a mission requirement for a nuclear pulse vehicle," *Missile/Space Daily* reported. "A Pentagon source said, 'If NASA says no, it's out.'"

By this time there was strong support for Orion not only from NASA's Marshall Space Flight Center in Huntsville but also from NASA's Ames Research Center in California, where a parallel study of Orion had issued a favorable report. The showdown came on July 17, 1964, at the Lawrence Radiation Laboratory in Livermore, California, when briefings on Orion were presented to NASA officials by Air Force, Los Alamos, and General Atomic personnel. Before the meetings, Hugh Dryden circulated a memo outlining NASA's "official position" that "in view of the shortage of NASA funds for both Fiscal Years 1964 and 1965, we are having to curtail a number of important projects which we believe offer much earlier possibilities of utilization than would Project ORION. Therefore, we do not expect to undertake any follow-on effort on that project in either of these two fiscal years."

"The purpose of the meeting was to acquaint the NASA representatives with the current status of Orion and proposed future plans and to solicit their interest and support," the Air Force explained. "Based on the comments of NASA representatives, it is apparent that the latter portion of the meeting objective was not achieved. No further action expressing interest or support by NASA of the Orion concept is anticipated." The Air Force then went back to General Atomic for their "rock bottom" cost to maintain a "minimum but meaningful" effort. General Atomic answered $500,000 to $1 million, without nuclear tests. According to *Aviation Week*, "The Air Force then approached NASA—this time unofficially—with a compromise proposal: each would put up $500,000 to keep Orion going through fiscal year 1966. Again NASA refused." One NASA official told *Missiles and Rockets* that Orion "probably is the only concept we have now that might permit manned missions to planets other than Mars" and another inside source commented that "you wouldn't expect this kind of furor to be raised over a piddling amount like that unless some people are afraid nuclear pulse will work."

Hope was running out. "Unless Jim Webb's or Harold Brown's mind can be changed during the next couple of months," Ted reported in early July, "ORION is likely to disappear as a government project as of January 1 of next year." Ted, now chairman of General Atomic's nascent Department of High Energy Fluid Dynamics—"because we reached a point where more money was coming in on nuclear weapons effects than on Orion"—decided to take a break. At the end of the summer, he took his family, including four children and a dog, up to the headwaters of the San Joaquin River near Huntington Lake in the Sierra Nevada, where they hiked to a remote campsite and settled in. After a couple of days in camp, remembers Ted, "we were sitting there cooking breakfast and here comes a young man with torn pants and his suit coat draped over his arm, carrying a big manila envelope, and in the manila envelope was an invitation to go out and see Harold Brown and General Donnelly at the Pentagon about a job." The messenger was Dan Baker, assistant to Art Rolander, General Atomic's chief counsel in Washington. "He had a terrible struggle getting up there," says Ted. "He ran into a rattlesnake, which he thought threatened him, but he delivered his envelope, we gave him some pancakes, and he went back down the path to the road."

The job was a new position as Deputy Director (Scientific) at the Defense Atomic Support Agency (DASA), the division of the Pentagon responsible for everything nuclear, from maintaining the stockpile to weapons testing to theoretical work on weapons effects. "I was being told, in effect, 'If you don't like the way it's working, come and fix it,'" says Ted. With the encouragement of General Atomic, he accepted the job, relinquished his stock options, uprooted his family, and moved to Washington. "It was a new job where a civilian was given in-line authority over all the R&D and weapons effects, so that I had the rank of a two-star general in the bowels of the Pentagon." Ted came up with one last plan to save Orion—the plan that Niels Bohr had suggested five years earlier at the Hotel Del Charro.

Besides the opposition from NASA and DDR&E, Orion now faced the Limited Test Ban Treaty of 1963, precluding flight-testing Orion with real bombs. "The treaty, however, provides procedures for its own amendment," wrote Paul Shipps in March 1965, "and the spirit of the treaty is clearly not to prevent the development of advanced space propulsion nor to hinder the scientific exploration of space." If the Air Force could not justify launching Orion *against* the Russians, why not launch Orion *with* the Russians? "Those of us working on the project believed that it should be carried through those test phases that were not prohibited by the treaty, because we were convinced that the practicality of the concept could be so tested in detail," Ted explained. "If the tests were successful, we argued, then the United States would have a sound basis for proposing what most of us had hoped for all along: a truly international effort to explore space on a big scale."

Ted remembers giving "an impassioned plea for going after Orion on the grounds that Apollo, which was quite far along by 1965, was a dead end. If it looked practical after another three years of hard work, we would follow through with the Russians on a round-trip to Mars, with the Saturn 5 booster taking the Orion engine up in two or three pieces, rendezvousing in orbit and then getting out far enough so there would be no hazard of radioactive material being dumped on the earth. The ship would be on its way to Mars, at escape velocity, before it went nuclear." The joint U.S.-U.S.S.R. Orion mission that Niels Bohr—who died in November 1962—and others believed in might have had a chance, if the issue of weapons testing and deployment in space could have been resolved. Andrei Sakharov, in his memoirs, describes "A Meeting of Party and Government Leaders with the Atomic Scientists" convened by Khrushchev on July 10, 1961. "I went on to describe some of my department's more exotic projects," says Sakharov, "such as the use of nuclear explosions to power spacecraft and other 'science fiction' schemes." Ted later became friends, in Vienna, with a Soviet nuclear physicist, Vladimir Shmelev, of the Kurchatov Institute, who admitted to having monitored what the Orion group was up to, but as far as Ted knows the Soviet weapons community never developed any equivalent project in response.

In early 1965, there were three developments in Orion's favor. Nance succeeded in getting the basic operating capabilities of the smaller Saturn-boosted Orion vehicles declassified, allowing limited discussion of the idea in public and in the open literature, minus technical details. Ted secured a commitment from DASA to support at least one underground nuclear test. There was growing determination in NASA to look at manned missions beyond the Moon, and official recognition that available vehicles were ill-suited to the job. "There appears to be a growing feeling within NASA that 400–500 day Mars missions are too long," explained *Missile/Space Daily* in a report on renewed interest in Orion, "both from the standpoint of reliability and a space crew's mental health."

Ted found an ally in Lieutenant Colonel John R. Burke, of the Air Force's Nuclear Power Division, who came from the nuclear-powered aircraft project and had been a consultant, at AEC headquarters, to Harry Finger on radiation effects. Burke, who later went to work for NASA, understood Finger's reasons for opposing Orion—"You can't blame him, he had his career and his position in NASA based on the NERVA engine"—but sided with Ted because "Orion had so much more capability than NERVA, and in reality they were both in about the same stage of development."

"ORION is not 'just another' advanced propulsion system," Burke argued in January 1965. "Practically every DOD/Air Force and NASA evaluation over the past 3 years has concluded that ORION provides the only capability for missions well beyond those achievable with chemical or nuclear rocket propulsion. The results point to a technique of rapidly traversing interplanetary distances substantially superior to any other method known today. Although the Department of Defense supports the concept as being technically sound, without NASA support the DOD and Air Force will not continue the program. All work on ORION technology is therefore scheduled to cease in April 1965."

Orion's future depended on conducting a nuclear test to find out whether the ablation predictions were sound. Ted Taylor and Moe Scharff designed an asymmetric, low-yield nuclear device—called Low Energy Nuclear Source, or LENS—which would fire a jet of high-velocity plasma at a sample pusher plate: a nuclear version of the high-explosive implosion tubes developed by Brian Dunne. Directing the energy equivalent of about a hundred tons of high explosive at an 8-foot-diameter pusher plate 20 feet away, it would finally give some indication whether ablation was survivable or not.

"Even Harold Brown was ready to sign off," Ted wrote to Freeman. The proposal was so clearly within the sphere of DASA's immediate responsibility, and within the bounds of the test-ban treaty, that everyone could get on board. "There was a moment in time, about six weeks, in which NASA, the AEC, and the key people following Orion agreed to fund a program in which all testing was done underground, not trying to fly a model or anything like that, a single test of our capacity to predict the effect of this material as it hit the pusher," remembers Ted. "General Atomic made a proposal for a three-year practicality demonstration program, and if that were successful so that things looked at least as good for Orion as they did at the start, then we'd go to the Russians and say let's do it together. And then NASA fell out of bed."

According to Nance, who spoke with NASA deputy administrator Earl Hilburn, the reasons for the negative decision, despite "no technical or mission objections," were that NASA had "no requirement for manned planetary missions," and that "if a big expansion is wanted it must be a political decision of Congress, not an internal NASA question." The decision, by all accounts, was close. "There were a lot of people down at Huntsville that were very much in favor of Orion," says Burke, "and there were a few people at headquarters, but like everybody else their hands were tied, and that was the end of it. Harry was a smart, capable individual and knew his way around NASA and the rest of it. So he prevailed, and we lost."

In February 1965, the Orion staff at General Atomic was down to nine and "formal research on this project was brought to a close." The only remaining effort was to close out the project's records and produce a final report. On June 30, 1965, Major John O. Berga of the Air Force Weapons Laboratory issued a terse, one-page Plan Change: "Objective: To establish the inherent feasibility of Nuclear Impulse Propulsion and to maintain currency in the technologies of other nuclear propulsion concepts. Results: None. This Project is hereby terminated." Orion was at an end.

Freeman completed his obituary on March 1, published four months later in *Science* under the title "Death of a Project: Research Is Stopped on a System of Space Propulsion Which Broke All the Rules of the Political Game." He summarized where the project succeeded and why it failed. "I understand that there is now no chance at all of saving ORION as a project," he explained to Stan Ulam. "My concern is to make sure that the public knows what has happened, so that they will be ready to come back to these ideas when the time is ripe."

He sent a copy to Robert Oppenheimer, describing it as "a partial answer to the question 'What does Christopher Robin do in the mornings?'"—a reference to the early days of the project, when his absences from the Institute in Princeton were as mysterious as Christopher Robin's absences from the 100-acre wood. "You will perhaps recognize the mixture of technical wisdom and political innocence with which we came to San Diego in 1958, as similar to the Los Alamos of 1943. You had to learn political wisdom by success, and we by failure. Often I do not know whether to be glad or sorry that we escaped the responsibilities of succeeding."

"The men who began the project in 1958," Freeman wrote, "aimed to create a propulsion system commensurate with the real size of the task of exploring the solar system, at a cost which would be politically acceptable, and they believe they have demonstrated the way to do it." But, after the initial euphoria came to an end, "there was no more brave talk of manned expeditions to Mars by 1965, and of sampling the rings of Saturn by 1970. What would have happened to us if the government had given full support to us in 1959, as it did to a similar bunch of amateurs in Los Alamos in 1943? Would we have achieved by now a cheap and rapid transportation system extending all over the Solar System? Or are we lucky to have our dreams intact?"

24

2001

"Between the first and last decades of the Twentieth Century lay a gulf greater than the wildest imagination could have conceived. It was the gulf between gunpowder and nuclear bomb, between messages tapped in Morse code and global television from the sky," wrote Arthur C. Clarke in 1964. "Above all, it was the gulf between the first hundred-foot flight at Kitty Hawk, and the first billion-mile mission to the moons of Jupiter."

Clarke left Ceylon for New York in April 1964 to collaborate with film director Stanley Kubrick, who had just released his cold war masterpiece, *Dr. Strangelove, or: How I Learned to Stop Worrying and Love the Bomb*. Kubrick was now developing a project provisionally titled *Journey Beyond the Stars* and commissioned Clarke to write a novel filling in some of the background that the film, suffused with the mystery of contact with a truly alien intelligence, would be unable to convey. "I felt that when the novel finally appeared it should be 'by Arthur Clarke and Stanley Kubrick; based on the screenplay by Stanley Kubrick and Arthur Clark'—whereas the movie should have the credits reversed," noted Clarke. While the two masters were incubating the odyssey of astronaut David Bowman and his ship *Discovery*, the odyssey of Orion was drawing to a close.

On October 5, 1964, General Atomic released a fourteen-page unclassified report, *Nuclear Pulse Propulsion*, by James Nance, explaining the basic principles of Orion without revealing any specifics such as the size, yield, standoff distance, or quantity of bombs. This was followed on March 19, 1965, by a thirty-three-page paper by Paul Shipps, *Manned Planetary Exploration Capability Using Nuclear Pulse Propulsion*, presented at the Canaveral Council of Technical Societies Second Space Congress, April 5–7, 1965. Nance hoped that open discussion of the project might lead to a last-minute reprieve. It was too late to influence the executioners at NASA, but not too late to influence the imaginations of Kubrick and Clarke.

"When we started work on *2001*, some of the Orion documents had just been declassified, and were passed on to us by scientists indignant about the demise of the project," Clarke explained. His diary for October 26, 1965—while the film, now titled *2001: A Space Odyssey*, was in production at MGM's studios at Boreham Wood near London—notes "a discussion with Stanley over his latest idea—that *Discovery* should be nuclear-pulse-driven. Read a recently declassified report on this and was quite impressed—but the design staff rather upset." The design department won. Orion survives, in Kubrick's film, in name but not in physics. "I think the main reason Stanley didn't want to go the Orion way," Clarke adds, thirty-six years later, "was that after *Dr. Strangelove*, he'd had enough of atomic bombs." In an early version of the screenplay, however, the *Discovery* enters the scene propelled by bombs:

> DISCOVERY 1,000,000 MILES FROM EARTH. SEE EARTH AND MOON SMALL. WE SEE A BLINDING FLASH EVERY 5 SECONDS FROM ITS NUCLEAR PULSE PROPULSION. IT STRIKES AGAINST THE SHIP'S THICK ABLATIVE TAIL PLATE.

Kubrick had been inspired by Clarke's 1950 short story "The Sentinel," in which an artifact, discovered on the Moon, is revealed to be monitoring our solar system for signs that advanced space-propulsion technology has emerged—and that the invention of nuclear weapons has not extinguished our civilization first. In the original screenplay, the Orion ship, leaving a trail of nuclear explosions against the dark background of interplanetary space, triggers the alarm:

> **Narrator:** A hundred million miles beyond Mars, in the cold loneliness where no man had yet travelled, Deep-Space-Monitor-79 drifts slowly among the tangled orbits of the asteroids.
>
> Radiation detectors noted and analyzed incoming cosmic rays from the galaxy and points beyond; neutron and X-ray telescopes kept watch on strange stars that no human eye would ever see; magnetometers observed the gusts and hurricanes of the solar winds, as the sun breathed million-mile-an-hour blasts of plasma into the faces of its circling children.
>
> All these things and many others were patiently noted by Deep-Space-Monitor-79, and recorded in its crystalline memory.
>
> But now it had noted something strange—the faint yet unmistakable disturbance rippling across the solar system, and quite unlike any natural phenomena it had ever observed in the past.
>
> It was also observed by Orbiter M-15, circling Mars twice a day; and High Inclination Probe-21, climbing slowly above the plane of the ecliptic; and even artificial Comet-5, heading out into the cold wastes beyond Pluto, along an orbit whose far point it would not reach for a thousand years.
>
> All noticed the peculiar burst of energy that leaped from the face of the Moon and moved across the solar system, throwing off a spray of radiation like the wake of a racing speedboat.

In the film, the *Discovery*'s voyage ends at Jupiter; in the novel the ship continues on to Saturn, taking advantage of a gravity assist. "Stanley and his special-effects team spent a great deal of time working on Saturn," said Clarke, "but the more accurately we reproduced this extraordinary world, the less believable it seemed." It was nature, not technology, that defied the imagination in 1965. The interplanetary ship *Discovery*, the Earth-to-orbit passenger shuttles, the circular space station, and lunar settlements all seemed plausible when the film was released in 1968. "Before the '70s had ended, the first permanent colony had been established on the Moon," Clarke's novel explained. "The cost of space travel had been slashed tenfold, and would be cut tenfold again with nuclear power. The brief age of the rocket dinosaurs, each capable of but a single flight, was drawing to its close."

Ted's vision for the year 2001 was much the same as Clarke's. "Nature has been kind to those who dream of space exploration on a vast scale, within the lifetimes of those of us assembled here," Ted told a Las Vegas audience in October 1961. "We always tend to underimagine the future more than a decade or so away; we tend to extrapolate only on the basis of what we have done, rather than what we know," he told an Austin, Texas, audience in 1962. By the time Kubrick began shooting his film, Ted was warning a Washington audience that "unless we take action soon, Apollo is likely to turn into a huge, expensive, dead-ended project that simply wasn't worth the effort. We must break away from the idea that we have to proceed slowly, one small step at a time."

Orion could make the steps all at once. "Bigger, higher-performance versions of Orion would make possible the detailed exploration of virtually all of the solar system in ships as large as ocean liners," he told a Vienna audience in 1966.

Ten million dollars had been spent over eight years on Project Orion; $10 million would be spent in four years on Kubrick's *2001*. Apollo, Clarke pointed out in 1965, was costing NASA $10 million a *day*. "Apollo costs too much and does too little," observed Freeman after the first Moon landing in 1969. "As soon as we are tired of this particular spectacle and wish to go farther than the moon, we shall find that we need ships of a different kind." Neither of the two next steps after Apollo—a manned Mars mission, or a lunar base—ever got off the ground. Costs rose astronomically; post-Apollo missions did not.

It now *is* 2001—and twenty-nine years since our last visit to the Moon. Orion has gone the way of the tail fin. "History has passed Orion by," says Freeman. "There will be no going back." What became of the future that appeared so promising in 1958?

Stan Ulam died in 1984. Orion remained his favorite invention, though the Teller-Ulam invention became better known. He stayed close to Ted, who credited his contributions, while growing increasingly estranged from Edward Teller, who did not. He never questioned whether Orion would have worked, and continued to hope for "its resurrection, which I, myself, believe will come."

Freddy de Hoffmann left General Atomic in 1968, after General Dynamics' support for his Shangri-la for physicists finally ran out. Few peaceful uses of atomic energy proved as successful as their progenitor, the bomb. De Hoffmann bet heavily, and lost, on commercializing a High Temperature Gas-Cooled Reactor, just before the market for large-scale nuclear power plants went into a decline. TRIGA succeeded by being small and quick; the nature of the nuclear power business forced HTGR to become large and slow. The unbounded optimism of Orion receded into memory, along with the 1956 Thunderbird convertibles that had dotted the parking lot at GA. De Hoffmann went on to become the director of the Salk Institute, a Shangri-la for biologists on the bluffs at Torrey Pines, and died in October 1989. "I still think Orion is the best way to get out there," he said at the thirtieth anniversary of General Atomic in 1985.

Gulf General Atomic, renamed Gulf Energy and Environmental Systems, was sold to Royal Dutch/Shell, who changed the name back to General Atomic, and then in turn sold it to Chevron, who named it GA Technologies. Since 1986 the company, now renamed General Atomics, has been privately owned by Neal and Linden Blue. When General Atomic was a division of General Dynamics, de Hoffmann ran the company as if it was a family business. Now, General Atomics *is* a family business, and the Blue family, including sons Linden P. Blue and Karsten Blue, has diversified into ventures ranging from unmanned reconnaissance aircraft to data networking, superconducting magnets, supercomputing, runway de-icing, and medical electronics—as well as defense work, including weapons dismantling for both East and West. General Atomics owns the largest privately operated controlled fusion facility in the United States, pursuing ideas that go back to the discussions held at the Barnard Street School during the summer of 1956. As one of its sidelines, it supplies the target fuel pellets for all United States inertial-confinement fusion experiments. If high enough energy densities can ever be achieved, the pellets may be beneficially exploded like a series of very small, clean bombs.

General Atomic's headquarters in La Jolla remain largely unchanged from when Project Orion closed up shop in 1965, although many peripheral facilities, including the linear accelerator, fuel-processing facility, and critical-assembly building, have been shut down. "We make the TRIGA fuel elements now in France," says Doug Fouquet, who has remained at General Atomic since 1959, "and we are working with the Russians on a modular helium reactor to burn up some of their old plutonium." The spirit of international cooperation in which General Atomic was founded is alive and well. With Russian scientists discussing the design of bomb-consuming reactors over lunch in the General Atomics cafeteria, Niels Bohr's vision of pursuing Orion as an international joint venture no longer seems as far-fetched as it did in 1959. Directly and through its affiliates, General Atomics controls 190 million pounds of uranium reserves in Texas, New Mexico, and Australia. If there is ever a reason to revive Orion, General Atomics would be a good place to start.

Michael Treshow, Carlo Riparbelli, Ed Day, Fred Ross, John Wild, Don Mixson, and others among the original Orion crew have passed on. Some of the group—including Freeman Dyson and Ted Taylor—moved elsewhere or returned to previous homes, but many of the Orion old-timers remain nearby. La Jolla is hard to leave—especially if you purchased a house between 1957 and 1965. The Hotel Del Charro, no longer host to visiting Orioneers, gradually lost the Hollywood horse-racing crowd to newer hotels in Del Mar, but remained known for its "secluded bungalows favored by visitors such as the late FBI chief J. Edgar Hoover," until its 3.7 acres were sold to developers, leaving the Andrea Villa Motel to preserve some mementos of the Del Charro on its walls.

Marshall Rosenbluth, now back in La Jolla, maintains a part-time office at General Atomics, pursuing controlled fusion with the same determination he brought to Project Sherwood in 1956. The offices in Rosenbluth's wing of Building H are still furnished with cold war–era steel desks, chairs, and bookshelves, and except for the desktop computers have not changed much from Orion times, when an IBM 7090 cost $597 per hour, and the swivel chairs were new. Rosenbluth

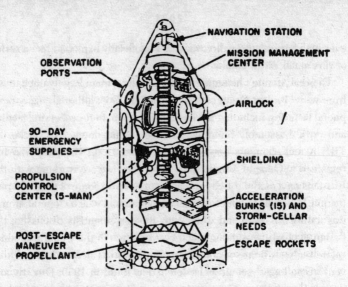

*Shielded command module, solar storm shelter, and escape vehicle for
a proposed 20-meter-diameter Jupiter exploration vehicle, 1964. Note
the navigation station and observation ports.*

reserves judgment on whether the proposal he and Ted made in 1958
for a 4,000-ton spaceship was technically sound. "Well, I can safely say
it wouldn't get off the ground now, politically, whether it would work or
not." As for post-Orion proposals by Los Alamos and Livermore to use
inertial-confinement fusion for space propulsion, he points out that "it
was sort of odd to think of doing it in space before you really knew how
to do it on Earth."

Herbert York's career at the forefront of the armament and disarmament establishments, before and after his involvement with Project
Orion, follows the title of his 1987 autobiography, *Making Weapons,
Talking Peace*. In 1961 he became the first chancellor of the University
of California at San Diego, adjacent to General Atomic, and lives just
south of Windansea. "We could live without nuclear fission," he says,
"and if I could abolish the fission process I would, the net would be
good." What keeps him awake at night are biological weapons, not
bombs. "It's the most dangerous thing on the horizon," he fears. "We in
the United States, in the name of examining what the possibilities are so

we can defend against it, are going to lead the world into a much greater trap than nuclear fission did."

York harbors no illusions about large government undertakings such as manned ventures into space. "Thinking broadly without thinking really stupidly is just hard to do—for the government," he observes. "While I was at ARPA trying to do things like supporting the initial thinking on Orion, my boss was saying we're going to send out contract proposals for anti-gravity and things like that." He has no regrets about helping to get Orion started—and no regrets about helping to bring the project to a halt. "Looked at in terms of what the whole country was doing it was an interesting thing that deserved some attention. But as a real project with real people and real money, it would have ended up with disappointed people, that's right." To York, it is not the feasibility but the *evolvability* of Orion that "was, and for a very long time to come will be, the showstopper." We arrived at successful technologies like airplanes or telephones, he points out, by building millions or billions of units, and making modifications one at a time. "Orion involved putting together simultaneously a number of novel technologies, most of which could not be meaningfully tested in isolation from each other or on small scale."

Brian Dunne, who lives high up on Mount Soledad in La Jolla, overlooking both the ocean and the Torrey Pines mesa, favors a middle approach: "You need to have three classes for decisions about projects: Yes, no, and suspended judgment." He thinks Orion should have been given a firm maybe, supporting continued research and engineering but postponing the political decision about whether development should go ahead. After leaving General Atomic when Orion and then Casaba-Howitzer were folded up, Dunne worked for a number of General Atomic spin-offs before starting his own company, Ship Systems, based in part on his shaped-charge and directed-plasma work. "They had some very weird projects, classified, so I cannot talk about it," says Jerry Astl. Dunne is through with weaponeering, but sees a busy future ahead. "I look for SDI [Star Wars] to have another renaissance," he explains. "I see the cold war all over again, except the Chinese are smarter—and better dispersed."

Dunne is an amateur archaeologist, and his perspective on Orion is

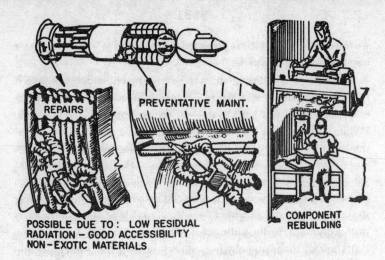

REPAIRS

PREVENTATIVE MAINT.

COMPONENT REBUILDING

POSSIBLE DUE TO : LOW RESIDUAL RADIATION - GOOD ACCESSIBILITY NON-EXOTIC MATERIALS

Except for brief acceleration periods, the ship is coasting through space with the engines off, allowing the crew to inspect the ship, keep up with routine maintenance, and make repairs.

similarly long term. "Orion will arise Phoenix-like from the ashes around 2040–2050," he says, predicting that we will eventually get to the Moon, find it uninteresting, and move on, via Orion, from there. The dates have slipped slightly from what he told Freeman in 1973: "I always thought that she should be grown from a huge Lunar base—who knows, perhaps in ~2020, she will!" In Dunne's office, a three-canister section of the Orion 1-meter-model charge-ejection system, and a piece of the model's perforated drag-skirt, sit under a shelf filled with archaeological texts.

Ten miles north of La Jolla, in Solana Beach, Jerry Astl's Orion artifacts go one layer further back than Dunne's. After leaving General Atomic in 1970, he became an independent consultant and founded Mar Den International Corporation in 1972. The 1:130-scale Orion model survives in his garage—and a wealth of undocumented details about the project survive in his mind. Explaining how the shock absorbers should have been reconfigured, he adds that "if they ever start Orion again they are going to find out pretty quick that they are going to need some ideas like that."

Moe Scharff now works for Science Applications International Corporation (SAIC), the earliest and most successful spin-off from General

Atomic. He is still engaged in concepts descended from Project Orion via Casaba-Howitzer, which was funded under ARPA's Project Defender in 1960. "Defender was there to look at advanced methods of missile defense," he explains, "and what I was proposing was certainly advanced. If you want to shut off the tape recorder I can tell you a little bit and then I can go back."

Burt Freeman lives on Mount Soledad slightly below Brian Dunne, and worked until recently at Maxwell Technologies, where the core of the Orion weapons effects group remained intact. He now works from home, modeling aerosols and magnetohydrodynamics, using a gigaherz desktop computer, with which, he says, "I'm able to do all of the tasks once requiring a big supporting staff. What more to want?" Conversation drifts quickly to radiation hydrodynamics, on both the "source" (bomb) and "interaction" (pusher) side—where so much progress has been made in the intervening years. "I haven't looked back," he says. "What impact that would have on Orion, now, I haven't the faintest idea. Or, really, interest, I must say." After some discussion of the problem of turbulent ablation, "an issue we never came to grips with," he changes his mind: "Yes, okay, I could get real interested! I think all these problems could be solved, particularly with an experimental program." He believes it would be easier to build Orion now, and even easier in the future, but "Orion shouldn't be developed now and I would choose not to work on it." He sees the same basic problem as Freeman and Ted: the dangerous nature of highly miniaturized bombs, and "whether it would be a good idea to have an industrial project that makes a lot more of them." He wonders if "maybe you could use some of the Russian stockpile—but I'd prefer just to dig holes and explode them all down there, to hell with the energy that they're potentially worth."

Kedar (Bud) Pyatt lives at the foot of Mount Soledad, not far from where the Hotel Del Charro has been replaced by condominiums at La Jolla shores. He remains convinced of Orion's feasibility and the ability of today's computers to answer many of the questions that were left unanswered in 1965. "For years and years and years the basic problem of calculating the behavior of a two-stage device and getting the yield right was an empirical treatment," he explains. "Nobody got the calculation absolutely right. There were fudge factors all over the place. In the last year with the advent of the new supercomputers some cohorts of mine at Los Alamos calculated from the high-explosive implosions through to the final yield and got it right."

Thomas Macken lives a few blocks from Windansea. As a hands-on aeronautical engineer, schooled in an era when you were expected to fly what you designed, he admits that "I was always skeptical about it. The thing that used to bug me most of all was the frequency of the delivery system, 1.1 seconds or something like that. It was really hard for me to visualize, maybe I'm too old-fashioned. I've always been very radical-minded—except when it comes to engineering." He was never comfort-able with putting so many people on top of such a large number of bombs.

Ten miles inland from General Atomic, past Miramar and Green Farm, Bill Vulliet is still doing physics, though no longer making the now-congested drive to Torrey Pines. He stayed at General Atomic long after the Orion group disbanded, and then worked for a series of smaller companies as a consultant on weapons effects. Unlike his former col-leagues who believe the project was technically sound, Vulliet now thinks that Orion could never have survived intact. "Opacity was only part of the problem," he says. "The other part of the problem is spalla-tion from the violent shock waves that go through that pusher. Any time a shock waves meets a surface, a rarefied surface, like air or gas on one side, metal plate on the other—it goes roaring through there, it comes to this air/steel interface, reflects, starts going back the other way and reflects as a rarefaction wave. This shock wave is strong enough that nothing would survive! There's no way you could design a pusher to do that job. It's nice to have specific impulse, but you don't want to grind the whole ship into powder on the first two or three shots! And if Ted Taylor were to approach me today, I would say, 'Let's go see if we can't pick daisies or do something useful around here. Because this isn't going to fly.'"

Seven miles up the coast highway from General Atomic, in Del Mar, David Weiss remains convinced that Orion—under international safe-guards—will eventually be revived. "It's not a matter of if it will ever be built," he says. "It's the German if/when, which means both if and when. After almost one hundred years of experience with flying machines it is difficult to realize that Orion is not really an aerospace vehicle, but

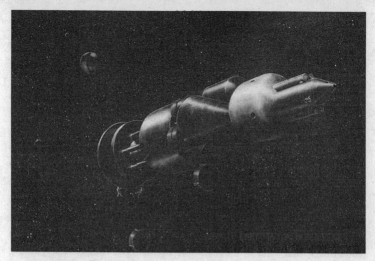

Empty propellant magazines are ejected and en route maintenance performed, two days after departure from Earth orbit for Mars.

rather a completely new animal: an orbital and/or interplanetary traveling colony. The intelligence and spirit of its inhabitants will be more determinate of its value and usefulness than any factor of its spectacular performance! You'll be doing the world a great service to finally let that rabbit out of its hat."

Lew Allen retired as chief of staff of the Air Force in 1982, moving to Pasadena to direct the Jet Propulsion Laboratory, whose interplanetary missions have all been unmanned flights. "The technology permits one to do more and more with less and less spacecraft," he explains. "Every day you are finding things you didn't expect, like 'Is there really water that one could exploit on the Moon? Is there helium 3, and if there were, would you know what to do with it? Could there possibly be life under the surface of Europa? How much water is there really at the polar caps of Mars?' Sending people has never made any real objective sense." Manned voyages would be sent in search of something else. "Orion was so bold, and so imaginative. Let's shove aside the obvious practical problems. I think all of us, even today, would say, 'Well, I don't know exactly why I want to do it, but I can't believe that there isn't a reason to do it,' that sort of thing. Maybe it's getting asteroids or, for one reason or another, just doing very ambitious missions. If we could sweep away the practical difficulties associated with bombs, I'd still be very excited about Orion as something we ought to do."

Bruno Augenstein maintains an office at RAND, in downtown Santa Monica, where he held positions ranging from vice president to chief scientist from 1967 to 1995, after serving as special assistant for Intelligence and Reconnaissance in the Department of Defense from 1961 to 1965. The top-secret Corona reconnaissance satellite program, which he believes distracted the Department of Defense from Orion, has now been declassified, revealing that "they had twelve failures on the Corona, partial success on the thirteenth try, and it was only the fourteenth that produced significant returns. You'd never get the opportunity today to go through that kind of a cycle. You would have Congress screaming after the second or third failure." RAND has the best institutional memory of the surviving cold war organizations, and Augenstein summarizes one of its later (and still classified) studies, *Orion: Future Space Propulsion System?*, as "a discussion of manned missions, primarily, and the possibility of establishing bases on the Moon and the planets. It was a report that recommended a full-fledged go-ahead." He remains convinced that Orion still deserves serious consideration, not only as a means of exploring the solar system, but as "a means of purposefully eliminating vast stockpiles of nuclear weapons; and an outlet for the hordes of skilled bomb designers, especially those of the former Soviet Union, whose efforts might otherwise be drawn in inappropriate directions."

Pierre Noyes remains at the Stanford Linear Accelerator, where he thinks seriously about antimatter, and semiseriously about how to use antimatter as fuel for interstellar transport—not with any expectation of building such vehicles, but to keep at least some science fiction grounded in fact. His nostalgia for Orion is tempered by an overwhelming fear of some of the other things that could be done with thousands of small, directed-energy bombs. "For a long time Freeman thought that this was the way we really would explore the solar system," he says, "when we had a lunar base and could launch where the fallout would be confined."

Edward Teller, the last of the Hungarian "Martians" who gave twentieth-century science and technology so many advances—John von Neumann, Theodore von Karman, Eugene Wigner, and Leo Szilard having predeceased him—still keeps one office at Livermore, and another at the Hoover Institution at Stanford. Teller played a background role in Orion, but as a mentor to de Hoffmann, Ted Taylor, and Freeman Dyson, he helped give the project its start. "It was the right idea in principle," he says in retrospect, "but many of the details were wrong."

Livermore and Los Alamos laboratories, then belonging to the AEC, now belong to the Department of Energy, or DOE. After Project Orion was over, both labs continued to consider Orion-like vehicles, especially whenever new developments renewed the possibility of small, clean bombs. In the early 1970s a revival of interest in Orion at Los Alamos resulted in a number of advances, including an experimental investigation of pusher-plate ablation at higher energy densities, and a proposal by Ted P. Cotter for a "rotating-cable pusher." Instead of a massive pusher plate backed by shock absorbers, the ship, spinning slowly around its central axis, would unreel a large number of steel cables, radiating outward like the arms of a giant squid. The cables, with flattened extremities, would absorb momentum from the explosions, transmitting it gently to the main body of the ship. Cotter credited this design to a still-classified proposal of Freeman Dyson's, circulated in November 1958 under the title *The Bolo and the Squid.*

The squid's latest incarnation at Los Alamos is a concept named *Medusa* by its inventor, Johndale Solem, coordinator for advanced concepts at the theoretical division. "Orion is mind-blowing compared to any other kind of spacecraft," he says. "As soon as you start thinking about nuclear explosives and how they might be used other than for breaking things and killing people—you think, 'Wow! Would this ever make a terrific propellant!'" Solem took a fresh look at the entire problem and came up with a small, lightweight spacecraft pulled along on elastic tethers behind a large, parachute-like canopy, billowing out under the pressure from the explosion of very small, low-yield bombs. Estimates of remarkable performance (Isp ranging from 4,000 to 40,000) are driven by Solem's knowledge that "to make a nuclear explosive with mass 25 kg and yield 2.5 kilotons is not much more difficult or expensive than to make a 25-kg, 25-ton yield device."

The last of the original Orion group still active at Los Alamos is Harris Mayer. "When you're a scientist you develop intuition," he says. "I knew that Orion would work. We knew how to make the bombs, there's no question about that. We knew how to make a structure that could stand 10 g's; we knew how to make a shock absorber that would reduce 100 g's to 10 g's. We even thought we knew about how to make an ablation pusher. There are all the elements. And we knew about how to launch through the atmosphere. The constraints may be important, but they're not given by nature. They're given by society and our culture and its values: 'At this time, no launches in the atmosphere.' That doesn't mean you can't launch in the atmosphere. And we passed it up not because people said the technology wouldn't work. I don't think we're going to be building Orion. But if we wanted to, we could be selling tickets for Orion like you do for an ocean liner.

"I didn't have the impression at the end of that year that it wasn't going anywhere. Quite the opposite. I thought that it had a grand start. These were days when we thought big. Now, whether it made economic sense to tour around the solar system and bring back asteroids, or pieces of asteroids, that I never thought made economic sense. But that wasn't the purpose of it. At that time we were a rich nation with unrestricted ambitions, so we thought of doing all these wonderful things. We're an even richer nation now, but with much restricted ambitions.

"Orion was a grand concept, which a rich nation with great vision and great opportunity could embrace. And it didn't even matter if it was a success. It was in working together toward a magnificent goal, and the camaraderie and intellectual stimulation in doing this had enduring benefit to the people involved and to the nation. We've lost this. You can't really think about something like Orion now. In talking with the old-timers about Orion, it's always a grand regret: a wonderful thing and we didn't get it done. It stepped on too many other toes. People were worried about being able to launch a thousand-pound payload, and we were talking about a thousand tons!"

Sixty miles south of the Los Alamos mesa lies Albuquerque and Kirtland Air Force Base, where AFSWC's physicists and administrators fought for Orion for seven difficult years. "In the final analysis, the Space Administration did not lend its wholehearted support to ORION and the Air Force was unable to carry the burden alone," AFSWC's historians concluded in their postmortem account. The Air Force Special Weapons Center became the Air Force Weapons Laboratory and then the Air Force Research Laboratory, with most of the nuclear weapons work shifting to Sandia National Laboratory, across a carefully guarded fence. Things that fly and things that explode are now kept in distinct administrative compartments, and in today's Air Force Project Orion would never stand a chance.

In the late 1950s, Don Prickett and Ed Giller purchased adjoining property in the foothills of the San Juan Mountains above Bayfield, Colorado, on Vallecito Creek. In late September, the summer visitors have left, elk-hunting season is just opening, and dark thunderstorms, bringing the first snow of the season, are swirling around the 12,000-foot peaks. "Black powder season's on," says Prickett. "The black powder people are up there in the hills." Elk-hunting season opens with bows and arrows, then black powder rifles, and finally conventional guns—a ritualized arms race where the more primitive weapons get first chance at the elk. "A miserable day for black powder," says Giller as the hail pounds on Prickett's roof. "Pretty hard to keep your powder dry." That sums up Prickett and Giller's careers as nuclear weaponeers: keep your powder dry, even if the purpose in doing so is to ensure it is never used.

Prickett attributes Orion's demise, as an Air Force project, to a specific Pentagon briefing where Department of Defense officials withdrew support. "I think we cut our own throat when we tried to push the Star Wars too soon, too fast," he explains. "At that final briefing, that the Pentagon insisted on, we should have just pushed the specific impulse capability and then you can worry about the details of what you are going to do with it later. We know what we're going to do with it eventually—but to try and sell it too soon was a big mistake. To turn it into Star Wars just didn't fly at that time." In Giller's opinion, "The concept was just too big a step to swallow. It was beyond the ability of the community, on the science and social side, to make such big steps, so it died."

Don Mixson, after leaving AFSWC for SAC, retired from the Air Force and moved to Northern California, where he pursued his artwork until his death in 1997. In 1979, Freeman Dyson's *Disturbing the Universe* referred to Mixson's 1959 study of possible military applications of Orion, prompting Mixson to respond: "It was written not to make Orion a military machine, but to con a military machine into yet another installment of funds to keep your beautiful big dream alive. You see, I shared that same dream and it was the only reason I was in the Air Force. NASA did not exist."

Ted Taylor left the Pentagon—and his Q clearance—in 1966. During two years in the Pentagon, he says, "I did a complete about-face in my attitude toward nuclear weapons. I discovered cases of willful deception, at all levels of government, concerning the effects of nuclear weapons on people, on buildings, on military equipment, on everything, if we ever used even a small fraction of the weapons in stockpile. Every nuclear weapon that is made makes the world a more dangerous place." He uprooted his family once again, this time to Vienna and the headquarters of the International Atomic Energy Agency, where, as a consultant to the United States Atomic Energy Commission, he sought to assess what the IAEA was doing to prevent diversion of nuclear material from peaceful to destructive purposes. He found that safeguards on the civilian side were as porous as the logic behind military justifications for stockpiling more and more bombs. "I vowed that I would use whatever energy I had left to try to stimulate the total abolition of nuclear weapons," he says. Ted knew what all those kilotons and megatons could do. "The awesomeness of it got to him after a while," says Don Prickett.

Ted, now living in retirement in upstate New York, tries to dream about space travel and solar energy, but finds he still dreams about bombs. "I had a dream last night, about a new form of nuclear weapon," he admits. "And I'm really scared of it. I have tried, I thought successfully, to hold on to a vow of just not thinking about new types of nuclear weapons anymore. And what's happened, to put it simply, is that it has gone from my conscious to my unconscious, and it's emerging as a dream; I cannot shut it off. I woke up at two A.M. and went back to bed at about six o'clock, and when I started writing I wound up filling up a page with notes, and it still makes sense. So it wasn't some weird possibility that I cannot describe, but I don't see any point in doing anything but just keeping it in my head, and, if I could, getting rid of it. What I am afraid is in the offing is people figuring out how to make a transition as spectacular as going from trying to kill a deer at two hundred yards with a pile of high explosive, to shooting at it.

"We haven't opened Pandora's box and found the really important content of that box, which was hope. Down in the bottom. If we just fiddle around at the surface, all kinds of terrible things come out. We just freeze up and say, 'No, no, no, no. That can't be done. Not allowable.'" Ted's hope is that the dream of Orion will one day be disentangled from the nightmare of the bomb.

"There is nothing indispensable about bombs," says Freeman, who, in retirement in Princeton, still thinks about space travel, but no longer expects to personally go along. He is more interested now in microspacecraft that fly on beams of light or use solar sails. The future of space, in Freeman's imagination, belongs to flocks of butterflies, not fleets of ships. Here on Earth, both military and peaceful uses of nuclear explosives have led us to dead ends. "There's nothing that nuclear explosions can do in the way of digging holes that you can't do without nuclear explosions. It takes only a little longer, and costs a little more." If you want to send a group of fifty people to Saturn in two years, however, nuclear-pulse propulsion is still worth a look. "The only thing that bombs can do that nothing else can do is something like Orion," he says.

The year 2001 is not *2001*. Orion—and Arthur C. Clarke's sentinel, if there is one—must wait until we have given up atomic energy as a weapon and are ready to step beyond.

Says Harris Mayer: "Look how young we all were in 1958."

2 5

The Sun Snarers

What if Project Orion were taken out of mothballs? Could an Orion ship be built? Would it work?

As I tracked down the original Orion crew—interrupting their retirement with questions about asymmetric explosions, shock absorbers, pusher plates, and anti-ablation grease—I was struck by how much undocumented knowledge is about to disappear. I kept imagining the opening scene of a film: Ted Taylor having coffee after picking up the mail in Wellsville, New York; Harris Mayer dismantling a camera in Los Alamos; Jerry Astl fixing his fence in Solana Beach; Bud Pyatt doing some weapons-effects calculations at Maxwell Technologies; Burt Freeman modeling magnetohydrodynamics; Brian Dunne in his study on Mount Soledad; Freeman Dyson in his office at the Institute in Princeton. One by one, their telephones ring.

The message: Orion is being built. This time, no political obstacles, and the entire United States and Russian stockpile is at your disposal, as well as the latest codes, supercomputers, and complete data on certain directed-energy devices, that, since you now have a need to know, exist.

Your Q clearance has been reactivated, and your family may join you once the existence of this project is revealed. One by one, the old-timers arrive back at Los Alamos and are ushered through maximum security into a conference room filled with colleagues they have not seen for forty years. The initial briefings to the Joint Chiefs of Staff and their Chinese and Russian counterparts begin. The chairman of the International Astronomical Union's working group on near-Earth objects is introduced. . . .

In the screenplay, the Orion ship would take a crew of *Armageddon* or *Deep Impact* heroes to wrestle with some Manhattan-sized piece of space debris. In reality, the emergency Orion fleet would be a cluster of small, unmanned vehicles, spawned by the realization, once the incoming hazard was identified, that the defense must be launched as quickly and as redundantly as possible, getting out there with enough time to nudge the assailant away from Earth.

Sending a chemical rocket out to meet a threatening object, armed with a large nuclear warhead to blast it out of the way, is backward, Johndale Solem of Los Alamos thinks. Multiple smaller bombs should be used to propel the interceptor, whose kinetic energy, if it gets there fast enough, can divert the threat. "The Orion aspect of it is," he tells me, in a conspicuously public part of the Los Alamos library, because the security mania is on and meeting privately might be misconstrued, "that when you look at the tactics for intercepting something that is on a terminal course with Earth, specific impulse comes very much into play. It gets you going faster, which has two parts to it. One is you get to it while it is still farther away, and the other part is that the kinetic energy you apply to it is going to be the mass times the square of that velocity."

In a three-page paper titled *Nuclear Explosive Propelled Interceptor for Deflecting Objects on Collision Course with Earth*, Solem goes back to Ulam's original idea and proposes an unmanned vehicle without either shock absorbers or shielding, driven by state-of-the-art 25 kg bombs of 2.5 kiloton yield. "Arming, fusing, and firing systems of artillery shells are routinely designed to withstand ~1,000 g," he explains. "An interceptor with similarly sturdy components can attain high velocities with only a few explosives and small shock absorbers, or no shock absorbers at all." Solem chooses as a sample target a "typical" chondritic asteroid 100 meters in diameter, weighing 14 million tons, with a closing speed of 25 km/sec, threatening us with an impact yield of 1,000 megatons if it hits Earth. The interceptor would be launched when the assailant is at a distance of 15 million km, or one week from impact, and would attempt to cause a deflection of 10,000 km to safely miss the earth. Solem estimates that a minimal Orion-type interceptor, weighing a mere 3.3 tons and without any warhead, could do the job. "The 115 nuclear explosives would have a total yield of 288 kilotons. . . . The time from launch to intercept is about five hours. Thus, there would be ample time to launch a second interceptor, should the first malfunction." The interceptors would be launched into deep orbit by chemical boosters, and start their engines from there. It would take a 6,000-ton chemically propelled interceptor to do the same job, and it would travel so slowly that it would have only one chance.

Solem envisions a Deep-Space Protection Force of unmanned vehicles, permanently stationed at stable Earth-Moon Lagrange points, under international control. We are unlikely to act on this suggestion in advance. A last-minute Project Orion might be our only viable response to the impending apocalypse of something large enough to give us a year or so of warning, but requiring something big, fast, and, if all else fails, surface-launched, to give it a kick. That's when NASA officials would suddenly start asking, "Who were those guys who were talking about that 4,000-ton Orion, and does anyone remember what we did with those plans?"

"With good enough detection systems we'll find the Earth-crossing asteroids and know their orbits ahead of time," says Harris Mayer. "But what we don't know is whether the extinctions that have occurred in the past, and may occur in the future, are not due to comets. A comet has only one chance to hit Earth, but we have only one chance to stop it. I have a terrible feeling that we'll solve one part of the problem, the Earth-crossing asteroids, and we won't solve the other one."

In the mountains north of Los Alamos, over sourdough pancakes with Don Prickett, I discuss this with retired Air Force General Ed Giller, who forty years ago was searching for a mission to justify Orion in terms of national defense. He answers that no one at the Pentagon gave this much thought in 1958—or today. "I don't know that any agency is in charge of defending the earth from an incoming asteroid," he says. "Is that Department of Defense? NASA? How about EPA? They tackle air pollution! It's only until somebody's given the mission, and nobody will get the mission until it is taken a little more seriously than it is today."

Don and Mary Prickett have kept their sourdough culture alive for fifty-four years. "Uninterrupted?" I ask. Not quite. One winter, a caretaker inadvertently threw it out—an extinction-scale event to the Pricketts. Fortunately, Ray Gilbert, an AFSWC colleague, had been maintaining a backup, and the culture was brought back to life. We have no backup copy of life on Earth.

In late spring of 1999, out of the blue, Freeman Dyson reported that "NASA officials have booked a conference room at the Institute for Advanced Study in Princeton for Monday morning next week and are flying up from Huntsville with twelve scientists who want to talk about Orion. Do they know something we don't?"

"The invasion from Huntsville is over," Freeman wrote after the visit. "They talked as if they are seriously intending to revive Orion as a long-range option for NASA. Only a few of them knew anything about the technical details, so I spent most of the time explaining the basics. I did not argue with them about whether anything of this sort is possible in the real world. I said the most useful thing they could do is a computer simulation of the entire Orion system, using modern radiation-hydrodynamics codes for the propellant-pusher interaction, modern neutron-transport codes for the internal radiation doses, and modern finite-element codes for the mechanical structures. With the enormous improvement of machines and codes since the 1960s, they could answer a lot of the questions that we could not answer in the old days. Especially if they could do three-dimensional hydrodynamics to find out how much the turbulent mixing of propellant with ablated pusher material would increase the ablation. This was the great unknown quantity that we needed a nuclear test to measure. Nowadays they could measure it pretty well with a computer simulation. So the basic questions of technical feasibility could now be answered without a nuclear test."

NASA *is* dusting off the old idea, both as a prospect for future interplanetary missions and as a near-term contingency plan for asteroid and comet defense. The Nuclear Pulse Propulsion of Orion times has been renamed "External Pulsed Plasma Propulsion"—removing most references to "nuclear" and all references to "bombs." "This is a brand-new propulsion research center, and it's supposed to do all the advanced propulsion," Joseph Bonometti, an engineer at NASA MSFC in Huntsville, explains to me shortly after his visit to Princeton. "They have hired a number of outside folks, which is unusual for NASA. So I started looking into Orion. Actually, I started looking into a few other things, nuclear gas core reactors and things like that, and I said, 'Well, this is not going anywhere. There is no way the engineering is going to make this feasible,' and they said, 'Well, how about looking into this Orion thing. It's kind of crazy but think about it.' So I did and I started saying, 'Well, gee, there's some very big inherent potential here.' All the other systems, as soon as you start building hardware, you start losing the maximum Isp you thought you were going to have and you end up with half or a third of what your maximum is. Orion is just the opposite. You say: 'Well, I know I can get three thousand, and if you do it right, you can go higher.'"

I make contact with Huntsville, thinking that NASA must surely have excavated the original Orion technical reports, and will by now have found Wernher von Braun's 1964 paper arguing the merits of Orion, which repeated Freedom of Information Act requests have failed to unearth. Unfortunately, NASA has had difficulty obtaining even the basic Orion literature, and wants to obtain copies—as soon as possible—from me! After reviewing a list of the documents I have collected they select 1,759 pages of old Orion reports. A message arrives from Huntsville: "It is very sad to say that the government is unable to get me even some of the references you have and it is somewhat convoluted to say that the government (i.e., NASA) is interested in buying copies of all the references you have obtained from the government! But I am seriously saying it." I make the copies, and ship them out by two-day UPS. After filling out a seven-page Request for Quotation form, followed by an eight-page purchase order, followed by three pages of ACH Payment Vendor System enrollment forms, requiring signature by an officer of a bank, I am officially a NASA vendor/contractor and reimbursement at $.07 per page is in the works.

Several months later, I receive a draft NASA report, *External Pulsed Plasma Propulsion and Its Potential for the Near Future*, by J. A. Bonometti, P. J. Morton, and G. R. Schmidt. It takes the reader straight back to 1958:

> For spacecraft applications, a momentum transfer mechanism translates the intense plasma wave energy into a vehicle acceleration that is tolerable to the rest of the spacecraft and its crew. This propulsion concept offers extremely high performance in terms of both specific impulse (Isp) and thrust-to-weight ratio, something that other concepts based on available technology cannot do. The political concerns that suspended work on this type of system (i.e. termination of Project ORION) may now not be as insurmountable as they were in 1965. The appeal of EPPP stems from its relatively low cost and reusability, fast interplanetary transit times, safety and reliability, and independence from major technological breakthroughs. In fact, a first generation EPPP system based on modern-day technology may very well be the only form of propulsion that could realistically be developed to perform ambitious human exploration beyond Mars in the 21st century. It could also provide the most effective approach for defense against collision between earth and small planetary objects—a growing concern over recent years.
>
> NASA is currently conducting research on advanced propulsion technologies capable of supporting ambitious human exploration of the solar system in the early part of the 21st century. The need for high power densities eliminates all but nuclear energy sources. The emphasis on known physics and affordability limits the scope still further to fission processes. Of the fission-based concepts that have been considered in the past (e.g., solid-core nuclear thermal, gas-core, internal and external nuclear pulse), only external nuclear pulse circumvents the Isp constraints imposed by containment of a heated gas, and provides the very high power densities needed for ambitious space

transportation. The physics behind creating a highly efficient fission burst is well understood, and in a vacuum, it produces a shell of ionized particles with an extremely high radial velocity. Thus, this concept of "riding on a plasma wave" is appropriately termed External Pulsed Plasma Propulsion or EPPP.

EPPP provides a technology that would allow us to seriously consider missions to the outer planets. It would also enable dramatically shorter trip times to Mars and other nearer-term destinations. The other and perhaps most compelling application for EPPP is its use in asteroid or comet defense. There is a low, but not negligible, probability of a collision with objects of sufficient size to cause catastrophic damage or an extinction-scale event. Good risk management would dictate that some effort be placed on devising countermeasures, if possible.

The ultimate hurdle in developing EPPP would be political in nature. However, there have been some important changes in the political landscape that may afford EPPP a chance where ORION failed. The Cold War is over and the fears of a large-scale nuclear conflict have abated somewhat. Unlike physics, the sociopolitical environment does change, and a propulsion system with this tremendous capability may be needed—possibly on rather short notice. Timing for development of EPPP may also be better than during the days of ORION. In many ways, international cooperation is more prevalent, and could conceivably be extended to the peaceful application of unused nuclear material. Stockpiles of fissionable material can be permanently disposed of and environmental contamination is negligible if used outside the earth's magnetosphere. Finally, the human race is at the threshold of truly exploring, developing resources and permanently inhabiting space.

Did someone in Huntsville find the lost paper on nuclear pulse propulsion by Wernher von Braun? Whether anything comes of this proposal in this century or not, having fresh copies of Orion documents in NASA files increases the chances that knowledge of Orion will be preserved. But what of the rest of Project Orion's documents, and

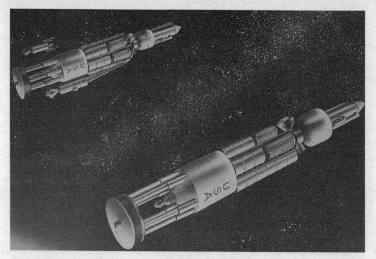

Two Mars exploration vehicles in convoy: note the "space taxis" for making transfers between separate ships. Upon return to Earth orbit the crew will transfer to reentry capsules, leaving the Orion vehicles in orbit to be refitted and refueled.

the unwritten knowledge accumulated by those who almost built Orion, the first time around? Is there any reason that the original plans for interplanetary Orion vehicles should be kept removed from public view?

At the end of this book is a list of known Project Orion technical reports. Many documents on this list are still classified "Secret—Restricted Data," whether or not they contain data that meet current standards for continued classification as S-RD. Besides preserving a detailed record of a cold war project and a review of the political arguments for and against the militarization of space, these reports constitute a collective scientific work that might be useful some day, even if, as Burt Freeman points out, "they might inhibit fresh thinking" if development was to proceed. As long as they remain secret, the whereabouts of copies, if any, will remain uncertain. Declassification is the way to ensure that copies are distributed and preserved. It is also the only way that the original authors can freely review and discuss their work.

Edward Teller wrote a short essay on secrecy titled "The Road to Nowhere," based on a tale from his Hungarian childhood about a band of runaway puppets who reach a fork in the road. One signpost points to "Nowhere" and one signpost points to "Everywhere." The puppets choose "Everywhere," get into all kinds of trouble, but eventually find their way home. "Science thrives on openness," Teller explains, "but during World War II we were obliged to put secrecy practices into effect. After the war, the question of secrecy was reconsidered, but the practice of classification continued; it was our 'security,' whether it worked or failed. We now have millions of classified technical documents. The limitations we impose on ourselves by restricting information are far greater than any advantage others could gain by copying our ideas. I do not claim that openness will never lead to trouble, but I am sure that it offers us the best possibility of getting safely home."

"There really are no important secrets anymore," says my father—making one exception: information that might enable terrorists to explode a small amount of fissionable material on the first try. The records of Project Orion could be opened without revealing these details, or becoming bogged down in deciding whether Orion is a technology worth developing or not. The theoretical question of whether it is technically possible to build Orion—now or in 1958—is separate from the political question of why. Proliferation of secrecy has not stopped the proliferation of bombs. Nuclear weapons, like mushrooms, grow best in the dark. Yes, there are active military implications associated with the low-yield, directed-energy devices that could be used to propel Orion, but it may be safer to have the potential for such threats in the open than to assume that others, to whom the same knowledge of physics is available, will not figure this out for themselves. The rabbit is out of the hat. No one can put it back.

Orion was too ambitious a leap in 1958. Both sides in the debate were right. Nuclear pulse propulsion had to wait, but nuclear pulse propulsion will be back. We are the sun snarers. "That first glimmering of speculation, that first story of achievement, that story-teller, bright-eyed and flushed under his matted hair, gesticulating to his gaping, incredulous listener, gripping his wrist to keep him attentive, was the most marvelous beginning this world has ever seen," wrote H. G. Wells, as the prospect of atomic energy began to dawn on us in 1914. "It doomed the mammoths, and it began the setting of that snare that shall catch the sun."

Orion the hunter and Orion the spaceship will meet among the stars.

Appendix

Project Orion Technical Reports, 1957–1965

Due to restrictions imposed under the Atomic Energy
Act of 1954, the following list is incomplete.

Taylor, T. B. *Note on the Possibility of Nuclear Propulsion of a Very Large Vehicle at Greater than Earth Escape Velocities.* GAMD-250, 3 November 1957.

Taylor, T. B., and Rosenbluth, M. N. GA-292. Title, date unknown.

GA-464. Author, title, date unknown.

GACP-340. Author, title, date unknown (proposal sent to ARPA ca. May 1958).

Feasibility Study of a Nuclear Bomb Propelled Space Vehicle. Contract AF 18(600)-1812, 30 June 1958, between United States Air Force Research and Development Command and General Atomic, a Division of General Dynamics Corporation.

Dyson, F. J. *Stability and Control of Space Vehicle.* GAMD-424, 8 July 1958.

Dyson, F. J. *A Note on Maximum Opacity.* GAMD-469, 8 July 1958.

Christy, R. F. *The Absorption of X-Rays by Cold Materials.* GAMD-470, 31 July 1958.

Ver Planck, D. W. *Flexural Vibrations and Stresses in a Flat Pusher.* GAMD-463, 6 August 1958.

Lewis, H. W. *Low-temperature Opacity by the Method of Moments.* GAMD-460, 7 August 1958.

Lewis, H. W. *Helmholtz Instability Over a Shallow Layer of Fluid.* GAMD-478, 11 August 1958.

Dyson, F. J. *IBM 650 Calculation of Equation-of-State and Opacity for (Poly)methylene (CH_2).* GAMD-483, 11 August 1958.

Ver Planck, D. W. *Compression Stress Waves and Energy Loss in the Pusher.* GAMD-472, 12 August 1958.

Dyson, F. J., and Noyes, H. P. *Free Expansion of a Gas* GAMD-476, 14 August 1958.

Ross, F. W. *Stability of Motion Induced by Blast.* GAMD-937, 18 August 1958.

Dyson, F. J. *Trips to Satellites of the Outer Planets.* GAMD-490, 20 August 1958.

APPENDIX

Noyes, H. P. *Separable One-Dimensional Hydrodynamic Solution with Rigid Wall Boundary.* GAMD-484, 22 August 1958.

Thornton, R. L. *A Survey of the Shock Absorber Problem.* GAMD-486, 25 August 1958.

Searcy, A. W. *The Vapor-Pressures of Refractories and Their Fugacities Under Very High External Pressures.* GAMD-498, 4 September 1958.

Dyson, F. J. *Free Expansion of a Gas (II). Gaussian Model.* GAMD-507, 5 September 1958.

Brueckner, K. A. *Random Walk of Trajectory Due to Bomb Misplacement.* GAMD-521, 9 September 1958.

Treshow, M. *Trajectories of a Rocket with Eccentric Thrust.* GAMD-541, 19 September 1958.

Brueckner, K. A. (with work by H. W. Lewis). *Collective Oscillations in an Atom.* GAMD-517, date unknown.

Dyson, F. J. *Supersonic Flow Past an Edge.* GAMD-565, 6 October 1958.

Dyson, F. J. *Free Expansion of a Gas, III.* GAMD-566, 17 October 1958.

Noyes, H. P. *Method for Calculating the Equation of State for AB_2.* GAMD-572, 21 October 1958.

Freeman, B. E. (with work by M. N. Rosenbluth). *Shock Structure in a Medium of Finite Radiation Opacity.* Part 2 (Part 1 classified). GAMD-578, 27 October 1958.

Rosenbluth, M. N. *The Two-Medium Radiative Diffusion Problem.* GAMD-583, 31 October 1958.

Dyson, F. J. *The Bolo and the Squid.* GAMD-599, 14 November 1958.

David, C. V. *Rocket Characteristics Determination.* GAMD-601, 24 November 1958.

Dyson, F. J. *Optimal Programming for Vertical Ascent in Atmosphere.* GAMD-619, 11 December 1958.

Treshow, M. *Project Orion: 4,000-Ton Vehicle, Mark 1* (title uncertain). GAMD-616, 12 December 1958.

Freeman, B. E. *Flight Characteristics During Takeoff Through the Atmosphere.* GAMD-622, 15 December 1958.

David, C. V. *Rocket-Assisted Takeoff and Landing on Planets and Satellites.* GAMD-625, 18 December 1958.

Bernstein, J. *Late Stage Ablation.* GAMD-630, 22 December 1958.

Brueckner, K. A. *Perturbation of Rocket Flight Through Wake.* GAMD-631, 22 December 1958.

Taylor, T. B. *Feasibility of a Nuclear Pulse Propelled Space Vehicle.* Preliminary progress report, GA number, date unknown.

Freeman, B. E. *Regular Gas Reflection Obliquely Incident on a Wall.* GAMD-668, 2 February 1959.

Freeman, B. E. *Minimum Energy Round Trips to Mars and Venus.* GAMD-672, 5 February 1959. Includes Appendix: *Landings on Mars' Satellites.*

Treshow, M. *Improved Stability of a Flexible Tore Shock Absorber.* GAMD-707, 10 March 1959.

Dyson, F. J. *Preliminary Study of Convective Ablation.* GAMD-710, 17 March 1959.

Dunne, B. B. *Diffracted Shock Wave Pressures.* GAMD-715, date unknown.

Dyson, F. J. (title classified). GAMD-752, April 1959.

Bell, C. W. (with work by J. H. Alexander, C. V. David, and C. F. Sprague). *Computer Program, Differential Equations, IBM 704, Fortran.* GAMD-794, 8 April 1959.

Treshow, M. *Project Orion, 4,000-Ton Vehicle, Mark 2.* GAMD-808, 18 April 1959.

Dyson, F. J. *Dimensional Study of Orion-type Spaceships*. GAMD-784, 23 April 1959.

Freeman, B. E. (with work by C. C. Loomis). *Properties of the Interaction of a Particle Stream with a Circular Disc*. GAMD-761, 24 April 1959.

Dunne, B. B., Dyson, F. J., Treshow, M., edited by T. B. Taylor. *Project Orion: Feasibility Study of a Nuclear-Bomb-Propelled Space Vehicle, Interim Annual Report, 1 July 1958–1 June 1959*. GAMD-837, April 1959.

Riparbelli, C. *Propagation of a Strain Wave in a Bar Across a Section Change*. GAMD-912, 1 May 1959.

Noyes, H. P. *Approximate Equation of State for* CH_2 *(0.1 - 2. 0 ev at 1 - 10^6 atm)*. GAMD-800, 19 May 1959.

David, C. V. *Nylon Rope Cycling Test*. GAMD-810, 25 May 1959.

Nowak, M. J. *Elementary Synopsis of Shock Absorber Problem*. GAMD-823, 1 June 1959.

Dyson, F. J. *Radioactive Fall-out from Bomb-Propelled Spaceships*. GAMD-835, 2 June 1959.

Dyson, F. J. *Effect of Bomb-Test Moratorium on Spaceship Development*. GAMD-851, 5 June 1959.

Treshow, M. *Toroidal Air Tubes for Two-Directional Shock Absorbers*. GAMD-839, 10 June 1959.

Dunne, B. B. *Project Orion Experimental Program*. GAMD-845, 16 June 1959.

Feasibility Study of a Nuclear-Bomb-Propelled Space Vehicle. Project Orion, Status Report 12. GAMD-864, 3 July 1959.

Bernstein, J. (with work by F. J. Dyson). *The Opacities and Equations of State of Some Mixtures of Light Elements*. GAMD-865, 6 July 1959.

Bernstein, J., and Dyson, F. J. *The Continuous Opacity and Equations of State of Light Elements at Low Densities*. GA-848, 13 July 1959.

Dunne, B. B. *Safety Procedures at Point Loma Experimental Site*. GAMD-915, 17 July 1959.

Dunne, B. B. *Measurement of High-Velocity Gases from an Explosive Cylinder*. GAMD-922, 24 July 1959.

Ross, F. W. *A Measure for Feasibility*. GAMD-897, 30 July 1959.

David, C. V. *A Study of Chemically Boosted Bomb-Propelled Vehicles*. GAMD-898, 31 July 1959.

Feasibility Study of a Nuclear-Bomb-Propelled Space Vehicle. Project Orion, Status Report 13. GAMD-911, 3 August 1959.

Baranger, M. (with work by J. C. Stewart). *The Calculation of Line Widths*. GAMD-927, 13 August 1959.

Case, K. M. *Stability of Inviscid Plane Couette Flow*. GA-918, 20 August 1959.

GAMD-929. Author, title, date unknown (concerns 1:130 scale model).

Dyson, F. J. *Proposal for an Experiment to Measure the Lifetime of the Neutron*. GAMD-957, 25 August 1959.

Berman, H. (with work by S. C. Choy). *Double-Skin Corrugation Construction*. GAMD-963, 1 September 1959.

Nowak, M. J. *Effect of Viscosity and Thermal Conductivity on Shock Structure*. GAMD-972, 4 September 1959.

DeWitt, B. S. *The Scientific Uses of Large Space Ships*. GAMD-965, 14 September 1959.

Vulliet, W. G. *Some Limits on the Resolution of an Earth-Surveying Orbital Telescope*. GAMD-986, 14 September 1959.

Case, K. M. *Stability of an Idealized Atmosphere.* GA-958, 15 September 1959.

Taylor, T. B. *Feasibility Study of a Nuclear Pulse Propelled Space Vehicle, Supplement to the Interim Final Report, 1 June 1959 to 15 September 1959.* GAMD-980, September 1959.

Treshow, M. *Preliminary Parameter Study.* GAMD-1036, 18 September 1959.

Li, Ta. *Pressure and Pressure Drag Coefficients from Hemispheres at All Speeds.* GAMD-992, 22 September 1959.

Baranger, M. (with work by J. C. Stewart). *The Photon Absorption Coefficient in the Windows Between Spectral Lines.* GAMD-996, 23 September 1959.

Riparbelli, C. *Deformation Analysis of a Plate-like Structure Represented as a Grid of Beams.* GAMD-998, 24 September 1959.

Dyson, F. J. *The Accessibility of the Satellites of the Outer Planets to a High-Thrust Nuclear Spaceship.* GAMD-1012, 25 September 1959.

Dyson, F. J. *Zeros of the Confluent Hypergeometric Function.* GA-999, 15 October 1959.

Astl, J. *Multi-ICBM Weapon System.* GAMD-1067, 2 November 1959.

Dunne, B. B. *Diffraction of a Shock Wave Around a Corner.* GAMD-1104, 19 November 1959.

Case, K. M. *Edge Effects and the Stability of Plane Couette Flow.* GA-994, 19 November 1959.

Case, K. M. *Taylor Instability of an Inverted Atmosphere.* GA-1009, 20 November 1959.

Riparbelli, C. *Mass and Stiffness Distribution of the Pusher for the 800-Ton Vehicle.* GAMD-1128, 7 December 1959.

Dunne, B. B., Ritter, P. B., and Ames, M. R. (with work by E. A. Day, J. Astl, M. J. Feeney, R. A. Cesena, R. D. Morton, R. Watson, R. Goddard, M. Young, J. W. Morris, R. N. House, L. Dial, W. B. McKinney, J. R. Pope, C. C. Loomis, F. W. Ross, T. B. Taylor). *Development of a Meter-Diameter Explosion-Propelled Flying Model.* GAMD-1212, 26 January 1960.

Weiss, D. C. (title classified). GAMD-1228, February 1960.

Wild, J. M. *General Descriptive Material on Orion.* GAMD-1240, February 1960.

Nowak, M. J. *The "Simplest" Extensional Vibration of a Circular Disc.* GAMD-1230, 8 February 1960.

Ross, F. W. *Propulsive System Specific Impulse.* GAMD-1293, 8 February 1960.

Vulliet, W. G. *Diffraction of Radiation Around an Opaque Disc.* GAMD-1256, 18 February 1960.

Riparbelli, C. *Influence of the Membrane Effect on the Bending of the Pusher Plate.* GAMD-1260, 22 February 1960.

Bell, C. W., and Loomis, C. C. (with work by C. F. Sprague). *PRESS: Computer Program in Fortran-II, IBM 704.* GAMD-1266, 25 February 1960.

Ross, F. W. *Disposable Mass-Equivalent for Fixed Mass.* GAMD-1294, 26 February l960.

Day, E. A. *A Pressure Pulse Simulator for Thick-Walled Structures.* GAMD-1273, 29 February 1960.

Taylor, T. B. *Nuclear Pulse-Propelled Vehicles.* GAMD-1276, March 1960.

Nowak, M. J. *The Equivalent Stiffness of Laminated Slabs.* GAMD-1267, 7 March 1960.

Dunne, B. B. *Jet Formation from Charges with Lined Cylindrical Cavities.* GAMD-1313, 7 March 1960.

Brown, H. D., Jr. (with work by J. H. Alexander and C. C. Loomis). *BUMP: Computer Program, Differential Equations, IBM 704.* GAMD-1292, 8 March 1960.

Riparbelli, C. *Response of a Cylindrical Shell to a Symmetrical Impulsive Load.* GAMD-1328, 24 March 1960.

APPENDIX

Ross, F. W. *System Specific Impulse for Staged Vehicles.* GAMD-1357, 7 April 1960.

Brown, H. D., Jr. *Betelgeuse.* GAMD-1393, 12 April 1960.

Nowak, M. J. *The Cone of Influence Method for the Wave Equation with Cylindrical Symmetry.* GAMD-1389, 27 April 1960.

Treshow, M. *Generalized Parameter Study.* GAMD-1402, 10 May 1960.

Astl, J. *Nuclear-Pulse Propelled Vehicle Launching System.* GAMD-1420, 16 May 1960.

Riparbelli, C. *Strain Wave Propagation Across the Pusher Plate and the Shock Absorber Attachments.* GAMD-1480, June 1960.

Weiss, D. C. *Nuclear Pulse Reaction Vehicle Configurations.* GAMD-1460, 20 June 1960.

Mautz, C. W. *Explosive Charges for Producing Gaseous Jets.* GAMD-1474, 22 June 1960.

Vulliet, W. G. *Conversion of Plasma Energy into Magnetic-Field Energy.* GAMD-1484, 23 June 1960.

David, C. V. *Specific Impulse of a Gas Jet Expanding Ideally.* GAMD-1488, 27 June 1960.

Project Orion—Interim Summary Report. GAMD-1816, July 1960.

Ross, F. W. *Space System Specific Impulse.* GA-1538, 22 July 1960.

Nowak, M. J. *More on Heat Conduction into the Pusher.* GAMD-1540, August 1960.

Weiss, D. C. *Orion Charge-Propellant Fire Control, Part 1, Deployment Systems.* GAMD-1579, 12 August 1960.

Treshow, M. *Integral Toroidal Shock Absorber—Advanced Developments.* GAMD-1615, 12 August 1960.

Peery, D. J. *Summary Report on Design of 880-Ton Vehicle.* GAMD-1632, 24 August 1960.

Riparbelli, C. *Large Deflections of a Lens-shaped Disc.* GAMD-1714, 8 September 1960 (with errata sheet, 27 April 1961).

Berman, H. (with work by C. W. Bell and C. Riparbelli). *Two-Dimensional Dynamic Analysis of Frames and Trusses Subjected to Arbitrary Forcing-Function. Part 1, Simple Symmetrical Truss.* GAMD-1871, 10 October 1960.

Riparbelli, C., and Brown, D. *Shells Under Impulsive Loads.* GAMD-1732, Part I, 12 October 1960.

Weiss, D. C., and Peery, D. J. *Some Mission Capabilities of Minimal Size Rocket-Boosted Orion Vehicles.* GAMD-1800, November 1960.

Pearlstine, L. D. (with work by R. Walsh). *A Comparison of Two Implicit Finite-Difference Schemes for Heat Diffusion Problems.* GAMD-1814, 11 November 1960.

Teichmann, T. *Motion of a Spring-Loaded Infinite Rod.* GAMD-1801, 15 November 1960.

Riparbelli, C. *Parameter Study—Cylinder with Piston.* GAMD-1830, 16 November 1960.

Teichmann, T., Day, E. A., Freeman, B. E., and Loomis, C. C. *Orion Practicality Demonstration Program.* GAMD-1861, 2 December 1960.

Berman, H. (with work by C. W. Bell and C. Riparbelli). *Two-Dimensional Dynamic Analysis of Frames and Trusses Subjected to Arbitrary Forcing-Function. Part 2, Simple Symmetrical Frame.* GAMD-1871, 8 December 1960.

Walsh, J. M. (with work by C. W. Mautz). *Jets from Steady-State Cavity Collapse.* GAMD-1912, 29 December 1960.

Loomis, C. C. *The Representation of Fluid Dynamics and Radiation Flow by the SPUTTER Code.* GAMD-2264, June 1961.

Treshow, M. (title classified). GAMD-1930, January 1961.

APPENDIX

Riparbelli, C. *Balloon-Type Shock Absorber With Grid*. GAMD-1977, January 1961.

David, C. V. *Minimum Energy Loss in a Two-Mass Spring System*. GAMD-2331, 16 January 1961.

Astl, J. *Split-Cylinder Long-Stroke Shock Absorber System*. GAMD-1978, February 1961.

Bell, C. W. *Dynamic Structural Analysis Frame, IBM 7090 Fortran Computer Program*. GAMD-1955, 7 February 1961.

Berman, H. *Pulse Shape Effects on Structural Dynamics*. GAMD-2030, 14 February 1961.

Berman, H. (with work by C. W. Bell and C. Riparbelli). *Two-Dimensional Dynamic Analysis of Frames and Trusses Subjected to Arbitrary Forcing-Function. Part 3, Complex Truss*. GAMD-1871, 17 February 1961.

Bell, C. W. (with work by D. Weiss). *Trip. A Computer Program Written in Fortran-II for the IBM 7090*. GAMD-2045, 22 February 1961.

Riparbelli, C. *Bending of a Lens-shaped Disc with Discrete Edge Supports*. GAMD-2046, 22 February 1961.

Peery, D. J. *Orion Design and Optimization Studies*. March 1961.

Preisendorfer, R. W. *Equations of Motion of Translating Pin-Joined Frames Subject to an Arbitrary Set of External Forces and Internal Restraints*. GAMD-2066, 1 March 1961.

Walsh, J. M. *On Non-Linear Plane Waves in Metal Plates (Pulse Attenuation and Pulse-Free Surface Interactions)*. GAMD-2115, 10 March 1961.

Nowak, M. J. *The General Fluid-Dynamics Equations, Particularly Lagrange's Equations*. GAMD-2116, 3 March 1961.

Lindley, W. B. *SC 4020 Plot Subroutine Package for Fortran Codes*. GAMD-2127, 22 March 1961.

Tillotson, J. H. *A Use for Radioisotopes in Ablation Experiments*. GAMD-2117, 6 April 1961.

Nowak, M. J. *A Summary Analysis of Ablation by Radiation Diffusion*. GAMD-2114, 11 April 1961.

Weiss, D. C. *Maneuvering Technique for Changing the Plane of Circular Orbits with Minimum Fuel Expenditure*. GA-2194, 13 April 1961.

Mautz, C. W. (with work by H. R. Kratz and J. C. Stewart). *Viscous Flow of Ablating Grease Films*. GAMD-2237, 17 April 1961.

Walsh, J. M. *Dynamic Cavitation Tensile Strengths of Metals*. GAMD-2222, 27 April 1961.

Riparbelli, C. *A Pneumatic Shock Absorber for Vehicles Driven by Explosions*. 28 April 1961.

Freeman, B. E. *Continuous Rezone in the Eulerian Hydrodynamic Formulation and the Moving Coordinate System*. GAMD-2228, 1 May 1961.

Teichmann, T. *The Behavior of a Thin Viscous Film Under Mechanical Forces and Thermal Forces*. GAMD-2257, 8 May 1961.

Tillotson, J. H. *An Optimum Shadow Shield*. GAMD-2271, 18 May 1961.

Nowak, M. J. *Application of the Single-Scattering Approximation for Atmospheric Side-Scattering of Gamma Radiation into a Nuclear Space Vehicle*. GA-2285, 29 May 1961.

Nowak. M. J. *Some Fundamental Properties of Shock Waves*. GAMD-2288, 1 June 1961.

Walsh, J. M. *Shock Attenuation for an Arbitrary Impulse*. GAMD-2341, 19 June 1961.

APPENDIX

Wild, J. M. *The Production of High Velocity, High Density Plasmas with High Explosives.* GA-2401, 11 July 1961.

Vulliet, W. G. (with work by L. D. Pearlstine). *Hydrodynamics in the Interaction of X-Rays and Cold Iron.* GAMD-2398, 12 July 1961.

Nowak, M. J. *The Simplest Extensional Vibration of a Circular Disc.* GA-2443, 27 July 1961.

The Nuclear/Chemical Pulse Reaction Propulsion Project (Project Orion). Summary Report for the Period 16 September 1959 through 30 June 1961. GA-2419, 28 July 1961.

Dunne, B. B. *Development of a Meter-Diameter Explosion-Propelled Flying Model.* GA-2188, 28 August 1961.

Stewart, J. C., and Pyatt, K. D. *Theoretical Study of Optical Properties: Photon Absorption Coefficients, Opacities, and Equations of State of Light Elements, Including the Effect of Lines.* Final Report, September 1961, Vol. 1. GA-2528/AFSWC-TR-61-71.

David, C. W. (with work by R. M. Feix and T. Teichmann). *Dynamics of a Two-Mass Spring System* GAMD-2596, 29 September 1961.

David, C. V. *Toroidal Shock-Absorber Scale-Model Testing (14-in. Pusher Plate).* GAMD-2554, 5 October 1961.

Nowak, M. J. *On the Conservation of Energy for Finite Difference Approximations.* GAMD-2728, 10 October 1961.

Taylor, T. B. *Advanced Propulsion Concepts.* GA-2592, 24 October 1961.

Case, K. M. *Stability of a Flow Against a Plate.* GA-2571, 6 November 1961.

Weiss, D. C. *Computation Techniques for Fast Transit Earth-Mars Trips.* GAMD-2626, 14 November 1961.

Teichmann, T. *The Kinematics of a Uniformly Expanding Cone of Particles.* GAMD-2637, 20 November 1961.

Vulliet, W. G. *Note on Thermal Conductivities at High Temperatures.* GAMD-2681, 13 December 1961.

Dunne, B. B., and Nowak, M. J. (with work by E. A. Day and P. B. Ritter). *Deformation of Aluminum Discs by Shock Waves from High Explosive Spherical Charges.* GAMD-2680, 15 December 1961.

Carlson, K. M. *Shapes of High-Altitude Balloons.* GAMD-2820, 5 January 1962.

David, C. V. *Double-Stage Shock Absorber Configuration (POGO)—Preliminary Study, Double-Spring System Configuration.* GAMD-2835, 19 January 1962.

Weiss, D. C. *Graphical Solution of Earth-Mars Trips.* GA-2661, 19 January 1962.

Freeman, B. E. *A Numerical Method for the Radiation Transport Equation in Plane Geometry.* GAMD-2874, 22 January 1962.

The Nuclear/Chemical Pulse Propulsion Project (Project Orion), Summary Report Supplement for the Period 1 July 1961 through 31 December 1961. GA-2863, date unknown.

Freeman, B. E., Kratz, H. R., and Wild, J. M. *The Nuclear/Chemical Pulse Reaction Propulsion Project, Quarterly Report, 1 Jan–31 Mar 1962.* GACD-3096, March 1962.

Teichmann, T. *An Avalanche Model for a Spherical Implosion in a Tenuous Atmosphere.* GAMD-3098, 7 March 1962.

Crafton, C. H. (with work by M. J. Nowak). *An Array vs. Index IBM Printer Plotter, Fortran Subroutine.* GAMD-3011, 9 March 1962.

Blackstock, A. W., Kratz, H. R., and Feeney, M. B. *Piezoelectric Gauge for Measuring Rapidly Varying Pressures up to Seven Kilobars.* GA-2444, 14 March 1962.

APPENDIX

Freeman, B. E. *Some Approximations in the Numerical Treatment of Radiation Transport Through Media with Frequency-Dependent Absorption Coefficients.* GAMD-3074, 1 April 1962.

Teichmann, T. (with work by D. R. Yates). *The Initial Behavior of an Explosion in a Cavity.* GAMD-3113, 12 April 1962.

Nowak, M. J. *Non-Steady Radiation Transport and the Thick-Thin Approximation.* GAMD-3095, 12 April 1962.

Ross, F. W. *Structural Factors and Optimization of Space Vehicles.* GA-1538, Supplement, 7 May 1962.

GAMD-3151. Author, title, date unknown (mid-1962, concerning payload/mission studies).

David, C. V. *Shock-Loaded-Plate Attachment Tests.* GAMD-3198, 11 June 1962.

Taylor, T. B. *Nuclear Propulsion in Space.* GA-3218, 12 June 1962.

Dunne, B. B., and Ritter, P. B. *Flash-Radiographs of Toroidally Imploded Cylindrical Implosion Charges.* GAMD-3284, 26 June 1962.

Proposed Nuclear Experiments. GAMD-3316, 1 August 1962.

Weiss, D. C. *A General Discussion of Earth-Mars Interplanetary Round Trips.* GA-3184, 13 August 1962.

Nowak, M. J. *BAMM—A Fortran IBM-7090 Code for the Calculation of Bending and Membrane Motion.* GAMD-3432, 28 August 1962.

Freeman, B. E. *Radiation-Transport in Spherically-Symmetric Configurations.* GAMD-3488, 4 September 1962.

Kratz, H. R. *Measurement of Ablation with Radiation the Dominant Mode of Energy Transfer.* GA-3569, October 1962.

Reetz, A. *Neutron and Gamma-Ray Heating in Iron Slabs.* GAMD-3690, 24 October 1962.

Treshow, M. *1962 Parameter Studies. Orion Parameter and Payload Study Based on 200- and 4,000-Ton Reference Design.* GAMD-3597, 25 October 1962.

Dunne, B. B. *Mass of High Velocity Gases from Toroidal Implosion Charges.* GAMD-3629, 31 October 1962.

Nowak, M. J. *Comments on the Boundary Conditions at an Ablating Surface.* GAMD-3639, 6 November 1962.

Mancini, R. J. *Stresses Induced in a Thin-Walled Tube by a Sudden Heat Input at the Inner Surface.* GAMD-3605, 9 November 1962.

Vulliet, W. G. *The Kinetics of Vaporization Below the Critical Point.* GA-3633, 14 December 1962.

Walsh, J. T. GAMD-3881. Title unknown. January 1963.

Treshow, M. *Vehicle Parameters as Influenced by Unloading of Fuel and Payload.* GAMD-3776, January 1963.

Teichmann, T. *Orion Fuel Requirements.* GAMD-4068, 19 February 1963.

Riparbelli, C. *Deformation Analysis of a Plate-like Structure Represented as a Grid of Beams.* Addendum to GAMD-998, 26 February 1963.

Davis, C. G. *A Numerical Calculation of a Nuclear Explosion at High Altitude.* GAMD-4301, 1963.

Overmyer, R. F., Hopkins, G. R., and Willis, D. E. *Radiation Effects Experiments on Instrumentation: Nuclear Pulse Propulsion Concept.* GAMD-4832, 14 May 1963.

Stahl, R. H. (with work by M. R. Ames, M. B. Feeney, and W. Simmons). *A Condenser Probe for Ablation Measurements.* GAMD-4255, 15 May 1963.

Mooney, W. E. *Orion Martian Excursion.* GA-P-359-1, 24 June 1963.

APPENDIX

General Atomic Briefing Charts for the Pre-Beginning Meeting, June 27, 1963. Nuclear Pulse Space Vehicle Preliminary Study, to be conducted by General Atomic for the Future Projects Office, Marshall Space Flight Center, NASA. GA-C-395, 25 June 1963.

Amtmann, H. H. *Preliminary Data on a Complete Life Support System for a Manned Space Vehicle.* GAMD-4507, 23 July 1963.

Mooney, W. E. *Study of the Effects of Using Lunar or Planetary Material for Propellant.* GA-0223, August 1963.

Amtmann, H. H. *Global and Spatial Information System, Part I, Basics of Sensors.* GAMD-4066, August 1963.

Weiss, D. C. *Arrested Rendezvous, a New Concept.* GA-3725A, 20 August 1963.

Weiss, D. C. *Comments on Use of Lunar or Planetary Material for Orion Propellant.* GA-P-363-1, 21 August 1963.

Mooney, W. E. *Orion Personnel Accommodations.* GA-P-363-2, 3 September 1963.

Mooney, W. E., Nance, J. C., Pyatt, K. D., Shipps, P. R., and Weiss, D. C. *Mid-Contract Status Presentation on the Nuclear Pulse Space Vehicle Preliminary Study.* GACD-4593, 25 September 1963.

Teichmann, T. *The Maximum Attainable Specific Impulse of Nuclear Pulse Propulsion Engines.* GAMD-4733, 31 October 1963.

Amtmann, H. H., and Day, E. A. *Experimental Techniques and Development Tasks for the Development of Nuclear Pulse Propulsion Engines. Final Report.* GAMD-4740, November 1963.

Reed, L. L. *Half Function, a Technique for Storing Two Floating-Point Numbers in a 36-Bit Computer Word.* GA-4805, December 1963.

Nuclear Pulse Propulsion Project (Project Orion) Technical Summary Report, RTD-TDR-63-3006 (1963–1964). GA-4205: Vol. 1, *Reference Vehicle Design Study* (October 1963); Vol. 2, *Interaction Effects* (March 1964); Vol. 3, *Pulse Systems* (March 1964); Vol. 4, *Experimental Structural Response* (July 1963).

Vulliet, W. G. *The Temperature Calculation of a Thin, Finite Slab from Measurement of Its Bremsstrahlung Radiation.* GAMD-4898, 9 January 1964.

Nuclear Pulse Vehicle Study, Condensed Summary Report. GA-4891, 14 January 1964.

Final Presentation on Nuclear-Pulse Vehicle Study. GACD-4914, 15 January 1964.

Nuclear Pulse Vehicle Program Status, Presentation to the USAF, Washington, D.C., 27 February 1964. GA-C-565-1.

Pyatt, K. D. *MOTET: A Computer Program to Solve the Time-Dependent Hydrodynamic Equations in Two Dimensions with Radiation Flow.* (GA number unknown), March 1964.

Sager, P. H. *Early System Applications of Nuclear Pulse Propulsion.* GA-5140, Preliminary Draft, 1 April 1964.

Teichmann, T. *The Performance Limits of Nuclear Pulse Propelled Rockets: I.* GAMD-5152, 7 April 1964.

Nance, J. C., and Taylor, T. B. *Proposed FY-1965 Orion Work Program Description.* Draft I by Nance, Draft II by Taylor. GA-C-622, 21 April 1964.

Poll, R. A. *Transient Radiation Effects in an Orion Pressure Transducer and a Time-of-Arrival Probe.* GA-3696, 24 April 1964.

Amtmann, H. H. *Cost Details for a Ground Oriented Development Plan for NPP System.* GAMD-4953, 5 May 1964.

Ground-Oriented Development Plan for a Nuclear Pulse Propulsion System. GAMD-5020, author, date unknown.

APPENDIX

Gerber, M. J., and Sager, P. H. *HAYO: A Computer Program for Sizing a Nuclear-Pulse Space Vehicle System.* GAMD-5267, 8 May 1964.

Arguments for a Research Program in Support of a Nuclear Pulse Propulsion Nuclear Test Program. GA-C-669, 2 June 1964.

Teichmann, T. *The Lateral Deformation of a Pressurized Torus.* GAMD-5347, 3 June 1964.

Amtmann, H. H., and Day, E. A. (with work by E. J. Wittenkeller). *Preliminary Investigation of a Repetitive-HE-Pulse Test Facility.* GAMD-5351, 4 June 1964. With Appendix by O. Boden, *Comments and Observations on Mechanism for Repetitive HE Pulse Test Facility,* 18 June 1964.

Boden, O. W., and Macken, T. *Review of Materials and Fabrication Problems for Intermediate Platform and Second-Stage Piston Tube.* GAMD-5408, 17 June 1964.

Hamrick, J. R., and Sager, P. H. *Masjet: An IBM 7044 Program for Flight Performance of a Propulsion System with Jettisoning of Mass at Discrete Intervals.* GAMD-5221, July 1964.

Freeman, B. E., and Lindley, W. B. *DIANE. Computer Program (Photon Absorption Coefficient Subroutine).* GAMD-5501, 1964 (date unknown).

Walsh, R. T. *The Diaphanous-II System: Computer Program (Opacity Subroutine for SPUTTER Code).* GAMD-5549, August 1964.

Proposed Test Program for the Dynamic Response of a Very Light, High-Capacity Gas-Filled Toroidal Shock Absorber System When Driven by High Explosive Impulsive Loads. GACP 42-283S, 31 August 1964.

Nance, J. C., Shipps, P. R., Amtmann, H. H., Day, E. A., David, C. V., Macken, T., Mooney, W., Pyatt, K. D., Sager, P. H., Stewart, G. W., Teichmann, T., Treshow, M., Weiss, D. C., Wikner, N. F., Ehricke, K. A., and Brown, B. *Nuclear Pulse Space Vehicle Study.* GA-5009, 19 September 1964. *Vol. 1: Summary Report; Vol. 2: Vehicle System Performance and Costs; Vol. 3: Conceptual Vehicle Designs and Operational Systems.*

David, C. V., and Day, E. A. *Repetitive Strong Shock Generation and Proposed Flexible Shock-Absorber System.* GA-5685, 29 September 1964.

Nance, J. C. *Nuclear Pulse Propulsion.* GAMD-5572, 5 October 1964.

Macken, T. *Compatibility and Characteristics of Launch Vehicle for Nuclear-Pulse-Propulsion Systems.* GAMD-5834, 15 October 1964.

Teichmann, T. *The Angular Effects Due to Asymmetric Placement of Axial Symmetric Explosives.* GAMD-5823, 26 October 1964.

Ames, M. R., and Muhl, W. O. *Transient Overload of Tektronix Oscilloscope.* GAMD-5852, November 1964.

Macken, T. (with work by A. Steeger). *Preliminary Analysis of Meteoroid Protection for the 10-M Diameter Orion Engine.* GAMD-5833, 12 November 1964.

David, C. V., and Hager, E. R. *Double-Stage Shock-Absorber Investigation.* GAMD-5911, December 1964.

David, C. V., et al. *Nuclear-Pulse-Propulsion-Module Characteristics as Predicted for Operation in the Early 1980's.* GAMD-5934, 5 December 1964.

Nuclear Pulse Propulsion Project (Project Orion). Technical Summary Report, 1 July 1963–30 June 1964. WL-TDR-64-93; GA-5386, 15 December 1964. *Vol. 1: Summary Report; Vol. 2: Theoretical and Experimental Physics; Vol. 3: Engine Design, Analysis, and Development Techniques; Vol. 4: Engineering Experimental Tests.*

David, C. V. *Axial and Lateral Rigidity of Pressurized Toroidal Filament Structures.* GAMD-6061, January 1965.

APPENDIX

David, C. V., Doering, D. A., and Leghorn, J. G. (with work by C. R. Dismukes, K. D. Pyatt, and S. J. Sand). *Nuclear-Pulse-Propulsion (Orion) Engine Optimization.* GAMD-6044, 8 February 1965. Includes Appendix A: *List of Input Parameters;* Appendix B: *List of Output Parameters;* Appendix C: *Key-Punch Form;* Appendix D: *OROP Program Listing;* Appendix E: *OROPLE Program Listing.*

Structural Analysis of Torus Spring Assembly. Author unknown. GAMD-5148, March 1965.

Triplett, J. R., et al. *SPUTTER—A General Purpose One-Dimensional Radiation and Fluid Mechanics Computer Program, Part 1.* GA-4820, 1 March 1965.

Potential Military Applications. Author unknown. GA-C-962 (Formerly GA-0-321). 1 March 1965.

ORION Space Propulsion: Technical Status and Mission Potential. Author unknown. GA-C-944, 1 March 1965.

Shipps, P. R. *Manned Planetary Exploration Capability Using Nuclear Pulse Propulsion.* GA-6224, 19 March 1965.

Monthly Progress Report—February 1965. Project Orion—Nuclear Pulse Propulsion Concept. GA-C-983, 19 March 1965.

David, C. V. *Nuclear Pulse Propulsion (ORION) 1965 Engineering Status.* GA-6280, April 1965.

David, C. V. *Stability Study of Nuclear Pulse Propulsion (Orion) Engine System.* GAMD-6213, 30 April 1965.

Day, E. A., and Nance, J. C. *Nuclear Pulse Propulsion (Orion) Technical Status Summary and Ground Development Plan.* GA-6307, 1 May 1965.

Nuclear Pulse Propulsion Project (Project Orion) Final Report, 1 July 1964–1 March 1965. GA-6261, July 1965 (AFWL TR 65-45).

Ehricke, K. A. *Nuclear-Pulse Space-Vehicle Study, Vol. 4: Mission Velocity Requirements and System Comparisons (with Supplement).* GA-5009, 28 February 1966.

Notes

All direct quotations not otherwise attributed
below are from the author's correspondence
and interviews, 1993–2001.

xiii–xiv   "Our poor old car . . . at 9 P.M.": F. J. Dyson to parents (Winchester, UK), 19 April 1959.

xiv   "will emit a trail . . . of a warhead": *La Jolla Journal*, 12 July 1958, p. 2B.

4   "go from downtown Jackass Flats . . . in a single stage": Scott Lowther, "The Large Orions: As Close as We've Come to a Starship," *Aerospace Projects Review* 2, no. 2 (March–April 2000), p. 15. See also: "Project Orion: Baseline Design," *Aerospace Projects Review* 1, no. 4 (September–October 1999), pp. 4–24; "Project Orion: Testing and Safety Issues," *Aerospace Projects Review* 1, no. 5 (September–October 1999), pp. 17–29; "Lunar Logistics Orion," *Aerospace Projects Review* 1, no. 6 (November–December 1999), pp. 19–26.

5   "Dr. Taylor estimated . . . $500,000,000": Ron Prater, Memo to Director, Research Directorate, AFSWC, 25 November 1958, Subject: Trip to General Atomic Division of General Dynamics Corporation, 18–20 November 1958. Extracted (p. 177) in "Project Orion: An Air Force Bid for Role in Aerospace," pp. 161–297 of the *1964 Annual History of the Air Force Weapons Laboratory, 1 January–December 1964*, compiled by Dr. Ward Alan Minge, Captain Harrell Roberts, and Sergeant Thomas L. Suminski. Unpublished (cited hereafter as AFWL 1964).

   "a hydrogen warhead . . . the United States": Dorence C. Jameson, Donald M. Mixson, Ronald F. Prater, AFSWC, "Nuclear Bomb Propelled Space Vehicle," draft (6 May 1959) of article for *ARDC Quarterly Review*, p. 3.

6   "Whoever controls . . . control the world": Taylor, Prickett, York, and Dyson recall slightly different versions of Power's statement; this is the version remembered by Ted Taylor.

NOTES

7   "included all the necessary . . . early in 1958": Major Lew Allen, USAF Office of Special Projects, to Ray DeGraff, Air Research and Development Command, 29 May 1958; AFWL 1964, p. 165.

"I have nothing . . . in this myself": F. J. Dyson to parents, 1 January 1958.

7–8 "I find myself . . . grow around us": F. J. Dyson to parents, 27 April 1958.

8   "Roy W. Johnson . . . fiscal year 1959": General Atomic, news release, Washington, D.C., 2 July 1958.

9   "Tonight when I . . . worms and clouds": F. J. Dyson to parents, 29 October 1957.

"The uses for ORION . . . space itself": AFWL 1964, p. 169.

"When I drove . . . to come along": Imme Jung to F. J. Dyson, in F. J. Dyson to parents, 22 June 1958.

10 "These atomic bombs . . . pretensions of war": H. G. Wells, *The World Set Free* (New York: Dutton, 1914), pp. 114–18.

11 "could get a colony . . . in about 150 years": F. J. Dyson, "High-Velocity Ships," General Atomic calculation sheets, 1959.

"Stars have a life cycle . . . that new stars may live": Hans Bethe, "Energy Production in Stars," *Physics Today*, September 1968, p. 44.

"When Bethe's fundamental . . . produced on Earth": Stanislaw Ulam, "Thermonuclear Devices," in R. E. Marshak, ed., *Perspectives in Modern Physics: Essays in Honor of Hans Bethe* (New York: Wiley Interscience, 1966), p. 593.

12 "The basic built-in characteristic . . . than a small one": F. J. Dyson, "The Future Development of Nuclear Weapons," *Foreign Affairs* 38, no. 3 (April 1960), p. 458.

"We were not bound . . . a 'Super' bomb": Edward Teller, "The Work of Many People," *Science*, 25 February 1955, p. 269.

13 "Its use would . . . the hopes of mankind": James B. Conant, Hartley Rowe, Cyril Stanley Smith, L. A. DuBridge, Oliver E. Buckley, J. R. Oppenheimer, I. I. Rabi, General Advisory Committee to the U. S. Atomic Energy Commission, Report of 30 October 1949, reprinted in Herbert F. York, *The Advisors: Oppenheimer, Teller, and the Super Bomb* (San Francisco: W. H. Freeman, 1976), p. 157.

"technically so sweet": J. Robert Oppenheimer, testimony before the AEC Personnel Security Board, 15 April 1954, *In the Matter of J. Robert Oppenheimer* (Washington, D.C.: Government Printing Office, 1954; Cambridge, MA: MIT Press, 1970), p. 251.

15 "a couple of people . . . have the time": Ralph Slutz, interview by Christopher Evans, June 1976, OH 086, Charles Babbage Institute, University of Minnesota at Minneapolis.

"As the results . . . he would say": Stan Ulam, *Adventures of a Mathematician* (New York: Scribner, 1976), pp. 216–17.

16 "Americans design . . . ballistic missiles": "Soviet Satellite Sends U.S. into a Tizzy," *Life*, 21 October 1957, p. 35.

"any country . . . with horses": F. J. Dyson, "The Future Development of Nuclear Weapons," *Foreign Affairs* 38, no. 3 (April 1960), p. 460.

"In 1940 . . . was unpopular": F. J. Dyson, 15 December 1958, to the editors, *Bulletin of the Atomic Scientists* (unpublished MS).

"He was sympathetic . . . in 1942": F. J. Dyson to parents, 31 July 1958.

20 "It does not . . . it is MY patent!": Francoise Ulam, unpublished memoirs.

"He was a maverick . . . his mind": Francoise Ulam, "Stanislaw Ulam, 1909–1984," *Los Alamos Science*, no. 15 (Special Issue, 1987), p. 6.

NOTES

20–21   "Many of us . . . think things out.'": Gian-Carlo Rota, "The Barrier of Meaning," *Letters in Mathematical Physics* 10 (1985), p. 97.

21   "Johnny answered . . . Santa Fe": Stan Ulam, *Adventures of a Mathematician* (New York: Scribner, 1976), pp. 141, 143, 144.

22   "In the entire . . . to the Moon'": Ibid., pp. 155, 156, 162.

"I found . . . precise relationships": Ibid., pp. 147–48.

"the group took . . . physics data": Frederic de Hoffmann, *Minutes of an Informal Meeting on Nuclear Rockets,* LAMS-836, 15 February 1949, p. 1.

22–23   "The idea . . . at high velocity": Stan Ulam, *Adventures of a Mathematician* (New York: Scribner, 1976), p. 252.

23   "Fission product decay . . . or exhausted": R. W. Bussard, in R. E. Schreiber, *The LASL Nuclear Rocket Propulsion Program,* LAMS-2036, April 1956, with Appendix by R. W. Bussard, *Nuclear Powered Rockets: A Historical Survey and Literature Summary,* p. 44.

24   "Repeated nuclear explosions . . . melting the vehicle": C. J. Everett and S. M. Ulam, *On a Method of Propulsion of Projectiles by Means of External Nuclear Explosions,* Los Alamos Scientific Laboratory Report, LAMS-1955 (August 1955), pp. 3–5.

"The vehicle is . . . to the vehicle": Ibid., pp. 6–7.

"The accelerations . . . are certainly large": Ibid., p. 20.

25   "it is almost like . . . to the moon": S. M. Ulam, testimony, 22 January 1958, before Subcommittee on Outer Space Propulsion of the Joint Committee on Atomic Energy, 85th Congress, 2nd session, p. 44.

"it appears that . . . such a ship": S. M. Ulam, manuscript text (undated) for "Talk Before the Joint Committee on Atomic Energy," U. S. House of Representatives, Hearings on Astronautics and Space Exploration, 85th Congress, 2nd session, April 15–May 12, 1958.

"Dr. Taylor . . . theoretical scheme": S. M. Ulam to Senator Clinton P. Anderson, 31 March 1960.

"The spaceship . . . not enthusiastic": Stan Ulam, *Adventures of a Mathematician* (New York: Scribner, 1976), p. 253.

26   "whose faculties . . . in its course": James Clerk Maxwell, *The Theory of Heat,* 2nd ed. (London, 1872), p. 308.

27   "As examples . . . very high velocities": S. M. Ulam, *On the Possibility of Extracting Energy from Gravitational Systems by Navigating Space Vehicles.* LAMS-2219 (written 1 April 1958, distributed 19 June 1958), pp. 3–7.

27–28   "The above discussion . . . some additional energy left": Ibid., p. 7.

28   "The computations . . . complication": Ibid., p. 7.

"Meteors . . . engineered for it": Ulam to Taylor, 19 March 1962.

29   "That nuclear fission . . . complete surprise": Frederic de Hoffmann, "A Novel Apprenticeship," in Jane Wilson, ed., *All in Our Time* (Chicago: Bulletin of the Atomic Scientists, 1974), p. 163.

30   "We had a rule . . . his hand": Ibid., p. 171.

"Making the bomb . . . experimentation": Ibid., p. 171.

"Even before . . . terrible restriction": Edward Teller, "The Work of Many People," *Science,* 25 February 1955, p. 272.

32   "He asked me . . . do the job right": Ed Creutz, *The Origin and Some Accomplishments of General Atomic,* MS, 20 February 1997, p. 6.

33   "Because the early . . . majority approval": Peter Kaye, "Future of Pueblo Lands to be Decided by Voters," *San Diego Union,* 27 May 1956.

NOTES

34   "Mayor Dail . . . they can see us'": Ed Creutz, *The Origin and Some Accomplishments of General Atomic*, MS, 20 February 1997, p. 7.

        "If science is . . . ideal as possible": Frederic de Hoffmann, "A Novel Apprenticeship," in Jane Wilson, ed., *All in Our Time* (Chicago: Bulletin of the Atomic Scientists, 1974), p. 164.

        "the distinction . . . was nonexistent": Frederic de Hoffmann, 18 July 1985, *GA Calendar* 17, no. 4 (August 1985), p. 3.

35   "Freddy . . . so little fuss": F. J. Dyson, *Disturbing the Universe* (New York: Harper & Row, 1979), p. 96.

41   "Those of us . . . words 9 to 5": Frederic de Hoffmann, 18 July 1985, *GA Calendar* 17, no. 4 (August 1985), p. 3.

        "We covered these . . . during lunch": Ed Creutz, *The Origin and Some Accomplishments of General Atomic*, MS, 20 February 1997, p. 7.

        "The drinking fountains . . . next to the floor": Brian Dunne, interview with Laurence Winn (partially published in *San Diego's Weekly*, 8 April 1976).

42   "We all knew . . . coal and oil": F. J. Dyson, *Disturbing the Universe* (New York: Harper & Row, 1979), p. 94.

        "There was a meeting . . . hydride reactor": Frederic de Hoffmann, 18 July 1985, *GA Calendar* 17, no. 4 (August 1985), p. 3.

43   "The result of . . . pulled the rods": F. J. Dyson, *Disturbing the Universe* (New York: Harper & Row, 1979), p. 98.

43–44   "safe even . . . with dynamite": Ibid.

44   "Some of his ideas . . . the electron": Ibid.

44–45   "I am amusing . . . who would play it": F. J. Dyson to parents, 12 August 1956.

45   "Niels Bohr pressed . . . really worked": F. J. Dyson, *Disturbing the Universe* (New York: Harper & Row, 1979), pp. 101–2.

46   "a strong letter on that subject": Frederic de Hoffmann, 18 July 1985, *GA Calendar* 17, no. 4 (August 1985), p. 3.

        "For about half . . . irreparably lost": F. J. Dyson to parents, 4 July 1959.

49   "When I heard . . . awesome events": T. B. Taylor, *Changes of Heart*, draft, 6 June 1986, chap. 1, "Full Circle."

        "Dreams of settling . . . looked grim": Ibid.

49–50   "I didn't know . . . didn't ask": Ibid.

50   "Within 24 hours . . . never do": T. B. Taylor, *Changes of Heart*, draft, 6 June 1986, chap. 2, "Los Alamos."

51   "I suddenly came . . . thirty-six years ago": T. B. Taylor, "From Bomb Designer to Disarmament Activist," talk presented to Nuclear Dialogue Project Meeting, Princeton, N. J., 21 October 1987.

        "I had complete freedom . . . I chose": T. B. Taylor, *Changes of Heart*, draft, 6 June 1986, chap. 2, "Los Alamos."

        "In my seven . . . single proposal": T. B. Taylor, "Elements of Technical Creativity," Symposium on Creativity in Science, Los Alamos National Laboratory, 13 August 1984.

51–52   "The laboratory's . . . was 'You bet!'": T. B. Taylor, *Changes of Heart*, draft, 6 June 1986, chap. 2, "Los Alamos."

52   "scarcely blew . . . at Livermore": Ibid.

        "a large part . . . without any degree": F. J. Dyson to parents, 1 July 1958.

52–53   "A great part . . . due to Ted": F. J. Dyson to parents, 1 July 1958.

NOTES

53–54 "The explosion . . . plain thrilling": T. B. Taylor, *Changes of Heart*, draft, 6 June 1986, chap. 2, "Los Alamos."

54–55 "Pursuing these limits . . . out of a gun?": Ibid.

55–56 "less than three years . . . considerably surpassed": T. B. Taylor, "Elements of Technical Creativity," Symposium on Creativity in Science, Los Alamos National Laboratory, 13 August 1984.

57 "The use of small . . . save the U.S.": T. B. Taylor, "Notes on Criminal or Terrorist Uses of Nuclear Explosives," 7 November 1966.
"At Nuclear Fuel . . . of any kind": T. B. Taylor, *Changes of Heart*, draft, 6 June 1986, chap. 4, "The Pentagon."

58–59 "'Accounting for . . . almost infinite'": F. J. Dyson, "Sir Phillip Roberts's Erolunar Collision" (1933) in *From Eros to Gaia* (New York: Pantheon, 1992), p. 5.

59 "When I thought . . . artillery shells": F. J. Dyson, letter to James Lukash, 15 August 1994.

60 "Herr Zucker . . . world distribution": P. E. Cleator, *Journal of the British Interplanetary Society* 1, no. 3 (July 1934), p. 27.
"In London . . . fighter aircraft": F. J. Dyson, "Mankind in the Universe," lecture given at Salzburg, 29 September 1969, at the meeting of the German and Austrian Physical Societies.

61 "I had my oil . . . as an experimenter": F. J. Dyson, *Disturbing the Universe* (New York: Harper & Row, 1979), p. 49.
"The sin . . . had sinned": Ibid., p. 53.
"The problem . . . absorbing light": Ibid., p. 48.
"Dick was . . . could understand": Ibid., p. 54.

62 "He was struggling . . . from the bottom up": F. J. Dyson, "This Side Idolatry," Foreword to *The Pleasure of Finding Things Out. The Best Short Works of Richard Feynman* (Cambridge, MA: Perseus Books, 1999), p. ix.
"Dyson was . . . both methods": Hans Bethe, review of *Disturbing the Universe*, in *Physics Today*, December 1979, p. 51.

63 "The roads . . . to write it down": F. J. Dyson, *Disturbing the Universe*, p. 67.
"the simplification . . . problem": F. J. Dyson, "The Radiation Theories of Tomonaga, Schwinger, and Feynman," *Physical Review* 75, no. 3 (1 February 1949), p. 486.
"The picture . . . earth in place": F. J. Dyson, "Field Theory," *Scientific American* 188, no. 4 (April 1953), pp. 62–63.

64 "In the first . . . are involved": F. J. Dyson, "Quantum Electrodynamics," *Physics Today*, September 1952, p. 6.
"What you need . . . little momentum": F. J. Dyson, interview with Gary Marcuse, 11 October 1999.

65 "We skimmed . . . physics and engineering": F. J. Dyson, "The Search for Extraterrestrial Technology," in R. E. Marshak, ed., *Perspectives in Modern Physics: Essays in Honor of Hans Bethe* (New York: Wiley Interscience, 1966), p. 641.
"In the early . . . ideas as possible": F. J. Dyson, "Experiments with Bomb-Propelled Spaceship Models," in Bogdan Maglich, ed., *Adventures in Experimental Physics*, Beta issue (1972), p. 324.
"When I left . . . place for us": F. J. Dyson, "Experiments with Bomb-Propelled Spaceship Models," pp. 323–24.

66 "even quite . . . scientists": Bruno Augenstein, "Some Aspects of Interstellar Space Exploration—New ORION Systems, Early Precursor Missions," 42nd Congress

315

of the International Astronautical Federation, Montreal, Canada, 5–11 October 1991, p. 1.

"I saw . . . life is good": F. J. Dyson to parents, 1 July 1958.

67   "I carefully extinguished . . . by mistake": T. B. Taylor, *Changes of Heart*, draft, 6 June 1986, chap. 2, "Los Alamos."

71   "A number of . . . nuclear blast": Bruno Augenstein, "Roles and Impacts of RAND in the Pre-Apollo Space Program of the United States," International Astronautical Federation 46th International Astronautical Congress, Oslo, 2–6 October 1995, p. 4.

"When placed . . . mass losses": Tom Wainwright, "Rocket Propulsion by Means of Nuclear Explosions," UCRL-4893, *Proceedings of the Joint AEC Weapons Laboratory Symposium, Livermore, CA, February 6–8, 1957*, p. 48.

74–75   "Several important . . . schemes of this kind": F. J. Dyson to parents, 8 June 1958.

75   "Do you believe . . . this planet too": S. M. Ulam, testimony, 22 January 1958, before Subcommittee on Outer Space Propulsion of the Joint Committee on Atomic Energy, 85th Congress, 2nd session, p. 53.

75–76   "Is there any theory . . . truly empty": Theodore Merkle, testimony, 22 January 1958, before Subcommittee on Outer Space Propulsion of the Joint Committee on Atomic Energy, 85th Congress, 2nd session, pp. 60–61.

78   "Luckily the work . . . as possible": F. J. Dyson to parents, 30 June 1958.

78–79   "We asked . . . to the end": Ibid.

79–80   "Conceptually . . . very high": Lew Allen (USAF Office of Special Projects) to Ray DeGraff (ARDC), 29 May 1958.

82   "the verbal understanding . . . first year": AFSWC, Project 3775, Nuclear Impulse Rocket Research Test Vehicle: R&D Project Card, 1 April 1960, p. 7.

"If the Concept . . . to the ship": Air Force Contract AF 18(600)-1812, "Feasibility Study of a Nuclear Bomb Propelled Space Vehicle," 30 June 1958, Exhibit "A"— Statement of Work, p. 1.

83   "We do not consider . . . per night": H. B. Fry (General Atomic) to Herbert R. Ash USAF (San Diego Air Procurement District), 18 July 1958.

84–85   "it looked screwball . . . working on it": Roy W. Johnson, quoted by Evert Clark, "Space Power Systems' Gains Reported: Project Orion Enters Engineering Feasibility Phase," *Aviation Week*, 29 February 1960, p. 26.

86   "We shall know . . . the ships": F. J. Dyson to parents, 19 May 1958.

87   "He is such . . . our enterprise": F. J. Dyson to parents, 28 June 1958.

"It was always . . . fatal flaw": F. J. Dyson, interview with Gary Marcuse, 11 October 1999.

92   "This summer . . . our project": F. J. Dyson to parents, 27 April 1958.

"Your bet with . . . ahead of us": F. J. Dyson to Pierre Noyes, 4 June 1958.

94   "Solar power . . . parallax measurement": T. B. Taylor, "Uses of Large Payloads," 17 January 1960.

"The importance . . . or two": Bryce DeWitt, *The Scientific Uses of Large Spaceships*, GAMD-965, 14 September 1959, pp. 1 and 16.

95   "The morale . . . into reality": AFSWC, Notes for "Project Orion Briefing," no author, no date, annotated as "Draft 1959," probably prepared by Don Mixson for ARPA final briefing on 30 April 1959, p. 2.

97   "When it was proclaimed . . . did not exist": Jorge Luis Borges, "The Library of Babel" (1941) in *Labyrinths* (New York: New Directions, 1964), pp. 54–55. Kurd Lasswitz's "The Universal Library," translated with a mathematical postscript by Willy Ley (the rocket pioneer) appears in Clifton Fadiman, ed., *Fantasia Mathe-*

NOTES

matica (New York: Simon and Schuster, 1958), pp. 237–47. Kevin Kelly's "In the Library of Form" appears in *Out of Control* (Reading, MA: Addison-Wesley, 1994), pp. 258–82.

97–98   "The variety . . . study them all!": T. B. Taylor, "Peaceful Uses of Nuclear Energy in Space," talk presented to the International Atomic Energy Agency, Vienna, Austria, 15 December 1966, p. 6.

98   "Random generation . . . strange idea indeed": T. B. Taylor, "Propulsion of Space Vehicles," in R. E. Marshak, ed., *Perspectives in Modern Physics: Essays in Honor of Hans Bethe* (New York: Wiley Interscience, 1966), p. 640.

105   "What range . . . size of the payload": F. J. Dyson, *Dimensional Study of Orion-type Spaceships*, GAMD-784, 23 April 1959, pp. 2–3.
"SATELLITE means . . . propelled by H-bombs": Ibid., p. 17.

105–6   "It is clear . . . significant levels": Ibid., p. 3.

106–7   "1,000 or 10,000 km/sec . . . in 150 years": F. J. Dyson, "High-Velocity Ships," General Atomic calculation sheets, 1959.

107   "Hydrogen bombs . . . to know exactly": F. J. Dyson, "Interstellar Transport," *Physics Today* 21 (October 1968), p. 42.
"The difficulty . . . smallest feasible ship": Ibid., p. 45.

108   "the building of a ship . . . $100 million today": Ibid., p. 45.
"These numbers represent . . . the solar system": Ibid., p. 44.
"By the time the first interstellar . . . by the home government": Ibid., p. 45.

111   "The AEC . . . ever heard": F. J. Dyson to parents, 26 August 1956.
"I finally managed . . . kinds of bombs": F. J. Dyson to parents, 20 September 1956.

113   "The model . . . of the model": F. J. Dyson, *Free Expansion of a Gas, Part 2, Gaussian Model*, GAMD-507, 5 September 1958, p. 1.

115   "A typical complete . . . IBM-7090": W. E. Mooney, J. C. Nance, K. D. Pyatt, P. R. Shipps, and D. C. Weiss, *Mid-Contract Status Presentation on the Nuclear Pulse Space Vehicle Preliminary Study*, GACD-4593, 25 September 1963, p. 9.

117   "its close prediction . . . of the code": General Atomic, *ORION Space Propulsion: Technical Status and Mission Potential*, GA-C-944, 1 March 1965, p. 7.

118   OROP and OROPLE are detailed in C. V. David, D. A. Doering, and J. G. Leghorn, *Nuclear-Pulse-Propulsion (Orion) Engine Optimization*, GAMD-6044, 8 February 1965.

120   "When the nuclear . . . toward the pusher": W. E. Mooney, J. C. Nance, K. D. Pyatt, P. R. Shipps, and D. C. Weiss, *Mid-Contract Status Presentation on the Nuclear Pulse Space Vehicle Preliminary Study*, GACD-4593, 25 September 1963, p. 7.

122   "I just did . . . pessimistic direction": F. J. Dyson to T. B. Taylor, 2 May 1958.

123   "If the opacity . . . seriously": AFSWC (draft, no date, ca. 1 August 1958), *Report of Meeting Between Lew Allen, Don Mixson, and Ted Taylor, 29 July at General Atomics*, p. 3.

125–26   "General Atomic . . . is urgent": Leonard A. Eddy (AFSWC) to Materials Laboratory, WADC, re: High Modulus of Elasticity Fiberglass, 24 September 1958.

126   "we are not familiar . . . size mentioned": Robert C. Tomashot (Senior Project Engineer, Materials Laboratory, WADC), Memo to Leonard A. Eddy, AFSWC, re: High Modulus of Elasticity Fiberglass, 8 October 1958.

128   "The explosive jets . . . more than that": F. J. Dyson, "Experiments with Bomb-Propelled Spaceship Models," in Bogdan Maglich, ed., *Adventures in Experimental Physics*, Beta issue (1972), p. 324.

NOTES

129 "that even much higher ... where the rates are small": J. Douglas Balcomb, Charles A. Bankston, Albert W. Blackstock, and James D. Hedstrom, *Pusher Plate Ablation Study: Final Report,* Los Alamos informal report LA-5152-MS, January 1973, pp. ix and 4.

130 "A specially selected ... is ablated": W. E. Mooney, J. C. Nance, K. D. Pyatt, P. R. Shipps, and D. C. Weiss, *Mid-Contract Status Presentation on the Nuclear Pulse Space Vehicle Preliminary Study,* GACD-4593, 25 September 1963, p. 10.

139 "in particular ... is not zero": F. J. Dyson, *Optimal Programming for Vertical Ascent in Atmosphere,* GAMD-619, 11 December 1958, p. 2.

140 "a very serious problem ... back motion": AFSWC (draft, no date, ca. 1 August 1958), *Report of Meeting Between Lew Allen, Don Mixson, and Ted Taylor, 29 July at General Atomics,* p. 6.

142 "With this test ... briefly discussed": Hans H. Amtmann and E. A. Day, *Preliminary Investigation of a Repetitive-HE-Pulse Test Facility,* GAMD-5351, 4 June 1964, p. ii.

143 "A test stand ... populated areas": Ibid., p. 35.

144–45 "Freddy asked ... take it out": T. B. Taylor, *Journal,* 28 October 1960.

146 "Detonators with long leads ... for small currents": Brian Dunne, *Safety Procedures at Point Loma Experimental Site,* GAMD-915, 17 July 1959, pp. 9, 11, 12.

147 "For charges ... experimental site": Ibid., p. 3.
"the tests involve ... certain materials": Robert V. Vallera (General Atomic) to U.S. Navy Electronics Laboratory, Subject: Request for Intermittent Use of Static Test Tower and Concrete Block House, 27 August 1958.

148 "I was shown ... than 50 shots": Donald M. Mixson, *Trip Report—Visit to General Atomic Division of General Dynamics Corporation, 25 February 1959,* 2 March 1959, p. 2.
"testing of ... significant results": Ronald F. Prater, USAF, *Trip Report: Visit to General Atomic and Hughes Aircraft, 23–26 March 1959,* 8 April 1959, p. 2.

149 "It was ARPA ... to pay for it": Donald M. Mixson to F. J. Dyson, 23 October 1979.
"The contractor shall ... for propulsion": AFSWC, *Amendment No. 1 to Exhibit "A," Statement of Work, Contract AF 18(600)-1812,* 19 June 1959.

150 "Three-pound charges ... all the tests": Dunne, Ritter, and Ames, *Development of a Meter-Diameter Explosion-Propelled Flying Model,* GAMD-1212, 26 January 1960, p. 44.

151 "penetrating fragments ... canister design": Ibid., notes for 26 June 1959, p. 50.
"It was decided ... safe as possible": Ibid., p. 7.

153 "In case ... fire a detonator": Ibid., p. 12.
"Under no circumstances ... or steel scissors": Brian Dunne, *Safety Procedures at Point Loma Experimental Site,* GAMD-915, 17 July 1959, pp. 4, 9.

153–54 "Excessive damage ... landed undamaged": Dunne, Ritter, and Ames, *Development of a Meter-Diameter Explosion-Propelled Flying Model,* GAMD-1212, 26 January 1960, pp. 49–54.

154 "Wish you could ... your room": Brian Dunne to F. J. Dyson, 16 November 1959.

157 "The purpose ... not just dreams": F. J. Dyson, "Experiments with Bomb-Propelled Spaceship Models," in Bogdan Maglich, ed., *Adventures in Experimental Physics,* Beta issue (1972), p. 325.

159 "Below a certain ... and extravagant": F. J. Dyson, "The Future Development of Nuclear Weapons," *Foreign Affairs* 38, no. 3 (April 1960), p. 458.

"As for the . . . contamination problems": AFSWC, *Report of Meeting Between Lew Allen, Don Mixson, and Ted Taylor, 29 July at General Atomics* (draft, no date, ca. 1 August 1958), p. 6.

"They have . . . for the pusher": Ibid., p. 7.

162 "As presently conceived . . . the pusher": Donald M. Mixson, *Memo, Subject: Trip to GA, 28–31 July 1958,* 7 August 1958, p. 2.

"They have been . . . is small": AFSWC, *Report of Meeting Between Lew Allen, Don Mixson, and Ted Taylor, 29 July* [1958] *at General Atomics*, p. 4.

165 "The latest method . . . about 500 tons": Donald M. Mixson and Ron F. Prater, (AFSWC), 5 September 1958, *Memorandum for Director, Research Directorate: Trip to General Atomic Division of General Dynamics Corporation, 27–29 August 1958,* p. 3.

166 "The first-stage . . . few g's or less": W. E. Mooney, J. C. Nance, K. D. Pyatt, P. R. Shipps, and D. C. Weiss, *Mid-Contract Status Presentation on the Nuclear Pulse Space Vehicle Preliminary Study,* GACD-4593, 25 September 1963, p. 5.

"The mechanical . . . present report": Carlo Riparbelli, *Parameter Study—Cylinder with Piston,* GAMD-1830, 16 November 1960, pp. 2–3.

166–67 "When a shock . . . takes place": C. V. David, *Minimum Energy Loss in a Two-Mass Spring System,* GAMD-2331, 16 January 1961, p. 1.

167 "An explosion timing . . . importance": C. V. David and E. R. Hager, *Double-Stage Shock-Absorber Investigation,* GAMD-5911, December 1964, p. 92.

169 "This body of water . . . powerful spring": Jules Verne, *From the Earth to the Moon, Direct in 97 Hours 20 Minutes; and a Trip Round It.* Translated from the French by Louis Mercier and Eleanor King. 9th edition (London: Sampson Low, Marston & Co., 1892), p. 122.

170 "In order to get . . . the time": AFSWC, *Report of Meeting Between Lew Allen, Don Mixson, and Ted Taylor, 29 July at General Atomics,* p. 6.

170–71 "studies under way . . . necessary duties": Leonard A. Eddy, Memo to Commander, Wright Air Development Center, 13 August 1958.

171 "The upper limit . . . instruments": F. J. Dyson, *Dimensional Study of Orion-type Spaceships,* GAMD-784, 23 April 1959, p. 10.

"They are now . . . factor of 2": Donald M. Mixson, *Memo, Subject: Trip to GA, 28–31 July 1958,* 7 August 1958, p. 3.

"The time available . . . order of 6 g": Michael Treshow, *Project Orion: 4,000-Ton Vehicle, Mark 2,* GAMD-808, 18 April 1959, p. 2.

173 "For the delivery . . . gun–type gadgets": AFSWC, *Report of Meeting Between Lew Allen, Don Mixson, and Ted Taylor, 29 July at General Atomics,* p. 6.

173–74 "Excellent progress . . . considered yet": Donald M. Mixson and Ron F. Prater (AFSWC), 5 September 1958, *Memorandum for Director, Research Directorate: Trip to General Atomic Division of General Dynamics Corporation, 27–29 August 1958,* p. 4.

174 "Dyson has looked . . . the bomb": AFSWC, *Report of Meeting Between Lew Allen, Don Mixson, and Ted Taylor, 29 July at General Atomics,* p. 6.

"Contrary to . . . shock absorbers": F. J. Dyson, "Experiments with Bomb-Propelled Spaceship Models," in Bogdan Maglich, ed., *Adventures in Experimental Physics,* Beta issue (1972), p. 324.

175 "I am recognized . . . early for me": Michael Treshow to Edward Creutz, GA, 28 November 1956.

176 "The takeoff rails . . . worked out": Michael Treshow, *Trajectories of a Rocket with Eccentric Thrust,* GAMD-541, 19 September 1958, pp. 2, 7, 14, 15.

"The charge will . . . of the blast": Michael Treshow, *Project Orion: 4,000-Ton Vehicle, Mark 2,* GAMD-808, 18 April 1959, p. 3.

176–77 "This allows . . . interplanetary travel": Ibid., p. 2.

177 "In order to save . . . conveyor rails": Ibid., p. 3.

179 "both the pulse frequency . . . from vertical": J. C. Nance et al., *Nuclear Pulse Space Vehicle Study,* GA-5009, *Vol. 1: Summary Report,* 19 September 1964, p. 14.

181 "The reception . . . very well": F. J. Dyson to parents, 16 August 1958.

182 "Advanced Interplanetary Ship": Undated table of design parameters (ca. 1959), reproduced in AFWL 1964, p. 187.

183 "We are about . . . were three": F. J. Dyson to parents, 31 July 1958.

"Within this first month . . . for this": AFSWC, *Report of Meeting Between Lew Allen, Don Mixson, and Ted Taylor, 29 July at General Atomics,* p. 8.

"slowly taking shape . . . of marble": F. J. Dyson to parents, 31 July 1958.

"We were all champing . . . the bombs": T. B. Taylor, *Changes of Heart,* draft, 6 June 1986, chap. 3, "La Jolla."

184 "I think the study . . . in general": F. J. Dyson to parents, 19 May 1958.

"approximate departure . . . actual flight": Burt Freeman, *Minimum Energy Round Trips to Mars and Venus,* GAMD-672, 5 February 1959, p. 2.

"the two satellites . . . jump off": Ibid., p. 10.

"Takeoff from Earth . . . during takeoff": Ibid., p. 2.

185 "This excursion . . . trip to Mars": W. E. Mooney, *Orion Martian Excursion,* GA-P-359-1, 24 June 1963, pp. 10–11.

186 "Either through inadvertence . . . skies to man": F. J. Dyson, *A Space Traveler's Manifesto,* MS, 5 July 1958.

188 "I was out . . . cliffs on the other": F. J. Dyson to parents, 13 July 1958.

189 "the controls . . . makes it exciting": F. J. Dyson to Verena Huber-Dyson, 2 August 1958.

"It is a fearsome . . . winch": F. J. Dyson to parents, 16 August 1958.

"I had five flights . . . the intended spot": Ibid.

"velocity decrement to land on satellite" in F. J. Dyson, *Trips to Satellites of the Outer Planets,* GAMD-490, 20 August 1958, p. 5.

189–90 "The satellites of the outer planets . . . landing on their satellites": Ibid., p. 2.

190 "The general nature . . . on the satellite": Ibid., p. 4.

"The meaning of these numbers . . . should not be built": Ibid., p. 8.

191 "It is quite likely . . . substantially reduced": Ibid., p. 9.

"We assume that . . . mass-ratio less than 2": Ibid., pp. 10–11.

191–92 "The Orion system . . . voyages to Mars": Ibid., p. 12.

196 "The situation of ARPA . . . no success": F. J. Dyson, "Death of a Project: Research Is Stopped on a System of Space Propulsion Which Broke All the Rules of the Political Game," *Science* 149, no. 3680 (9 July 1965), p. 142.

198 "We are happy . . . this opinion": F. J. Dyson to parents, 8 June 1958.

"The prospects . . . in the past": R. L. Belzer (assistant to President Frank Collbohm, RAND) to Major General W. M. Canterbury, AFSWC, 27 March 1959.

198–99 "We have to face . . . way things are: F. J. Dyson to parents, 24 May 1959.

199 "to have an observation . . . there first": F. J. Dyson to parents, 25 January 1956.

"Space platforms . . . and the like": Lew Allen, Major, USAF, Memo to Colonel Jameson, re: Don Mixson's Memo and Putt-Putt in General, 24 October 1958.

NOTES

200 "The Horrible weapon . . . as a deterrent": AFSWC, Notes for "Project Orion Briefing," no author, no date, annotated as "Draft 1959" (probably prepared by Don Mixson for ARPA final briefing on 30 April 1959), p. 9.

202 "Spent most . . . physics in it": T. B. Taylor, *Journal,* 11 October 1960.

"Had vile thoughts . . . call it quits": Ibid., 13 October 1960.

"Only delicate timing . . . or defensive": K. W. Baker and James W. Bothwell, Director, Plans and Requirements, CINCSAC, Omaha, Nebraska, to Commander, Air Defense Command, re: "Global Integration of Space Surveillance, Tracking, and Related Facilities (GISSTARF)," 31 May 1959, p. 3.

"There presently exist . . . military purposes": Dorence C. Jameson, Donald M. Mixson, Ronald F. Prater, AFSWC, "Nuclear Bomb Propelled Space Vehicle," draft (6 May 1959) of article for *ARDC Quarterly Review,* p. 3.

"Because the . . . operation of the ship": F. J. Dyson, interview with Gary Marcuse 11 October 1999.

203 "This was supposed . . . over mole hills": Donald M. Mixson, *Memo, Subject: Trip to GA, 28–31 July 1958,* 7 August 1958, p. 4.

204 "largely the work . . . an enemy first": AFWL 1964, p. 184.

"7 July . . . working on this": Donald M. Mixson, AFSWC, Memorandum for Record: Military Applications Briefings for Project Orion, 30 July 1959.

205–6 "Once a space ship is deployed . . . could not be recalled": General Atomic, *Potential Military Applications,* GA-C-962, 1 March 1965, pp. 16–21.

206 "Such a capability . . . seapower has": Paul H. Sager, *Early System Applications of Nuclear Pulse Propulsion,* GA-5140, Preliminary Draft, 1 April 1964, p. 32.

"had read Admiral . . . dominion of the world'": F. J. Dyson, *Weapons and Hope* (New York: Harper & Row, 1984), p. 66.

208 "General Atomic . . . manned ship": Lew Allen, Major, USAF, Memo to Colonel Dorence C. Jameson, re: Don Mixson's Memo and Putt-Putt in General, 24 October 1958.

208–9 "The latest . . . axis of the ship": Ronald F. Prater, USAF, *Trip Report: Visit to General Atomic and Hughes Aircraft, 23–26 March 1959,* 8 April 1959, p. 2

211 "a step by step . . . vehicle": Dorence C. Jameson, Donald M. Mixson, Ronald F. Prater, AFSWC, "Nuclear Bomb Propelled Space Vehicle," draft (6 May 1959) of article for *ARDC Quarterly Review,* p. 3.

"a small scale . . . atomic shots": Ronald F. Prater, USAF, *Trip Report: Visit to General Atomic and Hughes Aircraft, 23–26 March 1959,* 8 April 1959, p. 3.

"which will carry . . . atomic shots": Ibid., p. 4.

"Ted Taylor and I . . . hope to get (b)": F. J. Dyson to parents, 26 April 1959.

"reflected the high . . . soon would be": AFSWC, Project 3775, Nuclear Impulse Rocket Research Test Vehicle: R&D Project Card, 1 April 1960, p. 7.

211–12 "The people . . . until August": F. J. Dyson to parents, 4 July 1959.

212 "ARPA has about . . . the case": Major Lew Allen, Memo for Record, 19 August 1959: Trip Report to Washington, D.C., 27 July to 5 August 1959.

"Our space-ship . . . get the axe": F. J. Dyson to parents, 14 August 1959.

"It was felt . . . to NASA": AFWL 1964, p. 193.

213 "a plan for . . . military departments": Herbert F. York, ARPA, press release, 23 September 1959.

"this means . . . upon my return": Art Rolander, telegram to F. de Hoffmann, T. Taylor, E. Holles, GA, 23 September 1959.

NOTES

214 "Although the ORION . . . such support": Richard E. Horner, NASA, to Herbert F. York, DDR&E, 10 February 1960 (drafted by Harold B. Finger, 5 February 1960).

215 "We should think . . . to disappear": T. B. Taylor, *Journal,* 3 October 1960.
"Confidence in the . . . time period": AFSWC, Project 3775, Nuclear Impulse Rocket Research Test Vehicle: R&D Project Card, 1 April 1960, p. 1.
"placing the Research . . . by fiscal year '65": Captain Donald M. Mixson, USAF, Nuclear Impulse Rocket Research Test Vehicle, management report, FY 1961 Financial Plan Effort Program, 11 March 1960, p. 1.
"The successful completion . . . and navigation": Ibid.

216 "Marshall Rosenbluth . . . wins tomorrow!": T. B. Taylor, *Journal,* 7 November 1960.
"We must encourage . . . nuclear bombs": Jerome Wiesner, quoted in *New York Times,* 12 January 1961, p. 14C.
"which apparently . . . on the other": T. B. Taylor, *Journal,* 15 November 1960.
"Economical . . . costs now": T. B. Taylor, *Journal,* 19 October 1960.

218 "1) Establishment . . . of Mars": T. B. Taylor, *Journal,* 11 December 1960.
"Bruno Augenstein . . . end of 1964??": T. B. Taylor, *Journal,* 19 December 1960.
"much discussion . . . does not exist": T. B. Taylor, *Journal,* 28 December 1960.
"we are certainly . . . in space": T. B. Taylor, *Journal,* 26 January 1961.
"I took an instant . . . space travel": T. B. Taylor, *Journal,* 29 January 1961.
"We've kicked a field goal": T. B. Taylor, *Journal,* 29 March 1961.

219 "4 representatives from Boeing . . . 6 from Norair": George W. S. Johnson (Major, USAF, Ballistic Missile Division, ARDC), memo to Capt. Donald M. Mixson: List of Project Orion Briefing Attendees, 7 August 1959.

220 "the propellant could . . . acceleration of about 2 g": Michael Treshow, *ORION Parameter and Payload Study Based on 200- and 4,000-ton Reference Design,* GAMD-3597, 25 October 1962.

224 "I came back . . . the week": F. J. Dyson to parents, 31 October 1958.
"in laying plans . . . atomic devices": AFWL 1964, p. 186.

226 "The public is . . . of this fight": F. J. Dyson to parents, 31 October 1958.
"to build a building . . . as a side line": F. J. Dyson, "The Future Development of Nuclear Weapons," *Foreign Affairs* 38, no. 3 (April 1960), p. 462.
"the advantages . . . the same yield": Advanced Research Projects Agency / Institute for Defense Analyses, *Project GLIPAR: Guide Line Identification Program for Antimissile Research.* IDA-ARPA TR 60-2. Vol. 1: Summary (July 1960) section 3, p. 5.

227 "Only once . . . into my mind": F. J. Dyson, *Disturbing the Universe* (New York: Harper & Row, 1979), p. 127.
"no thought . . . contamination yet": Donald M. Mixson and Ron F. Prater [AFSWC], 5 September 1958, *Memorandum for Director, Research Directorate: Trip to General Atomic Division of General Dynamics Corporation, 27–29 August 1958,* p. 4.
"high explosive . . . and aerospace": AFWL 1964, p. 175.

231 "The concept . . . hired by General Atomic": Report, Briefing on ORION Project Putt-Putt, 20 February 1961, presented to Commander, ARDC, Lt. General Bernard A. Schriever, no sig., no date. Quoted in AFWL 1964, p. 207.

232 "He was more . . . design field": AFWL 1964, p. 212.
"The Soviets burst . . . 63 megatons": John S. Foster, Foreword to William E. Ogle, *An Account of the Return to Nuclear Weapons Testing by the United States After the Test Moratorium, 1958–1961* (DOE Nevada Operations Office, October 1985), p. 6.

NOTES

232–33 "Dr. Kavanu . . . nuclear weapons": Don Prickett, AFSWC, *Trip Report to Washington, D.C., on 14–16 August 1962*, 22 August 1962, pp. 2–3.

233–34 "I didn't want . . . within a matter of days": F. J. Dyson, interview with Gary Marcuse, 11 October 1999.

234 "the treaty . . . its development": T. B. Taylor, *The Effect of the "Treaty Banning Nuclear Weapons Test in Outer Space" on ORION*, draft, 7 August 1963, p. 1.
"Indeed . . . would be necessary": Ibid., p. 3.

235 "Our Orion . . . generates fallout": T. B. Taylor, *Journal*, 4 November 1960.
"Fission-product . . . penalty incurred": J. C. Nance et al., *Nuclear Pulse Space Vehicle Study*, GA-5009, *Vol. 3: Conceptual Vehicle Designs and Operational Systems*, 19 September 1964, p. 101.

235–36 "Pulse units for the 10-m . . . north or south": J. C. Nance et al., *Nuclear Pulse Space Vehicle Study*, GA-5009, *Vol. 1: Summary Report*, 19 September 1964, p. 38.

236 "trappage . . . almost negligible": J. C. Nance et al., *Nuclear Pulse Space Vehicle Study*, GA-5009, Vol. 3: *Conceptual Vehicle Designs and Operational Systems*, 19 September 1964, p. 81.
"there seems . . . fission-free bombs": F. J. Dyson, "The Future Development of Nuclear Weapons," *Foreign Affairs* 38, no. 3 (April 1960), p. 459.
"improvements . . . factors of 10^2 to 10^3": J. C. Nance et al., *Nuclear Pulse Space Vehicle Study*, GA-5009, *Vol. 1: Summary Report*, 19 September 1964, p. 38.

238 "Project Orion . . . Dr. von Braun": Donald M. Mixson, AFSWC, to T. B. Taylor, GA, 18 June 1959.
"out of small projects . . . to the stars": Frank H. Winter, *Prelude to the Space Age: The Rocket Societies, 1924–1940* (Washington, D.C.: Smithsonian Institution Press, 1983), p. 35.

240 "I am very curious . . . will be": T. B. Taylor to Stan Ulam, 29 August 1960.
"he seemed less . . . bureaucracy": T. B. Taylor, *Journal*, 27 November 1960.

241 "Sparked by Ross's . . . end of 1966": T. B. Taylor, *Journal*, 14 October 1960.
"The Air Force predicted . . . Nova II": USAF Project FORECAST, Propulsion Report, March 1964, Annex A: Nuclear Propulsion, reproduced in AFWL 1964, p. 283.
"This way . . . almost everywhere": T. B. Taylor, *Journal*, 15 October 1960.

243 "It is recommended . . . million a year": Thomas F. Dixon to Robert C. Seamans (cc. to H. Finger), 29 December 1961.

243–44 "There are always . . . as unsolvable": Don Prickett, 4 December 1961, in AFWL 1964, p. 222.

244 "I used the word . . . developed in flight": Harold Finger, "Mars—a Target for Advanced Propulsion," American Astronautical Society Symposium on the Exploration of Mars, Denver, CO, 6–7 June 1963, p. 19.
"Ted and I . . . von Braun and MSFC": James Nance to F. J. Dyson, 9 March 1965.

246 "An old analogy . . . in both cases": J. C. Nance, *Nuclear Pulse Propulsion*, GAMD-5572, 5 October 1964, p. 2.
"Vehicles utilizing . . . to Mars": Ibid., pp. 11, 13.
"Manned engines . . . train crews": E. A. Day and J. C. Nance, *Nuclear Pulse Propulsion (Orion) Technical Status Summary and Ground Development Plan*, GA-6307, 1 May 1965, p. 33.

247 "the engine/vehicle . . . pulse-engine startup": General Atomic/NASA, *Briefing Charts for the Pre-Beginning Meeting, 27 June 1963*, GA-C-395, 25 June 1963, p. 5.

NOTES

"The chemical rocket . . . space boosters": Ibid., p. 5.

248   "self-boosted . . . aboard in orbit": Ibid., p. 6.

"packaged in modules . . . of payload": Ibid., p. 7.

"NASA mission constraints . . . less demanding": General Atomic/NASA, *Nuclear Pulse Vehicle Study, Condensed Summary Report,* GA-4891, 14 January 1964, p. 1.

248–49   "Most of the significant . . . degraded specific impulse": Ibid., p. 3.

249   "2,782 pulses required per trip": J. C. Nance et al., *Nuclear Pulse Space Vehicle Study,* GA-5009, *Vol. 3: Conceptual Vehicle Designs and Operational Systems,* 19 September 1964, p. 28.

"During prolonged . . . exploration mission": J. C. Nance et al., *Nuclear Pulse Space Vehicle Study,* GA-5009, *Vol. 2: Vehicle System Performance and Costs,* 19 September 1964, p. 29.

250–51   "For short duration . . . long space missions": W. E. Mooney, *Orion Personnel Accommodations,* GA-P-363-2, 3 September 1963, p. 1.

251   "For the longer . . . may be desirable": W. E. Mooney, J. C. Nance, K. D. Pyatt, P. R. Shipps, and D. C. Weiss, *Mid-Contract Status Presentation on the Nuclear Pulse Space Vehicle Preliminary Study,* GACD-4593, 25 September 1963, p. 65.

"The propulsion modules . . . propulsion": J. C. Nance et al., *Nuclear Pulse Space Vehicle Study,* GA-5009, *Vol. 3: Conceptual Vehicle Designs and Operational Systems,* 19 September 1964, p. 29.

"there will also . . . colonization transport category": *General Atomic Briefing Charts for the Pre-Beginning Meeting, 27 June 1963,* p. 8.

252   "Vehicle A . . . nuclear-pulse operation": J. C. Nance et al., *Nuclear Pulse Space Vehicle Study,* GA-5009, *Vol. 1: Summary Report,* 19 September 1964, p. 37.

"4,000- and 16,000-ton ships": J. C. Nance et al., *Nuclear Pulse Space Vehicle Study,* GA-5009, *Vol. 2: Vehicle System Performance and Costs,* 19 September 1964, p. 81.

"Since high-altitude . . . unprotected eye": W. E. Mooney, J. C. Nance, K. D. Pyatt, P. R. Shipps, and D. C. Weiss, *Mid-Contract Status Presentation on the Nuclear Pulse Space Vehicle Preliminary Study,* GACD-4593, 25 September 1963, p. O-6.

"that approximately . . . hazard might exist": J. C. Nance et al., *Nuclear Pulse Space Vehicle Study,* GA-5009, *Vol. 3: Conceptual Vehicle Designs and Operational Systems,* 19 September 1964, pp. 94–95.

253   "Nuclear pulse . . . eighties or sooner": Krafft A. Ehricke, *Nuclear-Pulse Space-Vehicle Study,* GA-5009, *Vol. 4: Mission Velocity Requirements and System Comparisons,* 28 February 1966, p. O-6.

"ORION has crossed . . . few months": T. B. Taylor to F. J. Dyson, 11 July 1963.

"The great thing . . . wanted to do": F. J. Dyson to T. B. Taylor, 11 November 1963.

254   "withheld . . . for several months": AFWL 1964, p. 278.

"NASA headquarters . . . about 1990!": T. B. Taylor to F. J. Dyson, 23 December 1963.

254–55   "Orion had a unique . . . as long as it did": F. J. Dyson, "Death of a Project: Research Is Stopped on a System of Space Propulsion Which Broke All the Rules of the Political Game," *Science* 149, no. 3680 (9 July 1965), p. 144.

255   "For reasons . . . public support": T. B. Taylor to F. J. Dyson, 23 December 1963.

"$10.4 million over seven years": Don Prickett (AFSWC), *Nuclear Impulse Propulsion, Project 3775 (ORION): Summary of Program and Technical Status,* 12 January 1963, p. 8, table of financial history, January 1958–June 1963 (total $8,150,000). Also F. J. Dyson, *Orion: Notes on History* (no date, 1965).

NOTES

256   "The end result . . . unusually high": F. J. Dyson, "Death of a Project," p. 141.

"Orion, in its . . . well in hand": Ron F. Prater, AFSWC, Memorandum for the Record, 26 February 1963, p. 5.

259   "On 28 December . . . terminate it": AFWL 1964, pp. 231–32.

260–61   "Clearly the feasibility . . . this excellent group": Hans Bethe, telegram to Joseph V. Charyk, 18 January 1962.

261   "We have taken . . . penetration aids": Joseph V. Charyk to Hans Bethe, 25 January 1962.

"on the grounds . . . man in space": AFWL 1964, p. 248.

262   "Many who saw . . . a serious mistake": T. B. Taylor, *Changes of Heart,* draft, 6 June 1986, chap. 3, "La Jolla."

"capable of sustaining . . . payload limitations": AFWL 1964, p. 206.

"Men as wise . . . positively undesirable": F. J. Dyson, "Death of a Project," p. 142.

"There is certainly . . . about this change": *USAF Scientific Advisory Board Nuclear Panel Report on Orion/Helios,* 30 April 1964, p. 2.

263   "Fiscal Year 1965 . . . from Mr. Finger": AFWL 1964, p. 273.

"The in-house battle . . . emerged the champions": James Nance to F. J. Dyson, 9 March 1965.

"In accordance with . . . loss of continuity": Raymond D. Walker, Procurement Directorate, AFSWC, *Request for Determinations and Findings Pursuant to AFPI3-211, PR 146349,* 10 June 1963, pp. 1–2.

263–64   "The Air Force . . . and the AEC": Michael Yaffee, "Limited Work May Be Continued on Orion," *Aviation Week and Space Technology,* 10 May 1965, p. 67.

264   "Los Alamos was . . . we will play'": William Ogle, *An Account of the Return to Nuclear Weapons Testing by the United States After the Test Moratorium, 1958–1961,* U.S. DOE Nevada Operations Office, NVO-291, October 1985, p. 159.

"The result of the DOD . . . no, it's out'": "NASA, DOD, AEC at Loggerheads Over Project Orion," *Missile/Space Daily,* 11 December 1964, p. 13F.

"official position": George E. Mueller to Wernher von Braun (MSFC), re: Orion/Helios briefing at Livermore, 8 July 1964.

"in view of the shortage . . . two fiscal years": Hugh L. Dryden (NASA) to General James Ferguson, Deputy Chief of Staff, Research and Development, USAF, 11 June 1964 (rewritten by James Webb, 2 June 1964).

"The purpose . . . concept is anticipated": Colonel J. M. Silk, USAF, memo to RTD/RTG, Bolling AFB, re Orion Presentation to NASA, 22 July 1964.

265   "The Air Force . . . NASA refused": Michael Yaffee, "Limited Work May Be Continued on Orion," *Aviation Week and Space Technology,* 10 May 1965, p. 67.

"probably is the only . . . will work": Willard E. Wilks, "NASA Must Decide Orion Future," *Missiles and Rockets,* 14 December 1964, p. 12.

"Unless Jim Webb's . . . next year": T. B. Taylor to H. P. Noyes, 6 July 1964.

"I was being told . . . fix it": T. B. Taylor, *Changes of Heart,* draft, 6 June 1986, chap. 3, "La Jolla."

266   "The treaty . . . exploration of space": Paul R. Shipps, *Manned Planetary Exploration Capability Using Nuclear Pulse Propulsion,* GA-6224, 19 March 1965, p. 26.

"Those of us working . . . big scale": T. B. Taylor, *Nuclear Pulse Propulsion,* Third Conference on Planetology and Space Mission Planning, 28–30 October 1970, *Annals of the New York Academy of Sciences* 187 (25 January 1972), p. 339.

266–67   "A Meeting . . . other 'science fiction' schemes": Andrei Sakharov, *Memoirs,* translated from the Russian by Richard Lourie (New York: Knopf, 1990), p. 215.

267 "There appears to be . . . mental health": "NASA, DOD, AEC at Loggerheads Over Project Orion," *Missile/Space Daily*, 11 December 1964, p. 13F.
"ORION is not . . . April 1965": John R. Burke, Lt. Colonel, USAF, Nuclear Power Division, *AFRSTG Memorandum for Record: ORION Nuclear Pulse Propulsion*, 14 January 1965.

268 "Even Harold Brown . . . sign off": T. B. Taylor to F. J. Dyson, 1 March 1965.
"if a big expansion . . . internal NASA question": F. J. Dyson, *ORION: Notes on History*, undated notes from conversation with James Nance, 1965.
"formal research . . . to a close": *Project Orion—Nuclear Pulse Propulsion Concept: Monthly Progress Report—February 1965*, GA-C-983, 19 March 1965, p. 2.

268–69 "Objective . . . hereby terminated": John O. Berga, Major, USAF, *Research and Technology Resume, Nuclear Impulse Propulsion Technology Studies, Plan Change*, 30 June 1965.

269 "I understand . . . the time is ripe": F. J. Dyson to Stan Ulam, 26 January 1965.
"You will perhaps . . . of succeeding": F. J. Dyson to J. Robert Oppenheimer, 17 March 1965.
"The men who . . . the way to do it": F. J. Dyson, "Death of a Project: Research Is Stopped on a System of Space Propulsion Which Broke All the Rules of the Political Game," *Science* 149, no. 3680 (9 July 1965), p. 141.
"there was no more . . . dreams intact?": F. J. Dyson, "Experiments with Bomb-propelled Spaceship Models," in Bogdan Maglich, ed., *Adventures in Experimental Physics*, Beta issue (1972), p. 326.

270 "Between the first . . . moons of Jupiter": Arthur C. Clarke, 1964, in *The Lost Worlds of 2001* (New York: New American Library, 1972), p. 13.
"I felt that . . . credits reversed": Ibid., p. 31.

271 "When we started . . . the project": Ibid., p. 125.
"a discussion . . . staff rather upset": Ibid., p. 38.
"DISCOVERY . . . racing speedboat": Stanley Kubrick and Arthur C. Clarke, *2001: A*

271–72 *Space Odyssey*, screenplay (Hawk Films Ltd.), 13 October 1965.

272 "Stanley and his . . . seemed": Arthur C. Clarke, *The Lost Worlds of 2001* (New York: New American Library, 1972), p. 126.

273 "Before the '70s . . . to its close": Arthur C. Clarke, 1964, in *The Lost Worlds of 2001* (New York: New American Library, 1972), pp. 13–14.
"Nature has been . . . assembled here": T. B. Taylor, *Advanced Propulsion Concepts*, GA-2592, 24 October 1961, p. 14.
"We always tend . . . what we know": T. B. Taylor, *Nuclear Propulsion in Space*, GA-3218, 12 June 1962, p. 6.
"unless we take . . . step at a time": T. B. Taylor, *The Need for High Performance Nuclear Space Engines: A Talk to the AEC General Advisory Committee*, 30 March 1965, p. 2.
"Bigger, higher . . . ocean liners": T. B. Taylor, "Peaceful Uses of Nuclear Energy in Space," talk presented to the International Atomic Energy Agency, Vienna, Austria, 15 December 1966, pp. 15–16.
"Apollo costs . . . different kind": F. J. Dyson, "Mankind in the Universe," lecture given at Salzburg, 29 September 1969, at the meeting of the German and Austrian Physical Societies, p. 10.
"History has passed . . . going back": F. J. Dyson, *Disturbing the Universe* (New York: Harper & Row, 1979), p. 115.

NOTES

274   "its resurrection . . . will come": Stan Ulam to F. J. Dyson, 15 July 1965.
"I still think . . . out there": Frederic de Hoffmann, 18 July 1985, *GA Calendar* 17, no. 4 (August 1985), p. 3.

278   "I always thought . . . she will!": Brian Dunne to F. J. Dyson, 24 December 1973.

282   "a discussion . . . go-ahead": G. E. Gibson (RAND), *Orion: Future Space Propulsion System?* RAND/D-11007-PR, 26 February 1963.

283   "to make a nuclear . . . 25-ton yield device": Johndale Solem, *Some New Ideas for Nuclear Explosive Spacecraft Propulsion,* Los Alamos Report LA-12189-MS, October 1991, p. 11.

284   "In the final analysis . . . burden alone": AFWL 1964, p. 163.

285–86   "It was written . . . NASA did not exist": Donald M. Mixson to F. J. Dyson, 23 October 1979.

286   "I did a complete . . . dangerous place": T. B. Taylor, "From Bomb Designer to Disarmament Activist," presented to Nuclear Dialogue Project Meeting, Princeton, N. J., 21 October 1987.

287   "There is nothing . . . something like Orion": F. J. Dyson, interview with Gary Marcuse, 11 October 1999.

289–90   "Arming, fusing . . . first malfunction": Johndale Solem, "Nuclear Explosive Propelled Interceptor for Deflecting Objects on Collision Course with Earth," *Journal of Spacecraft and Rockets* 3, no. 4 (1994), pp. 708–9.

293–94   "For spacecraft applications . . . permanently inhabiting space": J. A. Bonometti, P. J. Morton and G. R. Schmidt, *External Pulsed Plasma Propulsion and its Potential for the Near Future,* NASA Marshall Space Flight Center, January 2000.

296   "Science thrives . . . safely home": Edward Teller, "The Road to Nowhere," *Technology Review,* 1981, reprinted in *Better a Shield Than a Sword* (New York: Free Press, 1987), pp. 118–20.

296–97   "That first glimmering . . . catch the sun": H. G. Wells, *The World Set Free* (New York: Dutton, 1914), p. 15.

Acknowledgments

"On Monday I went once again to Washington to talk with the very high authorities about our space-ship," my father reported to his parents on December 31, 1959. "Ted Taylor was also there. The people were sympathetic but said there is virtually no chance that the thing will be pushed ahead during the next few years. I came away feeling this is the end as far as I am concerned. I had a lot of fun working on the problem for a year, and the work I did remains available to anybody who wants to make use of it. The time will certainly come one day when the work will be renewed and pushed vigorously again. But for the next few years there is nothing more I can do. Ted and I agreed that if the work is stopped the thing for us to do is to write a book."

Ted Taylor and Freeman Dyson are the coauthors of this book. Many who helped them, forty-three years ago, in their attempt to build Orion were similarly generous in helping me. Herbert York, Brian Dunne, Moe Scharff, Bruno Augenstein, Thomas Macken, Jerry Astl, Carroll Walsh, Carlo Riparbelli, Bill Vulliet, John Burke, Ed Giller, Don Prickett, Harris Mayer, Pierre Noyes, Edward Teller, Lew Allen, Ed Creutz, Burt Freeman, Hans Amtmann, Ralph and Jonny Stahl, David Weiss,

Harold Finger, Bud Pyatt, Keith Brueckner, Francoise Ulam, Marshall Rosenbluth, Bill Simpson, and Doug Fouquet granted hundreds of hours of interviews without which it would have been impossible to reconstruct the story presented here. Any guesswork that has strayed into classified areas is my own.

There were other contributors to Project Orion whom I could not or did not speak with: Stan Ulam, Frederic de Hoffmann, Don Mixson, Michael Treshow, Ed Day, Michael Ames, John C. Stewart, Charles Loomis, Elizabeth Risberg, Lois Iles, James Nance, Howard Kratz, Perry Ritter, Ron Prater, Theodore Teichmann, Paul Shipps, Michael Nowak, Ray Gilbert, Fred W. Ross, Constant David, Charles Mautz, Ken Case, Ogden Boden, and Jeremy Bernstein. Their contributions are insufficiently recognized in this account.

General Atomic(s), Los Alamos National Laboratory, the History Office at Kirtland Air Force Base (in particular, Robert Duffner), the RAND Corporation, and NASA's Marshall Space Flight Center provided documents without which human memory of events of forty years ago would have been impossible to resolve. The United States Defense Technical Information Center was exceptionally useful in confirming the existence of certain documents, and is to be credited for preserving critical material that it will some day be authorized to release.

John Brockman, Katinka Matson, Stefan McGrath, William Patrick, and David Sobel helped turn my interest in Project Orion from nostalgia into a book. Fairhaven College and Western Washington University preserved my affiliation for three years. Patrick Ong supported travel to conduct interviews. Kenneth Brower opened a lot of doors, in 1978, when he published *The Starship and the Canoe*. Anthony Martin, Alan Bond, and the *Journal of the British Interplanetary Society* revealed, in 1979, just how in the dark we were about Project Orion after twenty years. Sylvan Schweber, Scott Lowther, Johndale Solem, and other fellow Orion researchers were generous with leads—as future Orion enthusiasts will, I hope, pursue the leads presented here.

Index

INDEX

INDEX

INDEX

Illustration Credits

Frontispiece: Jules Verne, *From the Earth to the Moon, Direct in 97 Hours 20 Minutes; and a Trip Round It* (first published 1865); engraving from the 9th edition, London, 1892.

Pages 6, 26, 62, 81, 135, 139, 141, 152, 156: Courtesy Jaromir Astl.

Page 14: Courtesy H. P. Noyes.

Pages 36, 101: Photos by the author.

Page 43: Courtesy General Atomic—now General Atomics (GA).

Pages 55, 175, 197, 213, 228: Artist(s) and date(s) unknown, courtesy U.S. Air Force Special Weapons Center, History Office, Kirtland Air Force Base (AFSWC/KHO).

Page 70: Drawing by Michael Treshow, GAMD-3597, 25 October 1962. Courtesy GA and Bruno Augenstein, RAND.

Page 90: Sketch by Walter Mooney, GA-C-395, 25 June 1963. Courtesy GA and Scott Lowther.

Pages 113, 178, 276: Artist(s) unknown, from GA-5009, 19 September 1964. Courtesy GA and NASA.

Pages 127, 163, 234: Artist(s) unknown, from GACD-4593, 25 September 1963. Courtesy GA, NASA, and Scott Lowther.

Page 151: Artist unknown, from GAMD-1212, 26 January 1960. Courtesy GA and Brian Dunne.

Pages 161, 250: Artist unknown, from GAMD-5911, December 1964. Courtesy GA and AFSWC/KHO.

Page 172: Drawing by Michael Treshow, GAMD-808, 18 April 1959. Courtesy GA, Defense Technical Information Center, and Scott Lowther.

Page 187: Courtesy F. J. Dyson.

Page 200: Artist unknown, from GA-C-962, 1 March 1965. Courtesy GA and AFSWC/KHO.

Pages 217, 245: Artist(s) and date(s) unknown, courtesy Thomas Macken.

Pages 242, 278, 281: Artist(s) unknown, from GA-6224, 19 March 1965. Courtesy GA and Thomas Macken.

Page 257: From GA-C-944, 1 March 1965. Courtesy GA and AFSWC/KHO.

Page 260: From GAMD-5351, 4 June 1964. Courtesy GA and AFSWC/KHO.

Page 295: Artist and date unknown, courtesy John R. Burke.